The Mathematics Survival Kit

SECOND EDITION

Jack Weiner

University of Guelph

 NELSON / EDUCATION

NELSON / EDUCATION

The Mathematics Survival Kit, Second Edition
by Jack Weiner

Associate Vice President, Editorial Director:
Evelyn Veitch

Editor-in-Chief, Higher Education:
Anne Williams

Executive Editor:
Paul Fam

Senior Marketing Manager:
Sean Chamberland

Developmental Editor:
My Editor Inc.

Senior Manufacturing Coordinator:
Charmaine Lee Wah

Design Director:
Ken Phipps

Managing Designer:
Katherine Strain

Cover Design:
Jennifer Leung

Cover Image:
Jennifer Leung

Printer:
Edwards Brothers

Library and Archives Canada Cataloguing in Publication

Weiner, Jack, 1949–
   The mathematics survival kit / Jack Weiner. — 2nd ed.

Includes index.
ISBN 978-0-17-650017-7

1. Algebra--Handbooks, manuals, etc. 2. Calculus--Handbooks, manuals, etc.

I. Title.

QA37.3.W43 2008   512'.15
C2008-906273-6

ISBN-13: 978-0-17-650017-7
ISBN-10: 0-17-650017-0

THE MATHEMATICS SURVIVAL KIT
TABLE OF CONTENTS

Giving the Third Degree to Second Degree Polynomials: Quadratics!

Solving Inequalities with Less (<) Difficulty, Greater (>) Ease

Increasing the Magnitude of Your Absolute Value Knowledge

Getting to the Root of Square Roots

Some Basic Graphs and Some Basics about Graphs

The Survival Kit Logs Powerful Time with Exponents and Logarithms

Drawing Your Attention to Some Basic Geometry

Angling Right in on Trigonometry

A Straightforward Approach to Limits

Continuity (There's a Hole in the Function, Dear Liza, Dear Liza)

Derivatives or Going on a Tangent about Slopes

Derivative Rules Rule

Integrating Your Knowledge about the Anti-Derivative

Inverse Functions: Now that's a Switch!

Warming Up to Polar Coordinates

Going to Any Lengths to Give You New Direction with Vectors

A Few Terms in Sequences and Series and a Sampling of Statistics

End Game

Introducing "The Mathematics Survival Kit"

It's 2 a.m. and you are stuck. You have forgotten how to "complete the square", which you need to complete a calculus question or an algebra question or a statistics question or ... Your text gives lots of examples but none of them review the completing the square technique.

Here comes **The Mathematics Survival Kit** to the rescue! Find the page you need in the **Survival Kit**. A quick 5 to 10 minute concise and friendly review gives you exactly what you need to continue with your homework.

The Mathematics Survival Kit contains **115*** topics just like that. Using high school course outlines, standard first year university calculus and algebra curricula, and my thirty years of teaching experience, I prepared a list of topics, from early high school to university, that plague students. Like completing the square. Like factoring cubics. Like those annoying log properties. Like ...

Each topic is covered in one page. Almost all consist of
  ➤ an introductory sentence or two
  ➤ a first very straightforward example
  ➤ a second example illustrating a common variation
  ➤ **TWO FOR YOU**: two extra questions with answers to reinforce the techniques (and space in between for you to **do the work!)**

I have three subtitles for this book and I believe in all three to the depths of my mathematics teacher's soul:

"Got a Math Problem? Give Me Five Minutes of Your Time!"

"I Remember How to Do That!"

"That's Easier Than I Remembered!"

Why "**Give me Five Minutes!**"? Pre-calculus and math review texts re-teach and do massive amounts of examples and exercises. They can be overwhelming. With the **Survival Kit**, I am saying, "Give me five minutes and together we will zero in on and solve **your** problem!" Also, pre-calculus math review texts miss many of these topics. I don't think there is any book available that covers them all because the topics span so much of the math curriculum. There is certainly no text out there that presents them in this one page per topic format.

That is a key point. You don't have to read pages 1 to 58 to understand page 59. Each page is like a dictionary definition. You have a vocabulary that allows you to understand the explanation of any word you look up in a dictionary. You have a mathematics vocabulary that does the same for **Mathematics Survival Kit** topics!

Why "**I Remember How to Do That!**"? You are smarter and know more than you often give yourself credit for. If I have done my job well and you have studied the material in an earlier course, you should be able to follow step by step the solutions to examples on any given page.

*This second edition, as you will read on page *x*, has 140 topics!

Why **"That's Easier Than I Remembered!"**? If you are using this book, you are probably strongly motivated and really into the math (or physics or chemistry or economics or ...) that you are currently studying. You have the background and motivation. You **can** do math. And most of the time, you will find that the topic you are reviewing is not nearly as intimidating as it once may have seemed.

I had a lot of fun writing this book and truly believe in its usefulness. Students, from **early high school to senior university**, who have seen drafts have said they want copies ASAP. Teachers have said it will save them loads of tutoring time because the extra help their students often need is background review—**The Survival Kit!**—rather than the current material. Parents have all said they want it not only for their offspring, but—I am not making this up—because it will be fun to see how much math they remember. Maybe enough to help junior!

I have several colleagues who deserve to take a bow.

Liisa Lahtinen, now a successful high school teacher, was one of my best Teaching Assistants ever. Guelph Professor Herb Kunze is that wonderful and rare combination of superb teacher and superb researcher. Both offered valuable advice and constructive criticism as the book took shape.

Guelph Professor Emeritus Hosh Pesotan gave me excellent suggestions to improve the book and kept me motivated by enthusing, **"The Mathematics Survival Kit** is such a neat idea. Why hasn't anyone done it before?"

Matthew Fisher recently completed his computer science undergraduate degree at the University of Guelph and is now successfully putting it to work for him. The index is 99% Matthew!

Dr. Lew Baxter, a mathematics teacher based in Toronto, meticulously worked through a copy of the book from the first printing. He generously took the time to send me dozens of suggestions which have resulted in a substantially improved **MSK**.

Penny Clemens, of Ydezign, worked her graphics magic on the layout of "How to Get an 'A' in Math" and "How to Get Extra Help", the first two and perhaps most valuable pages in the book.

Nelson Editor Anthony Rezek nurtured both me and **The Mathematics Survival Kit** through the writing process, patiently and promptly offering advice on all my editing questions. Nelson Manufacturing Coordinator Charmaine Lee Wah capably facilitated the production.

Finally, I am grateful to the literally tens of thousands of students I have had the honour to teach here at the University of Guelph and, in a previous geological age, at Parkside High School in Dundas, Ontario. I hope I have made a positive contribution to many of their lives. They certainly have enriched mine.

Of course, any imperfections that remain (and as the former editor of a mathematics journal, I know that achieving perfection is an "asymptotic" limit!) are mine and mine alone.

Professor Jack Weiner
Department of Mathematics and Statistics
University of Guelph
jweiner@uoguelph.ca

Introducing "The Mathematics Survival Kit", Edition 2

I began the introduction of the original Mathematics Survival Kit this way: "It's 2 a.m. and you are stuck. You have forgotten how to ..." Well, as I compose this introduction to the second edition, it is 2 p.m. and I am not stuck. I am in fact very happy to be sitting at a table in the gorgeous atrium of the New Science Complex at the University of Guelph, writing about the new edition of the MSK and the people who helped bring it to life.

The new edition has twenty five new topics. **All** were suggested by readers of the first edition, including students, teachers, and even parents! Moms and dads asked me to include more basics, which is why you will find sections on fractions and BEDMAS. A common request from students at several universities: create MSK pages for integration by parts. High school teachers and students wanted more on vectors. I'm especially grateful to Ivana Sunjic from Bishop Ryan Catholic Secondary School in Hamilton, Ontario. Ivana compiled a list of vector topics, every one of which became a Revised MSK section.

This book starts being useful in grade 9 and becomes progressively more useful right into college and university. However, I suggest that no matter what grade or year you are in, you photocopy (or download from the website given below) pages 1 and 2, **HOW TO GET AN A IN MATH** and **HOW TO GET EXTRA HELP**, and tape them to wall at your desk. These strategies work!

Sitting across from me are Sylvia Nguyen and George Hutchinson, diligently doing a final proof of the manuscript. Both are math majors entering second year. Both earned high 90's in the first year calculus course we navigated together last fall and winter. Both have been working with me to produce this second edition of the Mathematics Survival Kit. Both are doing a fabulous job.

I had terrific input and meticulous checking from Meghan Irvine. Meghan just graduated from Teachers' College with math and art as her two specialties. In her teaching placements, she experienced first hand the challenges students are finding with the evolving high school mathematics curriculum. She brought both the student and the new teacher perspective to the MSK table.

My colleague and friend, Professor Hosh Pesotan, patiently spent many, many hours working with me (on this edition and the original) as I searched for just the right examples, the best explanations, the clearest layouts. If this book works well (**and it does—no false modesty here**), give much credit to Hosh.

I am grateful for help and advice and support from Nelson Learning and in particular Executive Editor, Paul Fam, and My Editor Inc.'s developmental editor, Katherine Goodes.

I am pleased to report that the Mathematics Survival Kit is now available as an e-book, powered by the world's best math software, Maple! For more information and links to the Maple MSK site, go to www.mathematicssurvivalkit.ca.

Finally, **please** don't let this book gather dust. Work through the examples, pen or pencil in hand. If you have a suggestion on how I could improve a topic, email me. If you have a suggestion for a topic for edition three, email me. If you like the book, I want to know: email me.

Jack Weiner, jweiner@uoguelph.ca   June 16, 2008

x

Get an "A" in MATH!

After class, **DON'T** do your homework! Instead, *read over your class notes*. When you come to an example done in class...

DON'T read the example. Copy out the question, set your notes aside, and do the question yourself. Maybe you will get stuck. Even if you thought you understood the example completely when the teacher went over it in class, you may get stuck.

And this is **GOOD NEWS!** Now, you know what you don't know. So, consult your notes, look in the text, see your teacher/professor. Do whatever is necessary to figure out the steps in the example that troubled you.

Once you have sweated through the example, **DO IT AGAIN! And again**. Do it as often as you need so that it becomes, if not easy, then at least straightforward. Make sure you not only understand each line in the solution, but why each line is needed for the solution.

In part, you have memorized the solution. More importantly, you have made the subtleties of the problem unsubtle!

This is the great equalizer step. If your math or science aptitude is strong, then maybe you will have the example down pat after doing it twice. If not so strong, you may have to do it several times. But after you have done this for every class example...

DO YOUR HOMEWORK! If you follow this method and if the teacher chose the examples well, then most of the homework questions will relate easily back to problems done in class and the rest should extend or synthesize the ideas behind those problems.

Guess what you'll find on 80% or more of your tests and exams? The same kinds of problems! And you will have your "A". Good luck, although if you use this method, luck will have nothing to do with your INEVITABLE success.

Get Extra Help

Have your questions ready. When you see your teacher for extra help, **don't say anything like**, "I don't have a clue what's going on." Rather, work through your class notes – definitions, examples, theorems, and proofs – thoroughly, and be prepared to say, "I understand everything up to this point. How did we get from here to here?" In other words, **do your part!** Spend quality time with the material.

Get into study groups. Then one representative of your group can see your teacher for help with problems and report back to the others. Also, with group expertise, more often than not, you will solve most problems yourselves.

Struggle more than a little. Don't give up after one attempt. Make a sincere effort to sort out your problems. That way, when you say, "I am stuck RIGHT HERE!", you will be so **up** on the problem that your teacher's explanation will be clear.

Have you ever had this experience? A teacher is explaining a concept or technique in answer to your question. You are nodding your head, saying, "Uh huh! Uh huh! Yes, I understand." Yet you're thinking, "I don't have a clue what the teacher is talking about."

It can happen, but it's **rare**, that the teacher isn't explaining the problem well. Usually, though, the blame lies, yes, with the student, who hasn't struggled enough so that the teacher's explanation can work. **Struggle more than a little!**

- Review each day's notes as soon as possible – definitely before the next class.
- Do your homework before the next class.
- Participate in class.
- Form study groups with classmates.
- Don't fall behind.

BEDMAS (Order of Operations)

BEDMAS stands for $\boxed{B}$ $\boxed{E}$ $\boxed{D}$ $\boxed{M}$ $\boxed{A}$ $\boxed{S}$ and is a mnemonic (a
$\underset{\text{Brackets}}{} \underset{\text{Exponents}}{} \underset{\text{Division}}{} \underset{\text{Multiplication}}{} \underset{\text{Addition}}{} \underset{\text{Subtraction}}{}$

fancy word that means "easy memory trick") for the order in which we do arithmetic

operations. So, $\boxed{B}$rackets (or parentheses) come first, then $\boxed{E}$xponents, then $\boxed{D}$ivision

and $\boxed{M}$ultiplication **in the order they occur from left to right**, and finally, $\boxed{A}$ddition

and $\boxed{S}$ubtraction, **in the order they occur from left to right.**

Example 1) Evaluate (a) $4 \times 3 + 2$ (b) $2 + 4 \times 3$ (c) $(2 + 4) \times 3$ (d) 2×4^3

Solution (a) $4 \times 3 + 2 \overset{\boxed{\text{first} \times \text{then} +}}{=} 12 + 2 = 14$ (b) $2 + 4 \times 3 \overset{\boxed{\text{first} \times \text{then} +}}{=} 2 + 12 = 14$

(c) $(2 + 4) \times 3 \overset{\boxed{\text{first brackets then} \times}}{=} 6 \times 3 = 18$ (d) $2 \times 4^3 \overset{\boxed{\text{first exponents then} \times}}{=} 2 \times 64 = 128$

Example 2) Evaluate

(a) $6 \div 3 \times 5$ (b) $6 \div (3 \times 5)$ (c) $6 \times 3 \div 5$ (d) $6 \div 3 \div 5$ (e) $6 \div (3 \div 5)$

Solution (a) $6 \div 3 \times 5 \overset{\boxed{\text{first} \div \text{then} \times}}{=} 2 \times 5 = 10$ (b) $6 \div (3 \times 5) \overset{\boxed{\text{first ( ) then} \div}}{=} 6 \div 15 = \dfrac{6}{15} = \dfrac{2}{5}$

Note: In (a), BEDMAS had us divide first. In (b), with brackets, we first did the

multiplication. Different answers!

(c) $6 \times 3 \div 5 \overset{\boxed{\text{first x then} \div}}{=} 18 \div 5 = \dfrac{18}{5}$

. . . the answer is different again. BEDMAS is our friend. It brings (arithmetic) *order*

to our lives!

ALL HAIL BEDMAS!

(d) $6 \div 3 \div 5 \overset{\boxed{\text{Do the \textbf{first} division first.}}}{=} 2 \div 5 = \dfrac{2}{5}$

Note: Suppose in (d), we did the second division first. THIS IS WRONG!

(d) done incorrectly : $6 \div 3 \div 5 \overset{\boxed{\substack{\text{Do the \textbf{second} division first.} \\ \textbf{THIS IS WRONG!}}}}{=} 6 \div \dfrac{3}{5} \overset{\boxed{\substack{\text{Invert and} \\ \text{multiply.}}}}{=} \overset{2}{\cancel{6}} \times \dfrac{5}{\cancel{3}_1} = 10.$ Wrong!

The order of the $\div$ signs determines the order in which they are carried out. However, . . .

(e) $6 \div (3 \div 5) \overset{\boxed{\substack{\text{Do the second division first.} \\ \text{This is \textbf{correct} because of the brackets.}}}}{=} 6 \div \dfrac{3}{5} \overset{\boxed{\text{Invert and multiply.}}}{=} \overset{2}{\cancel{6}} \times \dfrac{5}{\cancel{3}_1} = 10$

Two for you.

1)(a) Evaluate: $22 + 14 \div 3 \times 4 - 3$

(b) The question in (a) was sent to me by the mom of a student who had won second prize in a Honda contest—$200 in CD's. First prize was a Honda motorcycle. Mom was relieved her son won second prize! He submitted the **correct** answer to the "skill testing question". However, Honda claimed the answer was 45 and withheld the prize.
(i) How did Honda arrive at 45?
(ii) Insert brackets into the expression so that the answer is 45.

(c) Mom asked me to write a letter to Honda explaining why her son's answer was correct. I did so. The good news: Honda agreed and gave him the prize. Mom was very grateful. However, I told her my time was valuable and that, while I was glad to help, I had a consultation fee. She was to pay me $1000 - 500×2.
(i) How much did she owe me using Honda's method?
(ii) How much did she owe me using BEDMAS?

Postscript: Mom told me a cheque was in the mail. I'm still waiting!

2) Evaluate: (a) $\dfrac{\left(\dfrac{2}{3}\right)}{\left(\dfrac{4}{5}\right)}$ (b) $\dfrac{\left(\dfrac{7}{5}\right)}{5}$ (c) $\dfrac{7}{\left(\dfrac{4}{5}\right)}$

Answers 1)(a) $37\dfrac{2}{3}$ (b)(i) Honda did each operation in the order in which it appeared.

(b)(ii) $(22+14) \div 3 \times 4 - 3$ (c)(i) $1000   (ii) $0

2)(a) $\dfrac{5}{6}$ (b) $\dfrac{7}{25}$ (c) $\dfrac{35}{4} = 8\dfrac{3}{4}$

Adding and Subtracting Fractions

Wouldn't it be great if " $\dfrac{a}{b}+\dfrac{c}{d}=\dfrac{a+c}{b+d}$ " $\boxed{\text{This is wrong!}}$, that is, when adding fractions, we just added the numerators and denominators?

Well, sorry, life is not that simple. But life is not that hard either. When you add or subtract fractions, you need a **common denominator**. Better still, you should use the **lowest common denominator**, as you will see. However, this method always works:

$$\boxed{\text{This is right!}}$$
$$\frac{a}{b}+\frac{c}{d}=\frac{a\times d}{b\times d}+\frac{c\times b}{d\times b}=\frac{ad+bc}{bd}$$

Example 1)(a) $\dfrac{1}{3}+\dfrac{5}{7}$ (b) $1\dfrac{5}{6}-2\dfrac{2}{5}$ (c) $\dfrac{5}{9}+\dfrac{5}{12}$

Solution (a) $\dfrac{1}{3}+\dfrac{5}{7}\underset{\boxed{\substack{\text{The common denominator}\\ \text{is}\\ 3\times 7=21.}}}{=}\dfrac{1\times 7}{3\times 7}+\dfrac{5\times 3}{7\times 3}=\dfrac{7+15}{21}=\dfrac{22}{21}\underset{\boxed{\text{and as a mixed fraction...}}}{=}1\dfrac{1}{21}$

(b) $1\dfrac{5}{6}-2\dfrac{2}{5}\underset{\boxed{\text{Make improper fractions.}}}{=}\dfrac{11}{6}-\dfrac{12}{5}\underset{\boxed{\substack{\text{The common denominator}\\ \text{is}\\ 6\times 5=30.}}}{=}\dfrac{55}{30}-\dfrac{72}{30}=-\dfrac{17}{30}$

(c) $\dfrac{5}{9}+\dfrac{5}{12}\underset{\boxed{\substack{\text{The \textbf{smallest} common denominator is}\\ 9\times 4=36 \text{ which is the}\\ \textbf{least common multiple} \text{ of } 9 \text{ and } 12!}}}{=}\dfrac{5\times 4}{9\times 4}+\dfrac{5\times 3}{12\times 3}=\dfrac{20}{36}+\dfrac{15}{36}=\dfrac{35}{36}$

Example 2)(a) $\dfrac{1}{3}+\dfrac{1}{5}-\dfrac{1}{7}$ (b) $\dfrac{2}{15}+\dfrac{3}{10}-\dfrac{1}{6}+3$

Solution (a) $\dfrac{1}{3}+\dfrac{1}{5}-\dfrac{1}{7}\underset{\boxed{\substack{\text{The common denominator}\\ \text{is}\\ 3\times 5\times 7=105.}}}{=}\dfrac{1\times 5\times 7}{105}+\dfrac{1\times 3\times 7}{105}-\dfrac{1\times 3\times 5}{105}=\dfrac{35+21-15}{105}=\dfrac{41}{105}$

(b) $\dfrac{2}{15}+\dfrac{3}{10}-\dfrac{1}{6}+3=\dfrac{2}{3\times 5}+\dfrac{3}{2\times 5}-\dfrac{1}{2\times 3}+\dfrac{3}{1}\underset{\boxed{\substack{\text{The \textbf{lowest}}\\ \text{common denominator}\\ \text{is}\\ 3\times 5\times 2=30.}}}{=}\dfrac{4}{30}+\dfrac{9}{30}-\dfrac{5}{30}+\dfrac{90}{30}=\dfrac{98}{30}=\dfrac{49}{15}$

Note: See page 23 for adding and subtracting polynomial fractions.

Two for you.

1)(a) $\dfrac{1}{5}+\dfrac{2}{9}$ (b) $3\dfrac{5}{7}-4\dfrac{1}{3}$ (c) $\dfrac{2}{11}+\dfrac{1}{22}$

2)(a) $\dfrac{1}{2}+\dfrac{2}{5}-1\dfrac{1}{10}$ (b) $5-2\dfrac{1}{4}+\dfrac{2}{3}$

Answers 1)(a) $\dfrac{19}{45}$ (b) $-\dfrac{13}{21}$ (c) $\dfrac{5}{22}$

2)(a) $-\dfrac{1}{5}$ (b) $\dfrac{41}{12}$ or $3\dfrac{5}{12}$

Multiplying and Dividing Fractions

When multiplying fractions, life is easy: $\boxed{\dfrac{a}{b} \times \dfrac{c}{d} = \dfrac{ac}{bd}}$

Dividing fractions causes a little heartache, but only because many of you don't understand the famous "**invert and multiply**" rule.

If you have divided five **whole** pizzas into thirds, then certainly you have fifteen portions. Well, you have just verified that $\dfrac{5 \text{ pizzas}}{\left(\dfrac{1}{3}\right)} = 15 \text{ pizza portions}$, that is, you have inverted

and multiplied: $\dfrac{5}{\left(\dfrac{1}{3}\right)} = 5 \times \underset{\text{Invert and multiply!}}{\left(\dfrac{3}{1}\right)} = 15$

Example 1)(a) $\dfrac{4}{5} \times \dfrac{3}{7}$ (b) $\dfrac{14}{9} \times \dfrac{3}{7}$ (c) $2\dfrac{2}{5} \times 3\dfrac{1}{4}$

Solution (a) $\dfrac{4}{5} \times \dfrac{3}{7} \overset{\boxed{\frac{a}{b} \times \frac{c}{d} = \frac{ac}{bd}}}{=} \dfrac{12}{35}$ (b) $\dfrac{14}{9} \times \dfrac{3}{7} \overset{\boxed{\text{Reduce first.}}}{=} \dfrac{\overset{2}{\cancel{14}}}{\underset{3}{\cancel{9}}} \times \dfrac{\overset{1}{\cancel{3}}}{\underset{1}{\cancel{7}}} = \dfrac{2}{3} \times \dfrac{1}{1} = \dfrac{2}{3}$

(c) $2\dfrac{2}{5} \times 3\dfrac{1}{4} \overset{\boxed{\text{Make improper fractions.}}}{=} \dfrac{\overset{3}{\cancel{12}}}{5} \times \dfrac{13}{\underset{1}{\cancel{4}}} = \dfrac{39}{5} \overset{\boxed{\text{or, as a mixed fraction, is ...}}}{=} 7\dfrac{4}{5}$

Example 2)(a) $\dfrac{\left(\dfrac{4}{5}\right)}{\left(\dfrac{3}{7}\right)}$ (b) $\dfrac{\left(\dfrac{7}{3}\right)}{4}$ (c) $\dfrac{7}{\left(\dfrac{3}{4}\right)}$

Solution (a) $\dfrac{\left(\dfrac{4}{5}\right)}{\left(\dfrac{3}{7}\right)} \overset{\boxed{\text{Invert and multiply!}}}{=} \dfrac{4}{5} \times \dfrac{7}{3} = \dfrac{28}{15}$ (b) $\dfrac{\left(\dfrac{7}{3}\right)}{4} = \dfrac{\left(\dfrac{7}{3}\right)}{\left(\dfrac{4}{1}\right)} = \dfrac{7}{3} \times \dfrac{1}{4} = \dfrac{7}{12}$

(c) $\dfrac{7}{\left(\dfrac{3}{4}\right)} = \dfrac{\left(\dfrac{7}{1}\right)}{\left(\dfrac{3}{4}\right)} = \dfrac{7}{1} \times \dfrac{4}{3} = \dfrac{28}{3}$

Two for you.

1)(a) $\dfrac{2}{9} \times \dfrac{4}{5}$ (b) $\dfrac{4}{5} \times \dfrac{15}{16}$ (c) $1\dfrac{1}{3} \times 2\dfrac{2}{7}$

2)(a) $\dfrac{\left(\dfrac{2}{9}\right)}{\left(\dfrac{5}{8}\right)}$ (b) $\dfrac{\left(\dfrac{2}{11}\right)}{3}$ (c) $\dfrac{5}{\left(\dfrac{1}{7}\right)}$

Answers 1)(a) $\dfrac{8}{45}$ (b) $\dfrac{3}{4}$ (c) $\dfrac{64}{21}$ or $3\dfrac{1}{21}$

2)(a) $\dfrac{16}{45}$ (b) $\dfrac{2}{33}$ (c) $\dfrac{35}{1} = 35$

Factoring Difference of Squares

Does anyone out there have a problem with $a^2 - b^2 = (a-b)(a+b)$? I didn't think so! Problems arise when it's not so obvious that difference of squares is what we are dealing with.

Example 1) Factor (a) $a^4 - b^8$ (b) $(x+y-z)^2 - (x-y-z)^2$

Solution (a) $a^4 - b^8 = (a^2 - b^4)(a^2 + b^4) \overset{\boxed{\text{Don't stop now!}}}{=} (a - b^2)(a + b^2)(a^2 + b^4)$

$\overset{\boxed{\text{for the obsessive}}}{=} (\sqrt{a} - b)(\sqrt{a} + b)(a + b^2)(a^2 + b^4)$

(b) $(x+y-z)^2 - (x-y-z)^2 \overset{\boxed{\begin{smallmatrix}a = x+y-z\\ b = x-y-z\end{smallmatrix}}}{=} \left(x+y-z-(x-y-z)\right)\left(x+y-z+x-y-z\right)$

$= 2y(2x - 2z) = 4y(x - z)$

Difference of squares is often used **SDRAWKCAB**, er, **BACKWARDS**, to rationalize expressions. This is especially useful in some limit questions.

Example 2) Rationalize the denominator in $\dfrac{1}{\sqrt{x} + \sqrt{y}}$.

Solution $\dfrac{1}{\sqrt{x} + \sqrt{y}} = \dfrac{1}{\sqrt{x} + \sqrt{y}}\left(\dfrac{\sqrt{x} - \sqrt{y}}{\sqrt{x} - \sqrt{y}}\right) = \dfrac{\sqrt{x} - \sqrt{y}}{x - y}$

Example 3) Evaluate: $\displaystyle\lim_{x \to 9} \dfrac{x - 9}{\sqrt{x} - 3}$

First Solution $\displaystyle\lim_{x \to 9} \dfrac{x - 9}{\sqrt{x} - 3} \overset{\boxed{\text{Factor the top...}}}{=} \lim_{x \to 9} \dfrac{(\sqrt{x} - 3)(\sqrt{x} + 3)}{\sqrt{x} - 3} = \lim_{x \to 9}(\sqrt{x} + 3) = 6$

Second Solution $\displaystyle\lim_{x \to 9} \dfrac{x - 9}{\sqrt{x} - 3} \overset{\boxed{\text{...or rationalize the bottom.}}}{=} \lim_{x \to 9} \dfrac{x - 9}{(\sqrt{x} - 3)}\left(\dfrac{\sqrt{x} + 3}{\sqrt{x} + 3}\right)$

$= \displaystyle\lim_{x \to 9} \dfrac{(x - 9)(\sqrt{x} + 3)}{x - 9} = \lim_{x \to 9}(\sqrt{x} + 3) = 6$

Two for you.

1) Factor: (a) $(x+y)^2 - (x-y)^2$ (b) $x^4 - z^{12}$

2)(a) Rationalize the numerator: $\dfrac{\sqrt{x+4} - \sqrt{3x-6}}{x-5}$

(b) Evaluate: $\displaystyle\lim_{x\to 5} \dfrac{\sqrt{x+4} - \sqrt{3x-6}}{x-5}$

Answers 1)(a) $4xy$ (b) $(x - z^3)(x + z^3)(x^2 + z^6)$

2)(a) $\dfrac{-2}{\sqrt{x+4} + \sqrt{3x-6}}$ (b) $-\dfrac{1}{3}$

Factoring Difference of Cubes

Lots of people have trouble with this one!

$a^3 - b^3 = (a-b)(a^2 + ab + b^2)$. Note that the coefficient of ab is +1. Note also that $a^2 + ab + b^2$ doesn't factor any further!

Example 1) Factor (a) $a^3 - b^6$ (b) $(x+h)^3 - x^3$

Solution (a) $a^3 - b^6 \overset{\boxed{a^3 - \left(b^2\right)^3}}{=} (a - b^2)(a^2 + ab^2 + b^4)$

$$\overset{\boxed{\substack{\text{For the obsessive:} \\ \text{use difference} \\ \text{of squares.}}}}{=} (\sqrt{a} - b)(\sqrt{a} + b)(a^2 + ab^2 + b^4)$$

(b) $(x+h)^3 - x^3 \overset{\boxed{\substack{\text{Here, } a=x+h \\ \text{and } b=x.}}}{=} (x+h-x)\left((x+h)^2 + (x+h)x + x^2\right)$

$$= h\left((x+h)^2 + (x+h)x + x^2\right)$$

(If you have taken calculus, this example should remind you of the derivative limit for $y = x^3$.) As with difference of squares, there are two approaches to limits with difference of cubes.

Example 2) Evaluate $\lim\limits_{x \to 64} \dfrac{x - 64}{x^{1/3} - 4}$.

First Solution $\lim\limits_{x \to 64} \dfrac{x - 64}{x^{1/3} - 4} \overset{\boxed{\substack{\text{Factor the top:} \\ a=x^{1/3} \text{ and } b=4}}}{=} \lim\limits_{x \to 64} \dfrac{(x^{1/3} - 4)(x^{2/3} + 4x^{1/3} + 16)}{x^{1/3} - 4}$

$= \lim\limits_{x \to 64}(x^{2/3} + 4x^{1/3} + 16) = 48$

Second solution $\lim\limits_{x \to 64} \dfrac{x - 64}{x^{1/3} - 4} \overset{\boxed{\text{Now rationalize the bottom.}}}{=} \lim\limits_{x \to 64} \dfrac{x - 64}{(x^{1/3} - 4)}\left(\dfrac{x^{2/3} + 4x^{1/3} + 16}{x^{2/3} + 4x^{1/3} + 16}\right)$

$= \lim\limits_{x \to 64} \dfrac{(x - 64)(x^{2/3} + 4x^{1/3} + 16)}{x - 64} = \lim\limits_{x \to 64}(x^{2/3} + 4x^{1/3} + 16) = 48$

Two for you.

1) Factor: $x^6 - y^6$

2) Evaluate the limits: (a) $\lim\limits_{x \to 5} \dfrac{x^3 - 125}{x^2 - 25}$ (b) $\lim\limits_{x \to 8} \dfrac{x - 8}{x^{1/3} - 2}$

Answers 1) $(x^2 - y^2)(x^4 + x^2 y^2 + y^4) = (x - y)(x + y)(x^4 + x^2 y^2 + y^4)$

2)(a) $\dfrac{15}{2}$ (b) 12

Factoring $a^n - b^n$ and $a^n + b^n$

First: Factoring $a^n - b^n$

First, please review these **Mathematics Survival Kit** topics:
Difference of Squares (page 9) and **Difference of Cubes** (page 11).

$$a^2 - b^2 = (a-b)(a+b)$$
$$a^3 - b^3 = (a-b)(a^2 + ab + b^2) \text{ Note that the coefficient of } ab \text{ is 1.}$$
$$a^4 - b^4 = (a-b)(a^3 + a^2b + ab^2 + b^3). \text{ So, for positive integers } n,$$
$$a^n - b^n = (a-b)(a^{n-1} + a^{n-2}b + a^{n-3}b^2 + a^{n-4}b^3 + \ldots + a^2b^{n-3} + ab^{n-2} + b^{n-1})$$

In the second bracket for the factored form of $a^n - b^n$, the exponent on a starts at $n-1$ and decreases one by one down to 0. The exponent on b starts at 0 and goes up one by one to $n-1$. **This formula works for any $n \in \mathbb{N}$, that is, for natural numbers.**

Second: Factoring $a^n + b^n$
(and we want n to be ODD!)

Face it: $a^2 + b^2$ **doesn't factor!** Well, all right, it does if you allow **complex numbers**.
$a^2 + b^2 = (a-bi)(a+bi)$, where $i = \sqrt{-1}$. For our purposes, restricted to real numbers, the sum of squares doesn't factor. Also, $a^4 + b^4$ and $a^8 + b^8$ have no easy linear factors like $a-b$ or $a+b$ (although they do have complicated quadratic factors! For now, don't ask!)
However, sum of cubes does factor: $a^3 + b^3 = (a+b)(a^2 - ab + b^2)$
Compare the difference of cubes: $a^3 - b^3 = (a-b)(a^2 + ab + b^2)$
Look at where $+$ changes to $-$. So, as long as n is $\boxed{\text{ODD}}$,
$$a^n + b^n = (a+b)(a^{n-1} - a^{n-2}b + a^{n-3}b^2 - a^{n-4}b^3 + \ldots + a^2b^{n-3} - ab^{n-2} + b^{n-1})$$

Example 1) Factor: (a) $a^5 - b^5$ (b) $a^5 + b^5$ (c) $a^7 + b^7$

Solution (a) $a^5 - b^5 = (a-b)(a^4 + a^3b + a^2b^2 + ab^3 + b^4)$
(b) $a^5 + b^5 = (a+b)(a^4 - a^3b + a^2b^2 - ab^3 + b^4)$
(c) $a^7 + b^7 = (a+b)(a^6 - a^5b + a^4b^2 - a^3b^3 + a^2b^4 - ab^5 + b^6)$

Two for you.

1) Factor: $a^5 - b^{10}$

2) Factor: $a^{15} + b^{30}$ (Hint: $a^{15} + b^{30} = (a^3)^5 + (b^6)^5$)

Answers 1) $(a - b^2)(a^4 + a^3b^2 + a^2b^4 + ab^6 + b^8)$

2) $(a^3 + b^6)(a^{12} - a^9b^6 + a^6b^{12} - a^3b^{18} + b^{24})$

optional

$= (a + b^2)(a^2 - ab^2 + b^4)(a^{12} - a^9b^6 + a^6b^{12} - a^3b^{18} + b^{24})$

Common Factors

The easiest kind of factoring is "common factoring". However, even common factors can be confusing when terms have factors like $(a+b)$ or negative exponents or fractional exponents! Let's do basics first and challenges second. Remember: $ax + ay - az = a(x + y - z)$.

Example 1) Factor (a) $2x^4y^2 + 4x^3y^3$ (b) $4(a+b)^2 - 7(a+b)^3 + a + b$

Solution (a) $2x^4y^2 + 4x^3y^3$ [$2x^3y^2$ is common to both terms.] $= 2x^3y^2(x + 2y)$

(b) $4(a+b)^2 - 7(a+b)^3 + a + b$ [$(a+b)$ is common to all three terms (treating the last $(a+b)$ as a single term)] $= (a+b)\left(4(a+b) - 7(a+b)^2 + 1\right)$

Example 2) Use common factoring to simplify the following:

(a) $\dfrac{(x-1)^3(3)(x+1)^2 - (x+1)^3(3)(x-1)^2}{(x-1)^6}$ (b) $x^{\frac{1}{3}}\left(\dfrac{2}{3}\right)(x-5)^{-\frac{1}{3}} + (x-5)^{\frac{2}{3}}\left(\dfrac{1}{3}\right)x^{-\frac{2}{3}}$

> Calculus students: these expressions appear with $\dfrac{d}{dx}\left(\dfrac{(x+1)^3}{(x-1)^3}\right)$ and $\dfrac{d}{dx}\left(x^{\frac{1}{3}}(x-5)^{\frac{2}{3}}\right)$.

Solution (a) $\dfrac{(x-1)^3(3)(x+1)^2 - (x+1)^3(3)(x-1)^2}{(x-1)^6}$

[$3(x-1)^2(x+1)^2$ is common to both terms in the numerator] $= \dfrac{3(x-1)^2(x+1)^2}{(x-1)^6}\left((x-1) - (x+1)\right) = -\dfrac{6(x+1)^2}{(x-1)^4}$

[The common factor is $\left(\dfrac{1}{3}\right)x^{-\frac{2}{3}}(x-5)^{-\frac{1}{3}}$. The **LOWER** exponent is the common exponent!]

(b) $x^{\frac{1}{3}}\left(\dfrac{2}{3}\right)(x-5)^{-\frac{1}{3}} + (x-5)^{\frac{2}{3}}\left(\dfrac{1}{3}\right)x^{-\frac{2}{3}}$

[I am including this optional step to show **EXPLICITLY** the common factor with the negative exponent in each of the first and second terms.]

[This is $x^{\frac{1}{3}}$ rewritten as $x^{-\frac{2}{3}}x^{\frac{3}{3}} = x^{-\frac{2}{3}}x$ in the first term to emphasize how to factor out $x^{-\frac{2}{3}}$ from this term.]

[This is $(x-5)^{\frac{2}{3}}$ rewritten as $(x-5)^{-\frac{1}{3}}(x-5)^{\frac{3}{3}} = (x-5)^{-\frac{1}{3}}(x-5)$ in the second term to emphasize how to factor $(x-5)^{-\frac{1}{3}}$ from this term.]

$= x^{-\frac{2}{3}}x \cdot \left(\dfrac{2}{3}\right)(x-5)^{-\frac{1}{3}} + (x-5)^{-\frac{1}{3}}(x-5) \cdot \left(\dfrac{1}{3}\right)x^{-\frac{2}{3}}$

$= \left(\dfrac{1}{3}\right)x^{-\frac{2}{3}}(x-5)^{-\frac{1}{3}}\left(\underbrace{2x}_{\text{This is all that is left in the \textbf{first} term after taking out the common factor.}} + \underbrace{x-5}_{\text{This is all that is left in the \textbf{second} term after taking out the common factor.}}\right)$

$= \left(\dfrac{1}{3}\right)x^{-\frac{2}{3}}(x-5)^{-\frac{1}{3}}(3x-5) = \dfrac{3x-5}{3x^{\frac{2}{3}}(x-5)^{\frac{1}{3}}}$

Two for you.

Factor each of the following:

1)(a) $3m^3n^2 - 6m^5n^5 + 9m^3n^3 - 12m^4n^2$ (b) $(x+y)^3 - (x+y)^5 + 2(x+y)$

2) $\left(\dfrac{1}{4}\right)(x-1)^{\frac{1}{2}}(x+1)^{-\frac{3}{4}} + \left(\dfrac{1}{2}\right)(x-1)^{-\frac{1}{2}}(x+1)^{\frac{1}{4}}$

Answers 1)(a) $3m^3n^2(1 - 2m^2n^3 + 3n - 4m)$ (b) $(x+y)\left((x+y)^2 - (x+y)^4 + 2\right)$

2) $\left(\dfrac{1}{4}\right)(x-1)^{-\frac{1}{2}}(x+1)^{-\frac{3}{4}}(3x+1) \overset{\boxed{\text{or}}}{=} \dfrac{3x+1}{4(x-1)^{\frac{1}{2}}(x+1)^{\frac{3}{4}}}$

Factoring (Easy) Quadratic Expressions/Trinomials Without Using the Quadratic Formula

Some quadratic expressions factor easily: $x^2 - 4x + 3 = (x-3)(x-1)$

When we need to factor quadratic expressions with equations like $2x^2 - x - 5 = 0$ (which in fact has **non-rational roots**) or $2x^2 - x + 3 = 0$ (which in fact has **non-real roots**), we can use the quadratic formula to make factoring foolproof. Go to page 51 for that method (and to see why the roots are non-rational and non-real, respectively.) However, when the quadratic expression/trinomial factors easily, using the quadratic formula is too much work when this simpler approach will do.

Assume a and b are positive and $a \le b$.

This is crucial to understanding the method below. There are four scenarios in the...

MATHEMATICS SURVIVAL KIT TRINOMIAL BOX

$$(1)\ (x-a)(x-b) = x^2 - ax - bx + ab = x^2 - (a+b)x + ab$$
$$(2)\ (x+a)(x+b) = x^2 + ax + bx + ab = x^2 + (a+b)x + ab$$
$$(3)\ (x-a)(x+b) = x^2 - ax + bx - ab = x^2 + (b-a)x - ab$$
$$(4)\ (x+a)(x-b) = x^2 + ax - bx - ab = x^2 - (b-a)x - ab$$

Example 1) Factor $x^2 - 4x + 3$.

Solution This trinomial fits the form (1) in the trinomial box above: $a + b = 4$ and $ab = 3$.

$$x^2 - 4x + 3 \ \overset{\boxed{\substack{a=1,\ b=3 \\ (x-a)(x-b)}}}{=}\ (x-1)(x-3).$$

Example 2) Factor: (i) $x^2 + 4x - 5$ (ii) $x^2 - 4x - 5$

Solution (i) Because of the -5 and the $+4$, we have form (3) in the Trinomial Box.

$$x^2 + 4x - 5 \ \overset{\boxed{\substack{a=1,\ b=5 \\ (x-a)(x+b)}}}{=}\ (x-1)(x+5)$$

(ii) Because of the -5 and the -4, we have form (4) in the Trinomial Box.

$$x^2 - 4x - 5 \ \overset{\boxed{\substack{a=1,\ b=5 \\ (x+a)(x-b)}}}{=}\ (x+1)(x-5)$$

Example 3) Factor: $3x^2 + 14x - 5$

Solution This doesn't fit into the Trinomial Box. It does factor pretty easily but we need a fair bit of trial and error to make the x^2 coefficient 3, the constant -5 and the x coefficient 14. My suggestion: it is easy and "trial and error" free to use the quadratic formula. You have (my) permission to do so. Go to page 51.

Two for you.

Factor each of the following:

1)(a) $x^2 + 11x + 10$ (b) $x^2 - 11x + 10$ 2)(a) $x^2 + 11x - 12$ (b) $x^2 - 11x - 12$

Answers 1)(a) $(x+10)(x+1)$ (b) $(x-10)(x-1)$

2)(a) $(x+12)(x-1)$ (b) $(x-12)(x+1)$

The Remainder and Factor Theorems for Polynomials

> **The Remainder Theorem** tells us that when we divide polynomial $P(x)$ by $x-a$ to obtain quotient $Q(x)$ and remainder R, then $R = P(a)$, that is, $P(x) = Q(x)(x-a) + P(a)$. So, if $P(a) = 0$, then $P(x) = Q(x)(x-a)$, that is, $x-a$ is a factor of $P(x)$. This is ...
>
> > **The Factor Theorem**
> > $x-a$ is a factor of polynomial $P(x) \Leftrightarrow P(a) = 0$
>
> Also, suppose $P(x) = a_n x^n + a_{n-1}x^{n-1} + ... + a_1 x + a_0$, where all the a_i's are integers, and $\dfrac{p}{q}$ is a root of $P(x)$. **Then q must divide a_n and p must divide a_0.**

Example 1) Using the Factor Theorem, find **rational roots** of $P(x) = x^3 - x^2 - 4x + 4$.

Solution The coefficient of x^3 is 1 and $a_0 = 4$. If $a = \dfrac{p}{q}$ is a rational root, then

p must divide 4 and q must divide 1. Therefore, we need to check $a = \pm 1, \pm 2, \pm 4$.

$P(1) = 0$, $P(-1) = 6$, $P(2) = 0$, $P(-2) = 0$, $P(4) = 36$, $P(-4) = -60$

Therefore the roots are 1, 2, and -2.

Two notes : 1) $P(x)$, a cubic, can have at most 3 roots. If we find 3, we are done!

2) $P(x) = (x-1)(x-2)(x+2)$

Example 2) Find the rational roots of $P(x) = 2x^4 - 5x^3 + 5x^2 - 5x + 3$.

Solution The coefficient of x^4 is 2 and $a_0 = 3$. If $a = \dfrac{p}{q}$ is a rational root, then

p must divide 3 and q must divide 2. We need to check $a = \pm 1, \pm\dfrac{1}{2}, \pm 3$, and $\pm\dfrac{3}{2}$.

$P(1) = 0$, $P(-1) = 20$, $P(3) = 60$, $P(-3) = 360$, $P\left(\dfrac{1}{2}\right) = \dfrac{5}{4}$, $P\left(-\dfrac{1}{2}\right) = \dfrac{15}{2}$, $P\left(\dfrac{3}{2}\right) = 0$,

$P\left(-\dfrac{3}{2}\right) = \dfrac{195}{4}$ Therefore the rational roots are 1 and $\dfrac{3}{2}$.

Three notes : 1) Since $P(x)$ is degree 4, the other roots are irrational or complex.

2) See **Polynomial Division** on page 27.
Divide $x-1$ into $P(x)$ and then $x - \dfrac{3}{2}$ into the resulting quotient.

The result: $P(x) = (x-1)\left(x - \dfrac{3}{2}\right)(2x^2 + 2)$ $\overset{\text{a little prettier...}}{=}$ $(x-1)(2x-3)(x^2+1)$.

3) The non-rational roots are $\pm i$, that is, $\pm\sqrt{-1}$.

Two for you.

Find the rational roots and then factor.

1) $P(x) = x^3 + 2x^2 - 5x - 6$ 2) $P(x) = 3x^4 - x^3 - 3x + 1$

Answers 1) $-1, \ 2, \ -3, \ P(x) = (x+1)(x-2)(x+3)$

2) $1, \ \dfrac{1}{3}, \ P(x) = (3x-1)(x-1)(x^2 + x + 1)$

Multiplying Expressions—FOIL: $(a+b)(c+d)$

In grades 9, 10, 11, 12, and yes, even university, there are students who believe $(x+y)^2 = x^2 + y^2$! NoNoNo!!! $(3+4)^2 = 7^2 = 49 \neq 3^2 + 4^2 = 9 + 16 = 25$!

Here is how we multiply two binomial expressions (expressions with **2** terms) and why. Everyone agrees that $A(x+y) = Ax + Ay$. Replace A with $(x+y)$:

$$(x+y)^2 = \overbrace{(x+y)(x+y)}^{\text{This is } A(x+y)!} = \overbrace{(x+y)\cdot x}^{A\cdot x} + \overbrace{(x+y)\cdot y}^{A\cdot y} = x^2 + yx + xy + y^2 = x^2 + 2xy + y^2$$

Each "term" in the first bracket (the terms are x and y) is multiplied by each term in the second (where the terms are again x and y.) Apply that reasoning to $(a+b)(c+d)$:

$$\underset{\underset{\text{FIRST}}{}\underset{\text{OUTSIDE}}{}\underset{\text{INSIDE}}{}\underset{\text{LAST}}{}}{\text{F}\quad\text{O}\quad\text{I}\quad\text{L}} : (a+b)(c+d) = \underset{\text{FIRST TERMS}}{ac} + \underset{\text{OUTSIDE TERMS}}{ad} + \underset{\text{INSIDE TERMS}}{bc} + \underset{\text{LAST TERMS}}{bd}$$

Example 1) Expand and simplify: (a) $(x+3)(x-2)$ (b) $(2a-3b)(2a+3b)$

Solution (a) $(x+3)(x-2) = \underset{\text{F}}{x^2} \underset{\text{O}}{-2x} + \underset{\text{I}}{3x} \underset{\text{L}}{-6} = x^2 + x - 6$

(b) $(2a-3b)(2a+3b)$ [This is an example of **Difference of Squares**.] $= \underset{\text{F}}{4a^2} + \underset{\text{O}}{6ab} \underset{\text{I}}{-6ab} \underset{\text{L}}{-9b^2} = 4a^2 - 9b^2$

Example 2) Expand and simplify:

(a) $(a+b+c)(x+y+z)$ (b) $(a+b+c)^2$ (c) $(a+b+c+d)^2$

Solution

(a) $(a+b+c)(x+y+z)$ [Multiply each of the three terms in the first bracket with each of the three terms in the second bracket.] $= ax + ay + az + bx + by + bz + cx + cy + cz$

(b) $(a+b+c)^2 = (a+b+c)(a+b+c)$

$\qquad = a^2 + ab + ac + ba + b^2 + bc + ca + cb + c^2$

[Collect like terms.] $= a^2 + b^2 + c^2 + 2ab + 2ac + 2cb$

(c) $(a+b+c+d)^2$ [using our experience from Example 2(b)...] $= a^2 + b^2 + c^2 + d^2 + 2ab + 2ac + 2ad + 2bc + 2bd + 2cd$

Note: In (a), there are 3 terms in each bracket. Since each term in the first is multiplied by each term in the second, the product has $3 \times 3 = 9$ terms in all. Of course, in (b) and (c), we collect like terms. So while the answer to (c) appears to have 10 terms, there were $4 \times 4 = 16$ terms before we simplified by collecting like terms.

Two for you.

Expand and simplify each of the following expressions:

1) $(x+3y)(2x-5y+1)$ 2) $(a+2b-3c)^2$

Answers 1) $2x^2+xy+x-15y^2+3y$ 2) $a^2+4b^2+9c^2+4ab-6ac-12bc$

Adding and Subtracting Polynomial Fractions

To simplify when we add or subtract fractions, we need to get the

lowest common denominator : $\dfrac{2}{3}+\dfrac{5}{9}-\dfrac{5}{12}=\dfrac{24}{36}+\dfrac{20}{36}-\dfrac{15}{36}=\dfrac{29}{36}$.

We use exactly the same method when adding and/or subtracting fractions with polynomials in the top and bottom.

Example 1) Simplify $\dfrac{3}{2a}-\dfrac{6}{5a}+\dfrac{3}{10a}$.

Solution $\dfrac{3}{2a}-\dfrac{6}{5a}+\dfrac{3}{10a}$

| Get the **lowest** common denominator! |
$= \dfrac{15}{10a}-\dfrac{12}{10a}+\dfrac{3}{10a}$

| Simplify the numerator. |
$= \dfrac{6}{10a}$

| Reduce more if you can! |
$= \dfrac{3}{5a}$

Example 2) Simplify $\dfrac{2x+1}{x-1}-\dfrac{x+1}{x+2}-\dfrac{5x+4}{x^2+x-2}$.

Solution $\dfrac{2x+1}{x-1}-\dfrac{x+1}{x+2}-\dfrac{5x+4}{x^2+x-2}$

| Factor the denominators! |
$= \dfrac{2x+1}{x-1}-\dfrac{x+1}{x+2}-\dfrac{5x+4}{(x-1)(x+2)}$

| Get the **lowest** common denominator. |
$= \dfrac{(2x+1)(x+2)}{(x-1)(x+2)}-\dfrac{(x+1)(x-1)}{(x-1)(x+2)}-\dfrac{5x+4}{(x-1)(x+2)}$

| Expand the numerator. |
$= \dfrac{2x^2+5x+2-(x^2-1)-(5x+4)}{(x-1)(x+2)}$

| Now simplify the numerator. |
$= \dfrac{x^2-1}{(x-1)(x+2)}$

| Check for and divide out any further common factors. |
$= \dfrac{\cancel{(x-1)}(x+1)}{\cancel{(x-1)}(x+2)}=\dfrac{x+1}{x+2}$

Two for you.

Simplify each of the following rational expressions:

1) $\dfrac{2x}{x-5} - \dfrac{x}{x-3} + \dfrac{1}{x^2-8x+15}$

2) $\dfrac{x-1}{x^2-16} + \dfrac{x}{x^2-5x+4} - \dfrac{1}{x^2+3x-4}$

Answers 1) $\dfrac{x^2-x+1}{(x-5)(x-3)}$ 2) $\dfrac{2x^2+x+5}{(x-4)(x+4)(x-1)}$

Multiplying and Dividing Polynomial Fractions

What we do with fractions having polynomials in the top and bottom is **exactly** what we do with fractions having numbers in the top and bottom.

$$\frac{4\cdot 7^3}{2\cdot 5^5}\times\frac{2^4\cdot 5^4}{4^2\cdot 7\cdot 11}\quad\boxed{\substack{\text{Get common}\\\text{factors and bases.}}}\quad=\quad\frac{2^2\cdot 7^3\cdot 2^4\cdot 5^4}{2\cdot 5^5\cdot 2^4\cdot 7\cdot 11}\quad\boxed{\substack{\text{Divide out the}\\\text{common factors.}}}\quad=\quad\frac{2\cdot 7^2}{5\cdot 11}\quad\boxed{\substack{\text{In the numerical case,}\\\text{work out the final value.}}}\quad=\quad\frac{98}{55}\ \boxed{\text{or}}\ 1\frac{43}{55}$$

Let's do the same question, setting it up so that it starts as **DIVISION!**

$$\frac{4\cdot 7^3}{2\cdot 5^5}\div\frac{4^2\cdot 7\cdot 11}{2^4\cdot 5^4}\quad\boxed{\text{Invert and multiply!}}\quad=\quad\frac{4\cdot 7^3}{2\cdot 5^5}\times\frac{2^4\cdot 5^4}{4^2\cdot 7\cdot 11}\quad\boxed{\text{Now repeat the steps above.}}\quad=\quad\dots=\frac{98}{55}$$

Example 1) Simplify the rational expression $\dfrac{(x^2-9)}{(x-3)^3}\times\dfrac{(x^2-3x)^2}{x^3+27}$.

Solution $\dfrac{(x^2-9)}{(x-3)^3}\times\dfrac{(x^2-3x)^2}{x^3+27}$

$\boxed{\substack{\text{Factor first! Then divide}\\\text{out the common factors.}}}$

$$=\ \frac{(x-3)(x+3)(x^2)(x-3)^2}{(x-3)^3(x+3)(x^2-3x+9)}$$

$$=\ \frac{x^2}{x^2-3x+9}$$

Example 2) Simplify: $\dfrac{m^2+3mn+2n^2}{m^2+2mn+n^2}\div\dfrac{m^2+2mn}{m^2+mn}$

Solution $\dfrac{m^2+3mn+2n^2}{m^2+2mn+n^2}\div\dfrac{m^2+2mn}{m^2+mn}$

$\boxed{\text{Invert and multiply!}}$

$$=\ \frac{m^2+3mn+2n^2}{m^2+2mn+n^2}\times\frac{m^2+mn}{m^2+2mn}$$

$\boxed{\substack{\text{Factor and divide}\\\text{out common factors!}}}$

$$=\ \frac{(m+n)(m+2n)}{(m+n)^2}\times\frac{m(m+n)}{m(m+2n)}$$

$$=\ 1$$

Two for you.

Simplify each of the following rational expressions:

1) $\dfrac{(x^2+5x+6)^2}{(x^2+6x+9)(x^2-9)} \times \dfrac{x^3-27}{x^2+4x+4}$

2) $\dfrac{(a^3+5a^2)^3}{a^2+10a+25} \div \dfrac{a^8(a^3+125)}{a^2-5a+25}$

Answers 1) $\dfrac{x^2+3x+9}{x+3}$ 2) $\dfrac{1}{a^2}$

Polynomial Division

Keep this example in mind: $3\overline{)28}$ with quotient 9, -27, remainder 1

| 3 divides into 28 approximately 9 times. |
| Multiply 9 by 3 and subtract to get the remainder. |

$D \equiv$ DIVIDEND $Q \equiv$ QUOTIENT $R \equiv$ REMAINDER $d \equiv$ DIVISOR

$$\dfrac{D}{d} = Q + \dfrac{R}{d} \quad \overset{\text{which, in the example above, gives...}}{\Rightarrow} \quad \dfrac{28}{3} = 9 + \dfrac{1}{3} \qquad D = Q \cdot d + R \quad \overset{\text{which, in the example above, gives...}}{\Rightarrow} \quad 28 = 9 \cdot 3 + 1$$

Example 1) Divide the polynomial $x^3 - 2x^2 + 5x - 7$ by $x + 2$.

Solution $x + 2$ divides into $x^3 - 2x^2 + 5x - 7$ approximately x^2 times, just like "3 into 28" above. Multiply $x + 2$ by x^2 and subtract to get the remainder. And so on...

$$
\begin{array}{r}
x^2 - 4x + 13 \\
x+2 \overline{)\ x^3 - 2x^2 + 5x - 7} \\
-(x^3 + 2x^2) \\
\hline
-4x^2 + 5x - 7 \\
-(-4x^2 - 8x) \\
\hline
13x - 7 \\
-(13x + 26) \\
\hline
-33
\end{array}
$$

Therefore, $\dfrac{x^3 - 2x^2 + 5x - 7}{x+2} \overset{\frac{D}{d}=Q+\frac{R}{d}}{=} x^2 - 4x + 13 - \dfrac{33}{x+2}$

Also, $x^3 - 2x^2 + 5x - 7 \overset{D=Q \cdot d+R}{=} (x^2 - 4x + 13)(x+2) - 33$

Example 2) Divide the polynomial $x^3 + 5x - 1$ by $x - 1$.

Solution For convenience, let's write $x^3 + 5x - 1 = x^3 + 0x^2 + 5x - 1$.

$$
\begin{array}{r}
x^2 + x + 6 \\
x-1 \overline{)\ x^3 + 0x^2 + 5x - 1} \\
-(x^3 - x^2) \\
\hline
x^2 + 5x - 1 \\
-(x^2 - x) \\
\hline
6x - 1 \\
-(6x - 6) \\
\hline
5
\end{array}
$$

Therefore, $\dfrac{x^3 + 5x - 1}{x-1} \overset{\frac{D}{d}=Q+\frac{R}{d}}{=} x^2 + x + 6 + \dfrac{5}{x-1}$

Also, $x^3 + 5x - 1 \overset{D=Q \cdot d+R}{=} (x^2 + x + 6)(x-1) + 5$

Two for you.

Divide the polynomial by the linear factor. Write your answer in the form $D = Q \cdot d + R$.

1) $x^3 + 2x^2 + 3x + 4$ by $x - 1$ 2) $x^4 - x^3 - 5x + 4$ by $x - 2$

Answers 1) $x^3 + 2x^2 + 3x + 4 = (x^2 + 3x + 6)(x - 1) + 10$

2) $x^4 - x^3 - 5x + 4 = (x^3 + x^2 + 2x - 1)(x - 2) + 2$

Finding the Equation of a Line

Given the slope and a point, or two points, there are **lots** of ways to find the equation of a line. The easiest method to cover all scenarios uses the equation $y - y_1 = m(x - x_1)$, where m is the slope and (x_1, y_1) is a point on the line.

Example 1) Find the equation of the line with slope -3 through the point $(2, -5)$.

Solution $y - (-5) \overset{\boxed{x_1 = 2, \, y_1 = -5, \, m = -3}}{=} -3(x - 2)$

$$y + 5 = -3x + 6$$
$$y = -3x + 1$$

Example 2) Find the equation of the line passing through the points $(2, 7)$ and $(4, 12)$.

Solution The slope $m = \dfrac{y_2 - y_1}{x_2 - x_1} = \dfrac{12 - 7}{4 - 2} = \dfrac{5}{2}$.

$$\boxed{\text{Note: } \dfrac{y_1 - y_2}{x_1 - x_2} = \dfrac{7 - 12}{2 - 4} = \dfrac{5}{2} \text{ as well.}}$$

Using $(2, 7)$ as (x_1, y_1): OR Using $(4, 12)$ as (x_1, y_1):

$$y - 7 = \frac{5}{2}(x - 2)$$ $$\qquad y - 12 = \frac{5}{2}(x - 4)$$

$$y - 7 = \frac{5}{2}x - 5$$ $$\qquad y - 12 = \frac{5}{2}x - 10$$

$$y = \frac{5}{2}x + 2$$ $$\qquad\qquad y = \frac{5}{2}x + 2$$

Example 3) Find the equation of the line passing through the points $(2, 1)$ and $(4, 1)$.

Solution The slope $m = \dfrac{y_2 - y_1}{x_2 - x_1} = \dfrac{1 - 1}{4 - 2} = \dfrac{0}{2} = 0$.

Using $(2, 1)$ as (x_1, y_1): OR Using $(4, 1)$ as (x_1, y_1):

$y - 1 = 0(x - 2)$ $\qquad\qquad y - 1 = 0(x - 4)$

$y - 1 = 0$ $\qquad\qquad\qquad y - 1 = 0$

$y = 1$ $\qquad\qquad\qquad\qquad y = 1$

Two for you.

1) Find the equation of the line through $(-1, -5)$ and $(3, 7)$.

2) Find the equation of the line with x intercept 4 and y intercept 7.
(Hint: use the points $(4, 0)$ and $(0, 7)$.)

Answers 1) $y = 3x - 2$ 2) $y = -\dfrac{7}{4}x + 7$

Slope m and y Intercept b

In the equation of the line $y = mx + b$, m is the slope and b is the y intercept.

Example 1) Find the slope and the y intercept for each of the following lines.

a) $y = 3x + 5$ b) $y = 7 - 2x$ c) $y = 4x$ d) $y = -7$ e) $2x + 3y = 4$

f) $4y - 5x - 2 = 0$ g) $x = 4$ h) $y = 0$ i) $x = 0$ j) $\dfrac{x}{3} + \dfrac{y}{2} = 1$

Solution

a) $m = 3,\ b = 5$ b) $m = -2,\ b = 7$ c) $m = 4,\ b = 0$ d) $m = 0,\ b = -7$

e) Rewrite the equation in the form $y = mx + b$:

$$2x + 3y = 4 \Leftrightarrow 3y = 4 - 2x \Leftrightarrow y = -\frac{2}{3}x + \frac{4}{3} \quad \text{and so} \quad m = -\frac{2}{3} \quad \text{and} \quad b = \frac{4}{3}$$

f) Rewrite the equation in the form $y = mx + b$:

$$4y - 5x - 2 = 0 \Leftrightarrow 4y = 5x + 2 \Leftrightarrow y = \frac{5}{4}x + \frac{1}{2} \quad \text{and so} \quad m = \frac{5}{4} \quad \text{and} \quad b = \frac{1}{2}$$

g) The slope is undefined (or infinite). This is the vertical line where x **always equals 4** while y can be any real number. It is parallel to the y axis and **there is no y intercept**.

h) $m = b = 0$. ($y = 0$ is the equation of the x axis.)

i) The slope is undefined (or infinite). $x = 0$ is the equation of the y axis, so there are **LOTS** of y intercepts!

j) Rewrite the equation in the form $y = mx + b$:

$$\frac{x}{3} + \frac{y}{2} = 1 \Leftrightarrow \frac{y}{2} = 1 - \frac{x}{3} \Leftrightarrow y = -\frac{2}{3}x + 2 \quad \text{and so} \quad m = -\frac{2}{3} \quad \text{and} \quad b = 2$$

Two for you.

Find the slope and the y intercept for the following lines:

1) $\pi y - 2x = 1$ 2) $3x - 4 = 0$

Answers 1) $m = \dfrac{2}{\pi}$, $b = \dfrac{1}{\pi}$ 2) undefined slope, no y intercept

Distance between Two Points and
Distance from a Point to a Line or Plane

Example 1) Find the distance from $(-1, 5)$ to $(6, 3)$.

Solution Distance $\overset{\sqrt{(x_2-x_1)^2+(y_2-y_1)^2}}{=} \sqrt{(6-(-1))^2+(3-5)^2} = \sqrt{7^2+(-2)^2} = \sqrt{53}$

Example 2) Find the (perpendicular) distance from the point $(3, 4)$ to the line $4x - 5y = 7$.

Solution The distance from (x_0, y_0) to $Ax + By + C = 0$ is given by the formula

$\dfrac{|Ax_0 + By_0 + C|}{\sqrt{A^2+B^2}}$. So, from the point $(3, 4)$ to the line $4x - 5y = 7$,

distance $\overset{\boxed{A=4,\ B=-5,\ \text{and}\ C=-7}}{=} \dfrac{|(4)(3)+(-5)(4)-7|}{\sqrt{4^2+5^2}} = \dfrac{|-15|}{\sqrt{41}} = \dfrac{15}{\sqrt{41}}$

Example 3) Find the distance from $(3, 4, -1)$ to $(0, 5, -2)$.

Solution Distance $= \sqrt{(x_2-x_1)^2+(y_2-y_1)^2+(z_2-z_1)^2}$

$= \sqrt{(0-3)^2+(5-4)^2+(-2-(-1))^2} = \sqrt{(-3)^2+(1)^2+(-1)^2} = \sqrt{11}$

Example 4) Find the perpendicular distance from the point $(1, 2, 3)$ to the plane $2x + 4y - 5z = 7$.

Solution The distance from (x_0, y_0, z_0) to $Ax + By + Cz + D = 0$ is given by the formula

$\dfrac{|Ax_0 + By_0 + Cz_0 + D|}{\sqrt{A^2+B^2+C^2}}$. So, from the point $(1, 2, 3)$ to the plane $2x + 4y - 5z = 7$,

distance $\overset{\boxed{A=2,\ B=4,\ C=-5,\ \text{and}\ D=-7}}{=} \dfrac{|(2)(1)+(4)(2)+(-5)(3)-7|}{\sqrt{2^2+4^2+(-5)^2}}$

$= \dfrac{|-12|}{\sqrt{45}} = \dfrac{12}{\sqrt{45}} = \dfrac{12}{3\sqrt{5}} = \dfrac{4}{\sqrt{5}} \overset{\boxed{\text{for fans of BOB}\ (\text{Back Of the Book!})}}{=} \dfrac{4\sqrt{5}}{5}$

Two for you.
1) Find the distance between $(-3, 0, 1)$ and $(5, 2, 0)$.

2) Find the distance from the point $(1, 2, 3)$ to the plane $3x - 7z = 0$.

(Hint: $A = 3$, $B = 0$, $C = -7$, and $D = 0$.)

Answers 1) $\sqrt{69}$ 2) $\dfrac{18}{\sqrt{58}}$ $\boxed{\text{BOB!}}$ $= \dfrac{9\sqrt{58}}{29}$ $\boxed{\text{BOB} \equiv \text{BACK OF BOOK}}$

Visually Identifying Slopes of Lines

This page is all about visually recognizing the slope of a line. Assume the scales on the x and y axes are equal in all cases. Slope tells you how much y increases for a unit change in x. So a slope of 3 means if x **increases** by 1, then y **increases** by 3. If x goes up by 5, then y goes up by $3 \times 5 = 15$, that is, y goes up 3 times as much as x. A slope of -3 means that if x **increases** by 1, then y **decreases** by 3.

Given points (x_1, y_1) and (x_2, y_2), the slope of the segment joining these points is

$$m = \frac{y_2 - y_1}{x_2 - x_1} = \frac{y_1 - y_2}{x_1 - x_2} = \frac{\Delta y}{\Delta x} = \frac{\text{rise}}{\text{run}} = \frac{\text{change in } y}{\text{change in } x}$$

Warning! Don't confuse the symbol "*m*" for slope with the lines labelled "m" below.

Positive Slope
y **goes up**
as *x* **goes up**.

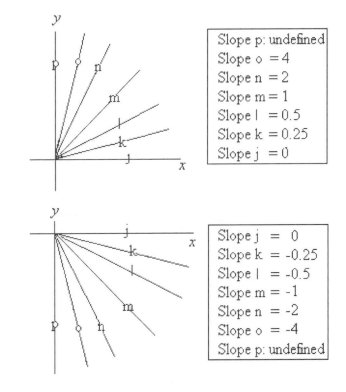

Negative slope
y **goes down**
as *x* **goes up**.

Note:

Horizontal lines (line **j** in both pictures) have **slope 0**.

Vertical lines (line **p** in both pictures) have **undefined (or infinite) slope**.

One for you.

1) Match the slopes 3, -4, 0, 0.5, -0.5, and undefined with the segments.

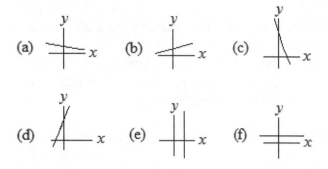

Answer (a) -0.5 (b) 0.5 (c) -4 (d) 3 (e) undefined (f) 0

Parallel and Perpendicular Lines

If line l_1 with slope m_1 is parallel
to line l_2 with slope m_2, then $m_1 = m_2$.

If line l_1 with slope $m_1 \neq 0$ is perpendicular
to line l_2 with slope m_2, then $m_2 = -\dfrac{1}{m_1}$,

that is, the slope of l_2 is the **negative reciprocal** of the slope of l_1.

In the case of perpendicular lines, if $m_1 = 0$, then l_1 is
horizontal, that is, l_1 is parallel to the x axis. In this case,
l_2 is vertical, that is, parallel to the y axis, and its slope
is undefined, that is, l_2 has "infinite slope".

Example 1) Find the equation of the line which is (a) parallel (b) perpendicular
to the line $y = -3x + 5$ which passes through the point $(-4, 3)$.

Solution (a) The slope of a parallel line is -3. Using $y - y_1 = m(x - x_1)$, we have
$y - 3 = -3(x - (-4))$ and so $y = -3x - 9$.

(b) The slope of a perpendicular line is $-\dfrac{1}{(-3)} = \dfrac{1}{3}$. Therefore,

$y - 3 = \dfrac{1}{3}(x + 4)$ and so $y = \dfrac{1}{3}x + \dfrac{13}{3}$.

Example 2) Find the equation of the line which is
(a) parallel (b) perpendicular
to the line $y = -1$ which passes
through the point $(1, 2)$.

Solution (a) The slope of a parallel line is 0

$y = mx + b$
$m = 0$ and $b = 2$

and y is always 2: $y = 2$
(b) The slope of a perpendicular line is undefined
and on this line, x is always 1: $x = 1$

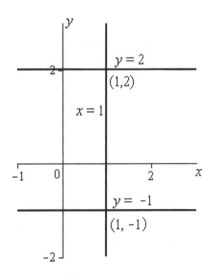

37

Two for you.

1) Find the equation of the line through the point $(1, 1)$ that is

(a) parallel to the line through the points $(1, 1)$ and $(3, 11)$

(b) perpendicular to the line through the points $(1, 1)$ and $(3, 11)$.

2) Find the equation of the line with x intercept 1 that is

(a) parallel to $y = 4$ (b) perpendicular to $y = 4$.

Answers 1)(a) $y = 5x - 4$ (b) $y = -\dfrac{1}{5}x + \dfrac{6}{5}$

2)(a) $y = 0$ (Note: here, every real number is an x intercept!)   (b) $x = 1$

Finding Tangent and Normal Lines to a Curve

Let $y = f(x)$. The slope of the tangent line to this function at the point $(a, f(a))$ is given by $f'(a)$ and the slope of the normal line by $-\dfrac{1}{f'(a)}$.

Example 1) Let $f(x) = x^3 - 8x + 9$.
Find the equation of the tangent
and normal lines at the point where $x = 2$.

Solution $f'(x) = 3x^2 - 8$.
Now $f(2) = 1$ and $f'(2) = 4$. Using
$y - y_1 = m(x - x_1)$, the tangent line
is $y - 1 = 4(x - 2)$ and so $y = 4x - 7$.
For the normal line, we still use the

point $(2,1)$ but the slope is $-\dfrac{1}{4}$.

Therefore, the normal equation is

$y - 1 = -\dfrac{1}{4}(x - 2)$ and so

$y = -\dfrac{1}{4}x + \dfrac{1}{2} + 1 = -\dfrac{1}{4}x + \dfrac{3}{2}.$

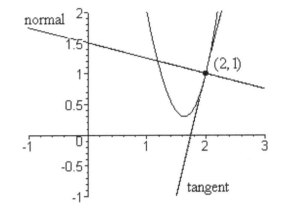

Example 2) Let $xy + e^{y-1} = 2$. Find the equation of the tangent and normal lines at the point where $y = 1$.

Solution Substituting $y = 1$ gives (remember $e^0 = 1$) $x + 1 = 2$ and so $x = 1$.

Differentiating implicitly: $x\dfrac{dy}{dx} + y + e^{y-1}\dfrac{dy}{dx} = 0$ $\therefore$ $\dfrac{dy}{dx}(x + e^{y-1}) = -y$

and so $\dfrac{dy}{dx} = \dfrac{-y}{x + e^{y-1}}.$

At $(1,1)$, $\dfrac{dy}{dx} = -\dfrac{1}{2}.$

The tangent line is $y - 1 = -\dfrac{1}{2}(x - 1)$ and so $y = -\dfrac{1}{2}x + \dfrac{3}{2}.$

The normal line is $y - 1 = 2(x - 1)$ and so $y = 2x - 1$.

Two for you.

1) Find the tangent and normal lines to $y = x^2 - x$ at $x = -1$.

2) Find the tangent and normal lines to $x + y + \ln y = 4$ at $y = 1$.

Answers 1) tangent: $y = -3x - 1$ normal: $y = \dfrac{1}{3}x + \dfrac{7}{3}$

2) tangent: $y = -\dfrac{1}{2}x + \dfrac{5}{2}$ normal: $y = 2x - 5$

Solving Two Linear Equations Using Substitution

In the earlier high school grades, we usually solve two linear equations by either the "substitution" or "elimination" methods. There is a method called "row reduction" which works much better when you have **three or more** equations. (See pages 43 and 45.) In fact, elimination is just a simple version of row reduction. However, for two equations, substitution is usually the best. So in this section, **substitution rules** rule!

Example 1) Solve E1: $x + 3y = 5$ and E2: $4x - 5y = 3$ using substitution.

Solution Solve for x in E1: $x + 3y = 5 \Rightarrow x = 5 - 3y$. Call this equation E3. Substitute this into E2:

$4(5 - 3y) - 5y = 3$

$\Rightarrow 20 - 12y - 5y = 3$

$\Rightarrow -17y = -17$

$\Rightarrow y = 1$

Now we substitute $y = 1$ into E3: $x = 5 - 3(1) = 5 - 3 = 2$

Geometrically, we have found that the two straight lines $x + 3y = 5$ and $4x - 5y = 3$ intersect at the point $(2,1)$.

Example 2) Solve E1: $5y - 3x = -6$ and E2: $5x - 8y = 0$ using substitution.

Solution First, solve for y in E1:

$5y = 3x - 6 \Rightarrow 5y - 3x = -6 \Rightarrow y = \dfrac{3x - 6}{5}$. Call this equation E3.

Now substitute this into E2:

$5x - 8\left(\dfrac{3x - 6}{5}\right) = 0 \quad \boxed{\text{Clear the denominator by multiplying the equation by 5.}} \Rightarrow \quad 25x - 8(3x - 6) = 0$

$\Rightarrow 25x - 24x + 48 = 0 \Rightarrow x = -48$.

Now substitute this into the equation for E3: $y = \dfrac{3(-48) - 6}{5} = \dfrac{-144 - 6}{5} = \dfrac{-150}{5} = -30$

Note: You can solve for x first and then find y or solve first for y and then find x. Do what seems easiest for the particular example. In Example 1, it was best to solve for x first because, well, you tell me! (Hint: Can you say, "Fractions!"?)

Two for you.

Solve the linear systems using the substitution method:

1) $x - 2y = 3,\ 2x + y = 1$ 2) $4x + 3y = -1,\ 7x + 2y = 8$

Answers 1) $x = 1,\ y = -1$ 2) $x = 2,\ y = -3$

Solving Two Linear Equations Using "Row Reduction"

Let's use row reduction to solve these pairs of equations. There are other methods, and in fact some of these are easier than row reduction when you have only two equations, **but this is the easiest method to generalize to three, four, and more linear equations.**

Example Solve each of the following pairs of linear equations:

1) $x + 3y = 5$ and $4x - 5y = 3$ 2) $3x - 5y = 6$ and $5x - 8y = 0$

3) $2x - y = 7$ and $4x - 2y = 14$ 4) $2x - y = 7$ and $4x - 2y = 6$

Solution 1)
$$\begin{array}{|ll|} x + 3y = 5 & \text{E1} \\ 4x - 5y = 3 & \text{E2} \end{array}$$
$\overset{\boxed{\substack{\text{Leave E1 alone!} \\ -4 \times \text{E1} + \text{E2} = \text{E3}}}}{\Longleftrightarrow}$
$$\begin{array}{|ll|} x + 3y = 5 & \text{E1} \\ -17y = -17 & \text{E3} \end{array}$$

From $-17y = -17$, we find $y = 1$.

Substitute $y = 1$ into E1: $x + 3(1) = 5$ and so $x = 2$. The solution is $(x, y) = (2, 1)$.

2)
$$\begin{array}{|ll|} 3x - 5y = 6 & \text{E1} \\ 5x - 8y = 0 & \text{E2} \end{array}$$
$\overset{\boxed{\substack{\frac{1}{3} \times \text{E1} = \text{E3} \\ \text{Leave E2 alone!}}}}{\Longleftrightarrow}$
$$\begin{array}{|ll|} x - \dfrac{5}{3}y = 2 & \text{E3} \\ 5x - 8y = 0 & \text{E2} \end{array}$$

$\overset{\boxed{\substack{\text{Leave E3 alone!} \\ -5 \times \text{E3} + \text{E2} = \text{E4}}}}{\Longleftrightarrow}$
$$\begin{array}{|ll|} x - \dfrac{5}{3}y = 2 & \text{E3} \\ \dfrac{1}{3}y = -10 & \text{E4} \end{array}$$

From $\dfrac{1}{3}y = -10$, we have $y = -30$.

Substitute $y = -30$ into E1: $3x - 5(-30) = 6$ and so $3x = -144$ and $x = -48$.

3) Solving the same way as in 1) and 2) yields the equation $0 = 0$. These lines are **COINCIDENT**, that is, both equations represent the same line. The solutions are $x \in \mathbb{R}$ and $y = 2x - 7$.

4) This time, we obtain the equation $0 = 8$. **FALSE**! There is no solution. These are non-intersecting parallel lines.

Two for you.

Solve the linear systems:

1) $5x - 7y = 10$, $15x + 4y = 5$ 2) $4x + 3y = -1$, $7x + 2y = 8$

Answers 1) $x = \dfrac{3}{5}$, $y = -1$ 2) $x = 2$, $y = -3$

Solving Three Linear Equations

We will use row reduction here just as we did with two equations in two unknowns on page 43. The method is **looooooonnnnnng**, tedious, and it's easy to make mechanical errors. The good news is that the steps are pretty straightforward.

Example Solve the following systems of linear equations:

1) $\begin{array}{l} x+2y-6z=5 \\ 4x+5y-21z=5 \\ -3x+3y+17z=-2 \end{array}$

2) $\begin{array}{l} 2x+y-2z=10 \\ 3x+2y+2z=1 \\ 5x+4y+3z=4 \end{array}$

Solution

1)

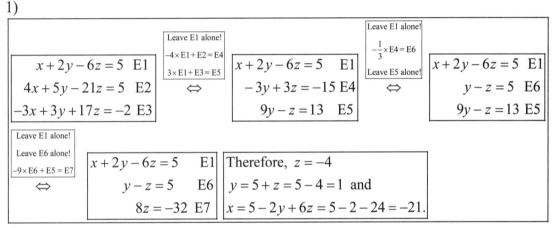

$\begin{array}{ll} x+2y-6z=5 & \text{E1} \\ 4x+5y-21z=5 & \text{E2} \\ -3x+3y+17z=-2 & \text{E3} \end{array}$

Leave E1 alone!
$-4\times\text{E1}+\text{E2}=\text{E4}$
$3\times\text{E1}+\text{E3}=\text{E5}$
$\Leftrightarrow$

$\begin{array}{ll} x+2y-6z=5 & \text{E1} \\ -3y+3z=-15 & \text{E4} \\ 9y-z=13 & \text{E5} \end{array}$

Leave E1 alone!
$-\frac{1}{3}\times\text{E4}=\text{E6}$
Leave E5 alone!
$\Leftrightarrow$

$\begin{array}{ll} x+2y-6z=5 & \text{E1} \\ y-z=5 & \text{E6} \\ 9y-z=13 & \text{E5} \end{array}$

Leave E1 alone!
Leave E6 alone!
$-9\times\text{E6}+\text{E5}=\text{E7}$
$\Leftrightarrow$

$\begin{array}{ll} x+2y-6z=5 & \text{E1} \\ y-z=5 & \text{E6} \\ 8z=-32 & \text{E7} \end{array}$

Therefore, $z=-4$
$y=5+z=5-4=1$ and
$x=5-2y+6z=5-2-24=-21.$

2)

$\begin{array}{ll} 2x+y-2z=10 & \text{E1} \\ 3x+2y+2z=1 & \text{E2} \\ 5x+4y+3z=4 & \text{E3} \end{array}$

$\frac{1}{2}\times\text{E1}=\text{E4}$
Leave E2 alone!
Leave E3 alone!
$\Leftrightarrow$

$\begin{array}{ll} x+y/2-z=5 & \text{E4} \\ 3x+2y+2z=1 & \text{E2} \\ 5x+4y+3z=4 & \text{E3} \end{array}$

Leave E4 alone!
$-3\times\text{E4}+\text{E2}=\text{E5}$
$-5\times\text{E4}+\text{E3}=\text{E6}$
$\Leftrightarrow$

$\begin{array}{ll} x+y/2-z=5 & \text{E4} \\ y/2+5z=-14 & \text{E5} \\ 3y/2+8z=-21 & \text{E6} \end{array}$

Leave E4 alone!
$2\times\text{E5}=\text{E7}$
Leave E6 alone!
$\Leftrightarrow$

$\begin{array}{ll} x+y/2-z=5 & \text{E4} \\ y+10z=-28 & \text{E7} \\ 3y/2+8z=-21 & \text{E6} \end{array}$

Leave E4 alone!
Leave E7 alone!
$-\frac{3}{2}\text{E7}+\text{E6}=\text{E8}$
$\Leftrightarrow$

$\begin{array}{ll} x+y/2-z=5 & \text{E4} \\ y+10z=-28 & \text{E7} \\ -7z=21 & \text{E8} \end{array}$

Therefore, $z=-3$
$y=-28-10z=-28+30=2$ and
$x=5-y/2+z=5-1-3=1.$

Two for you.

Solve the linear systems:

1) $x - 2y + z = 7$, $\ 2x - y + 4z = 17$, $\ 3x - 2y + 2z = 14$

2) $2x + y - 3z = 5$, $\ 3x - 2y + 2z = 5$, $\ 5x - 3y - z = 16$

Answers 1) $x = 2$, $y = -1$, $z = 3$ 2) $x = 1$, $y = -3$, $z = -2$

Consistent vs Inconsistent vs Dependent vs Unique Solutions of Three Linear Equations in 3 Unknowns

Example 1) For each of the following systems of equations, using "**row reduction**", the system has been reduced so that the solution can be easily (**trust me!**) determined. State the solutions for each system.

(a)
$$\begin{array}{c} x+2y-6z=5 \\ 4x+5y-21z=5 \\ -3x+3y+17z=-2 \end{array}$$
which can be reduced to
$$\begin{array}{c} x+2y-6z=5 \\ y-z=5 \\ z=-4 \end{array}$$

(b)
$$\begin{array}{c} x-2y+4z=2 \\ 2x-3y+5z=3 \\ 3x-4y+6z=7 \end{array}$$
which can be reduced to
$$\begin{array}{c} x-2y+4z=2 \\ y-3z=-1 \\ 0=3 \end{array}$$

(c)
$$\begin{array}{c} x+2y+3z=3 \\ 2x+3y+8z=4 \\ 3x+2y+17z=1 \end{array}$$
which can be reduced to
$$\begin{array}{c} x+2y+3z=3 \\ y-2z=2 \\ 0=0 \end{array}$$

Solution 1)(a) Unique solution. The three planes intersect in a single point: $z=-4$, $y=1$, and $x=-21$.

(b) **Inconsistent solution.** The three planes have no common point of intersection. This can happen when at least two of the planes are parallel but not coincident.

(c) **Consistent (dependent) solution.** This happens when at least two of the planes coincide or no two of the three are parallel but they have a common line of intersection. If all three planes coincide, you obtain only one non-trivial equation, that is one non-"$0=0$" equation. Here, with "free" variable (or "parameter") z, we have $y=2+2z$ and so $x=3-3z-2(2+2z)=3-3z-4-4z=-1-7z$.

47

Four for you.

The following equations are the reduced forms of four linear systems in three variables. State the solution for each and whether it is dependent, inconsistent, and/or unique.

1) $x + y + z = 3$, $y - z = 5$, $z = 1$

2) $x + y + z = 3$, $y - z = 5$, $0 = 0$

3) $x + y + z = 3$, $0 = 0$, $0 = 0$

4) $x + y + z = 3$, $y - z = 5$, $0 = 1$

Answers 1) $z = 1$, $y = 6$, $x = -4$; unique solution

2) $z \in \mathbb{R}$, $y = 5 + z$, $x = -2 - 2z$; dependent system with infinite solutions (one free variable)

3) $z \in \mathbb{R}$, $y \in \mathbb{R}$, $x = 3 - y - z$; dependent system with infinite solutions (two free variables)

4) no solution; inconsistent.

Solving Quadratic Equations Using the Quadratic Formula

Some quadratics factor and solve very easily, such as $x^2 - 4x + 3 = (x-3)(x-1) = 0$. Others, such as $2x^2 - x - 5 = 0$, have "less pleasant" real roots. Still others, such as $2x^2 - x + 3 = 0$, have non-real roots. In these latter cases, the quadratic formula makes solving for x much simpler.

Remember the quadratic formula : if $ax^2 + bx + c = 0$, then $x = \dfrac{-b \pm \sqrt{b^2 - 4ac}}{2a}$.

Note the relationship between finding the roots and factoring the expression :

$$ax^2 + bx + c = a\left(x - \frac{-b + \sqrt{b^2 - 4ac}}{2a}\right)\left(x - \frac{-b - \sqrt{b^2 - 4ac}}{2a}\right)$$

Example 1) Solve the equation $2x^2 - x - 5 = 0$ using the quadratic formula.

Solution $a = 2, \; b = -1, \; c = -5$

$$\therefore \; x = \frac{-(-1) \pm \sqrt{(-1)^2 - 4(2)(-5)}}{2(2)} = \frac{1 \pm \sqrt{41}}{4}$$

The roots are $x = \dfrac{1 + \sqrt{41}}{4}$ and $x = \dfrac{1 - \sqrt{41}}{4}$.

Note the relationship between finding the roots and factoring the expression :

$$2x^2 - x - 5 = 2\left(x - \frac{1 + \sqrt{41}}{4}\right)\left(x - \frac{1 - \sqrt{41}}{4}\right)$$

Example 2) Solve the equation $2x^2 - x + 3 = 0$ using the quadratic formula.

Solution $a = 2, \; b = -1, \; c = 3$

$$\therefore \; x = \frac{-(-1) \pm \sqrt{(-1)^2 - 4(2)(3)}}{2(2)} = \frac{1 \pm \sqrt{-23}}{4} = \frac{1 \pm \sqrt{23}\,i}{4}$$

The roots are $x = \dfrac{1 + i\sqrt{23}}{4}$ and $x = \dfrac{1 - i\sqrt{23}}{4}$.

Note the relationship between finding the roots and factoring the expression :

$$2x^2 - x + 3 = 2\left(x - \frac{1 + i\sqrt{23}}{4}\right)\left(x - \frac{1 - i\sqrt{23}}{4}\right)$$

Two for you.

Solve each of the following using the quadratic formula:

1) $3x^2 - 4x - 1 = 0$ 2) $5x^2 + 6x + 5 = 0$

Answers 1) $\dfrac{2+\sqrt{7}}{3}$, $\dfrac{2-\sqrt{7}}{3}$ 2) $\dfrac{-3+4i}{5}$, $\dfrac{-3-4i}{5}$

Factoring Quadratic Expressions
Using the Quadratic Formula

Some quadratic expressions factor very easily, such as $x^2 - 4x + 3 = (x-3)(x-1)$. When we need to factor quadratic expressions whose corresponding equations have "unpleasant" real roots, such as $2x^2 - x - 5 = 0$, or non-real roots, such as $2x^2 - x + 3 = 0$, we can use the quadratic formula to make factoring simple.

Remember the quadratic formula : if $ax^2 + bx + c = 0$, then $x = \dfrac{-b \pm \sqrt{b^2 - 4ac}}{2a}$.

Here is a quadratic fact of life. Let $f(x) = ax^2 + bx + c$ have roots r_1 and r_2. Then we can factor $f(x) = ax^2 + bx + c = a(x - r_1)(x - r_2)$. **Note the "*a*" in the factored form.**

Example 1) Factor $f(x) = 2x^2 - x - 5$ using the quadratic formula.

Solution $a = 2$, $b = -1$, $c = -5$ $\therefore$ $x = \dfrac{-(-1) \pm \sqrt{(-1)^2 - 4(2)(-5)}}{2(2)} = \dfrac{1 \pm \sqrt{41}}{4}$

The roots are $r_1 = \dfrac{1 + \sqrt{41}}{4}$ and $r_2 = \dfrac{1 - \sqrt{41}}{4}$

$\therefore$ $f(x) \overset{a(x-r_1)(x-r_2)}{=} 2\left(x - \dfrac{1+\sqrt{41}}{4}\right)\left(x - \dfrac{1-\sqrt{41}}{4}\right) \overset{\text{or if you prefer...}}{=} \left(2x - \dfrac{1+\sqrt{41}}{2}\right)\left(x - \dfrac{1-\sqrt{41}}{4}\right)$

Example 2) Factor the expression $g(x) = 2x^2 - x + 3$ using the quadratic formula.

Solution $a = 2$, $b = -1$, $c = 3$ $\therefore$ $x = \dfrac{-(-1) \pm \sqrt{(-1)^2 - 4(2)(3)}}{2(2)} = \dfrac{1 \pm \sqrt{-23}}{4} = \dfrac{1 \pm \sqrt{23}\,i}{4}$

The roots are $r_1 = \dfrac{1 + i\sqrt{23}}{4}$ and $r_2 = \dfrac{1 - i\sqrt{23}}{4}$

$\therefore$ $g(x) \overset{a(x-r_1)(x-r_2)}{=} 2\left(x - \dfrac{1+i\sqrt{23}}{4}\right)\left(x - \dfrac{1-i\sqrt{23}}{4}\right) \overset{\text{or if you prefer...}}{=} \left(2x - \dfrac{1+i\sqrt{23}}{2}\right)\left(x - \dfrac{1-i\sqrt{23}}{4}\right)$

Two for you.

Factor each of the following using the quadratic formula:

1) $3x^2 - 4x - 1$ 2) $5x^2 + 6x + 5$

Answers 1) $3\left(x - \dfrac{2 + \sqrt{7}}{3}\right)\left(x - \dfrac{2 - \sqrt{7}}{3}\right) \overset{\boxed{\text{or if you prefer...}}}{=} \left(3x - 2 - \sqrt{7}\right)\left(x - \dfrac{2 - \sqrt{7}}{3}\right)$

2) $5\left(x - \dfrac{-3 + 4i}{5}\right)\left(x - \dfrac{-3 - 4i}{5}\right) \overset{\boxed{\text{or if you prefer...}}}{=} \left(5x + 3 - 4i\right)\left(x + \dfrac{3 + 4i}{5}\right)$

Problems Involving the Sum and Product of the Roots of a Quadratic Equation

> **Remember the quadratic formula :** if $ax^2 + bx + c = 0$, then $x = \dfrac{-b \pm \sqrt{b^2 - 4ac}}{2a}$.

Adding the two roots:

$$r_1 + r_2 = \frac{-b + \sqrt{b^2 - 4ac}}{2a} + \frac{-b - \sqrt{b^2 - 4ac}}{2a} = \frac{-2b}{2a} = -\frac{b}{a}$$

Multiplying the two roots:

$$r_1 r_2 = \left(\frac{-b + \sqrt{b^2 - 4ac}}{2a} \right)\left(\frac{-b - \sqrt{b^2 - 4ac}}{2a} \right) \overset{\substack{\text{The numerator expands} \\ \text{to a } \textbf{difference of squares!}}}{=} \frac{b^2 - (b^2 - 4ac)}{4a^2} = \frac{4ac}{4a^2} = \frac{c}{a}$$

Example 1) Identify the sum and product of the roots of $3x^2 - 4x - 2 = 0$ **without solving for the roots!**

Solution $a = 3, \ b = -4, \ c = -2$

$$\therefore \ r_1 + r_2 \ \overset{\boxed{\text{Sum} = -\frac{b}{a}}}{=} \ -\frac{(-4)}{3} = \frac{4}{3} \quad \text{and} \quad r_1 r_2 \ \overset{\boxed{\text{Product} = \frac{c}{a}}}{=} \ -\frac{2}{3}$$

Example 2) The sum and product of the roots of a quadratic equation are $\dfrac{4}{3}$ and $-\dfrac{2}{3}$, respectively. Find the quadratic equation.

Solution Rewrite $ax^2 + bx + c = 0$ as $x^2 + \dfrac{b}{a}x + \dfrac{c}{a} = 0 = x^2 - \left(-\dfrac{b}{a} \right)x + \dfrac{c}{a}$.

We are given $r_1 + r_2 = \dfrac{4}{3} = -\dfrac{b}{a}$ and $r_1 r_2 = -\dfrac{2}{3} = \dfrac{c}{a}$.

Therefore, the required quadratic equation is

$$x^2 - \left(\frac{4}{3} \right)x - \frac{2}{3} = 0 \ \text{ or } \ 3x^2 - 4x - 2 = 0.$$

Two for you.

1) Identify the sum and product of the roots of $\pi x^2 + ex - 1 = 0$ **without solving for the roots!**

2) The sum and product of the roots of a quadratic equation are $-\dfrac{2}{5}$ and 3, respectively. Find the quadratic equation.

Answers 1) $\text{Sum} = -\dfrac{e}{\pi}$, $\text{Product} = -\dfrac{1}{\pi}$

2) $x^2 + \dfrac{2}{5}x + 3 = 0$ or $5x^2 + 2x + 15 = 0$

The Graph of $y = a(x - b)^2 + c$

Given the parabola $y = a(x - b)^2 + c$, the vertex is (b, c) and the graph opens up if $a > 0$ and down if $a < 0$. The y intercept (where $x = 0$) is $ab^2 + c$.

Example 1) State the vertex and y intercept and draw the graph for each of the following: (a) $y = (x - 2)^2 + 1$ (b) $y = -2(x + 2)^2 + 4$

Solution

(a) vertex: $(2, 1)$; y intercept = 5   (b) vertex: $(-2, 4)$; y intercept = -4

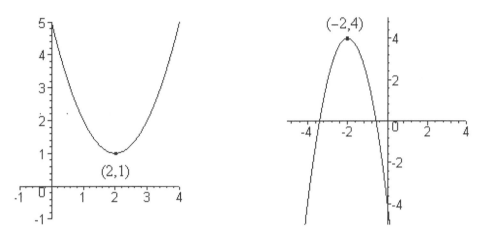

Example 2) Let $y = x - x^2$. Find the vertex and draw the graph.

Solution To find the vertex, **complete the square**.

$$y = x - x^2 = -(x^2 - x) \qquad = \qquad -\left(x^2 - x + \frac{1}{4}\right) + \frac{1}{4} = -\left(x - \frac{1}{2}\right)^2 + \frac{1}{4}$$

The coefficient of x is -1. Divide by 2 and square!

We subtracted 1/4 so we add 1/4.

The vertex is $\left(\dfrac{1}{2}, \dfrac{1}{4}\right)$

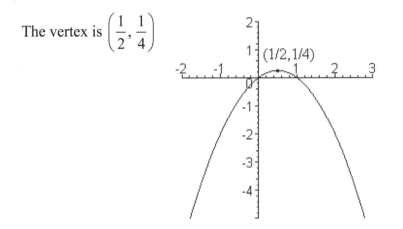

Two for you.

Find the vertex, the y intercept, and state whether the parabola opens up or down:

1) $y = 2(x+3)^2 - 5$ 2) $y = 1 - 8x - 2x^2$

Answers

1) vertex: $(-3,-5)$; y intercept $= 13$; up

2) vertex: $(-2,9)$; y intercept $= 1$; down

Completing the Square

Let's set this up so that we always have $a > 0$:

$$(x+a)^2 = x^2 + 2ax + a^2 \qquad (x-a)^2 = x^2 - 2ax + a^2$$

Note the sequence a, $2a$, and a^2. Completing the square is easy!

1) **Identify the $2a$ term.**

2) **Divide by 2 to get the a term.**

3) **Square to get the a^2 term.**

Example 1) Complete the square in the expression $4x^2 + 12x - 17$.

Solution $4x^2 + 12x - 17$

> Factor the 4 from the x^2 term and the x term **but not the constant!**

$$= 4(x^2 + 3x) - 17$$

> Now, $2a = 3$, so $a = 3/2$ and $a^2 = 9/4$. By the way, note how we got "$3x$": $3x = 12x/4$ Keep this in mind for the **next** example.

$$= 4(x^2 + 3x + \frac{9}{4}) - 17 - 4(9/4)$$ $\boxed{\text{We add } 4\left(\dfrac{9}{4}\right) \text{ so we subtract } 4\left(\dfrac{9}{4}\right).}$

$$= 4\left(x + \frac{3}{2}\right)^2 - 26$$

Always factor out the coefficient of x^2. Factor it from the x term as well but **NOT** the constant.

Example 2) Complete the square in the expression $5 - \frac{3}{2}x^2 + 2x$.

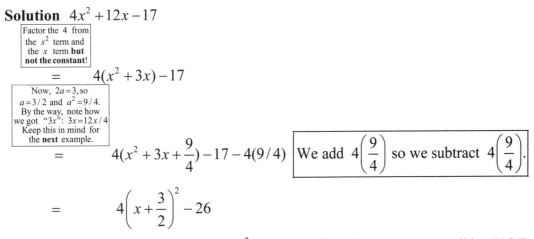

Solution $5 - \dfrac{3}{2}x^2 + 2x$ $\qquad$ $\boxed{\text{Factor out } -\tfrac{3}{2}. \text{ Note: } -\dfrac{4}{3}x = \dfrac{2x}{\left(-\tfrac{3}{2}\right)}}$ $\qquad = -\dfrac{3}{2}\left(x^2 - \dfrac{4}{3}x\right) + 5$

$$= -\frac{3}{2}\left(x^2 - \frac{4}{3}x + \frac{4}{9}\right) + 5 + \frac{3}{2}\left(\frac{4}{9}\right)$$
$\boxed{\begin{array}{l}\text{Note } 2a = -4/3, \text{ so } a = -2/3, \text{ and } a^2 = 4/9. \\[4pt] \text{Also, we } \textbf{SUBTRACT } \dfrac{3}{2}\left(\dfrac{4}{9}\right) \text{ so,} \\[6pt] \text{to compensate, we } \textbf{ADD } \dfrac{3}{2}\left(\dfrac{4}{9}\right).\end{array}}$

$$= -\frac{3}{2}\left(x - \frac{2}{3}\right)^2 + 5 + \frac{2}{3} = -\frac{3}{2}\left(x - \frac{2}{3}\right)^2 + \frac{17}{3}$$

Two for you.

Complete the square for each of the following:

1) $3x^2 - 30x - 11$ 2) $x - x^2$

Answers 1) $3(x-5)^2 - 86$ 2) $\dfrac{1}{4} - \left(x - \dfrac{1}{2}\right)^2$

Solving Linear Inequalities

Now pay attention!

1) One of math's cardinal rules: **what you do to one side you do to the other!**

2) Another: when you multiply or divide an **inequality** by a **negative**, the direction of the inequality **reverses**.

> For example, $-2 < 4$. Multiply both sides by -3 and you get $6 \;>\; -12$. | The direction is reversed!

Example 1) Solve the inequality $4 - 2x < 5 + 8x$.

Solution $\quad 4 - 2x < 5 + 8x$

Bring the x terms to the left and the numbers to the right: $-10x < 1$

Now divide both sides by -10: $\quad x \;>\; -\dfrac{1}{10}$ | We divided by a negative so the inequality reverses!

OR

$4 - 2x < 5 + 8x$

Bring the numbers to the left and the x terms to the right: $-1 < 10x$

Now divide both sides by 10: $\quad -\dfrac{1}{10} \;<\; x$ | This time the inequality direction **DID NOT CHANGE** because we divided by a **POSITIVE** number!

Example 2) Solve the inequality $3 \le 2x - 5 < 7$.

Solution $\quad 3 \le 2x - 5 < 7 \quad \Leftrightarrow \quad 8 \le 2x < 12 \quad \Leftrightarrow \quad 4 \le x < 6$

[Add 5 to each of the three parts of the inequality...] [...and divide by 2.]

Example 3) Solve the inequality $3 - 2x < 6 + 4x < 7$.

Solution This time we **MUST** solve two inequalities separately, because x appears more than once.

We need to say "**and**" because **both** inequalities must be satisfied!

$$3 - 2x < 6 + 4x \qquad \text{and} \qquad 6 + 4x < 7$$
$$-6x < 3 \qquad\qquad \text{and} \qquad\qquad x < 1$$
$$x > -\frac{1}{2} \qquad\qquad \text{and} \qquad\qquad x < \frac{1}{4} \qquad \therefore \quad -\frac{1}{2} < x < \frac{1}{4}$$

Two for you.

Solve these inequalities:

1) $3 > 5 - 6x \geq 2$ 2) $3x + 7 < 4x + 5 < -x + 5$

Answers 1) $\dfrac{1}{3} < x \leq \dfrac{1}{2}$

2) No solution.

($3x + 7 < 4x + 5 \Leftrightarrow x > 2$ while $4x + 5 < -x + 5 \Leftrightarrow x < 0$.

There are no numbers than are greater than 2 **AND** less than 0!)

Solving Quadratic Inequalities

Some of these inequalities factor and solve very easily. Some don't factor, which means there are no intercepts: the parabola is either always above or always below the x axis. Some factor if you first **complete the square** and then use **difference of squares**.

Example 1) Solve the inequality $x^2 - 3x - 4 > 0$.

Solution $x^2 - 3x - 4 > 0 \Leftrightarrow (x-4)(x+1) > 0$
The solution is $x \in (-\infty, -1) \cup (4, \infty)$.

$$\boxed{\begin{array}{l} x+1 < 0 \\ x-4 < 0 \end{array}} \quad \boxed{\begin{array}{l} x+1 > 0 \\ x-4 < 0 \end{array}} \quad \boxed{\begin{array}{l} x+1 > 0 \\ x-4 > 0 \end{array}}$$

$(-)(-) \qquad (+)(-) \qquad (+)(+)$

$$\begin{array}{ccccc} & + & & - & + \\ \hline & -1 & & 4 & \end{array}$$

$y = x^2 - 3x - 4$

Example 2) Solve the inequality $x^2 - x + 1 < 0$.

Solution $x^2 - x + 1 < 0$

$\boxed{\begin{array}{l} \text{Completing the square} \\ (x+a)^2 = x^2 + 2ax + a^2 \\ \text{Here, } a = -\frac{1}{2}. \end{array}}$

$$\Leftrightarrow x^2 - x + \frac{1}{4} + 1 - \frac{1}{4} < 0 \Leftrightarrow \left(x - \frac{1}{2}\right)^2 + \frac{3}{4} < 0$$

Since $\left(x - \frac{1}{2}\right)^2 + \frac{3}{4} \geq \frac{3}{4} \overset{\boxed{\text{Always!}}}{>} 0$, there is no solution.

$y = x^2 - x + 1$

(Sometimes **BOB** – that is, the **B**ack **O**f the **B**ook – calls no solution "**the null set**" or "**the empty set**".)

Example 3) Solve the inequality $x^2 - x - 1 < 0$.

Solution $x^2 - x - 1 < 0 \Leftrightarrow x^2 - x + \frac{1}{4} - 1 - \frac{1}{4} < 0 \Leftrightarrow \left(x - \frac{1}{2}\right)^2 - \frac{5}{4} < 0$

$\boxed{\begin{array}{l} a^2 - b^2 = (a-b)(a+b) \\ a = x - \frac{1}{2} \quad b = \frac{\sqrt{5}}{2} \end{array}}$

$\boxed{\begin{array}{l} \text{Be careful with "}-\text{"} \\ \text{when you make} \\ \text{"2" a common} \\ \text{denominator for} \\ \text{each root.} \end{array}}$

$$\Leftrightarrow \left(x - \frac{1}{2} - \frac{\sqrt{5}}{2}\right)\left(x - \frac{1}{2} + \frac{\sqrt{5}}{2}\right) < 0 \Leftrightarrow \left(x - \frac{1+\sqrt{5}}{2}\right)\left(x - \frac{1-\sqrt{5}}{2}\right) < 0$$

$(-)(-) \qquad (+)(-) \qquad (+)(+)$

$$\begin{array}{ccccc} & + & & - & + \\ \hline & \frac{1-\sqrt{5}}{2} & & \frac{1+\sqrt{5}}{2} & \end{array}$$

$\therefore x \in \left(\dfrac{1-\sqrt{5}}{2}, \dfrac{1+\sqrt{5}}{2}\right)$

Two for you.

Solve the inequalities: 1) $x^2 + 7x + 12 > 0$ 2) $x^2 + 2x - 1 < 0$

Answers 1) $x \in (-\infty, -4) \cup (-3, \infty)$ 2) $x \in \left(-1 - \sqrt{2}, -1 + \sqrt{2}\right)$

Solving Inequalities with Two or More Factors

Here, you will have an inequality where

1) on one side you will have a **product** and/or **quotient** of factors in the form $x \pm a$;

2) on the other side **you must have 0!**

Example 1) Solve the inequality $(x+3)x(x-4) < 0$.

Solution

$$
\begin{array}{cccc}
(-)(-)(-) & (+)(-)(-) & (+)(+)(-) & (+)(+)(+)
\end{array}
$$

$$
\underset{\displaystyle -\;\;\;\; -3 \;\;\;\; + \;\;\;\; 0 \;\;\;\; - \;\;\;\; 4 \;\;\;\; +}{\rule{8cm}{0.4pt}}
$$

$\therefore \; x \in (-\infty, -3) \cup (0, 4)$

Example 2) Solve the inequality $(x+3)^2 (x+1)^3 x^{1/3} (x-4) \le 0$.

Solution This time, the factor $(x+3)$ **DOESN'T MATTER** because it is raised to an **EVEN** exponent: $(x+3)^2 \ge 0$ **ALWAYS.** I will include -3 on the number line just for emphasis! However, $x+1$ is raised to an **ODD** exponent and so it will change from $-$ to $+$ as x goes from less than -1 to greater than -1. Ditto for the $x^{1/3}$ term as x goes from less than 0 to greater than 0.

$$
\begin{array}{ccccc}
(-)(-)(-) & (-)(-)(-) & (+)(-)(-) & (+)(+)(-) & (+)(+)(+)
\end{array}
$$

$$
\underset{\displaystyle -\;\;\;\; -3 \;\;\;\; - \;\;\;\; -1 \;\;\;\; + \;\;\;\; 0 \;\;\;\; - \;\;\;\; 4 \;\;\;\; +}{\rule{9cm}{0.4pt}}
$$

The solution is $x \in (-\infty, -1] \cup [0, 4]$.

Example 3) Solve the inequality $\dfrac{(x+3)(x+1)x}{(x-4)} \le 0$.

Solution Watch out for division by 0: we **can't** let x be 4.

$$
\begin{array}{ccccc}
(-)(-)(-)(-) & (+)(-)(-)(-) & (+)(+)(-)(-) & (+)(+)(+)(-) & (+)(+)(+)(+)
\end{array}
$$

$$
\underset{\displaystyle +\;\;\;\; -3 \;\;\;\; - \;\;\;\; -1 \;\;\;\; + \;\;\;\; 0 \;\;\;\; - \;\;\;\; 4 \;\;\;\; +}{\rule{9cm}{0.4pt}}
$$

$\therefore \; x \in [-3, -1] \cup [0, 4)$

Two for you.

Solve these inequalities:

1) $(2x-3)(4-x)(x-7)^3(x+1)^2 > 0$

$\left(\text{Hint: write the inequality as } -2\left(x-\dfrac{3}{2}\right)(x-4)(x-7)^3(x+1)^2 > 0 \text{ and then} \right.$

$\left. \left(x-\dfrac{3}{2}\right)(x-4)(x-7)^3(x+1)^2 < 0. \right)$

2) $\dfrac{(x+3)^2(x-1)}{(x+5)^{3/2}(x-2)(x-4)^3} \le 0$ (Hint: $x > -5$; otherwise, $1/(x+5)^{3/2}$ is undefined.)

Answers 1) $x \in \left(-\infty, \dfrac{3}{2}\right) \cup (4,7)$ 2) $x \in (-5,1] \cup (2,4)$

Solving Rational Inequalities

In these questions, if you **cross multiply**, you need **SEPARATE CASES**.

Multiply by a " + " and the direction stays the same!
Multiply by a " – " and the direction reverses!

HERE IS AN EASIER WAY…

Example 1) Solve the inequality $\dfrac{1}{x+2} \leq \dfrac{2}{3x+1}$.

Solution $\dfrac{1}{x+2} \leq \dfrac{2}{3x+1}$ $\boxed{\text{Do not cross-mulitply!}}$ $\Leftrightarrow$ $\dfrac{1}{x+2} - \dfrac{2}{3x+1} \leq 0$

$\boxed{\text{Get a common denominator.}}$ $\Leftrightarrow$ $\dfrac{3x+1-2(x+2)}{(x+2)(3x+1)} \leq 0$ $\boxed{\text{Simplify.}}$ $\Leftrightarrow$ $\dfrac{x-3}{3(x+2)\left(x+\dfrac{1}{3}\right)} \leq 0$

$$\begin{array}{ccccccc}
(-)(-)(-) & & (+)(-)(-) & & (+)(+)(-) & & (+)(+)(+) \\
\hline
- & -2 & + & -\dfrac{1}{3} & - & 3 & +
\end{array}$$

The solution is $x \in (-\infty, -2) \cup \left(-\dfrac{1}{3}, 3\right]$.

Example 2) Solve the inequality $\dfrac{2x-1}{3x+1} \geq \dfrac{x+2}{x-2}$.

Solution $\dfrac{2x-1}{3x+1} \geq \dfrac{x+2}{x-2}$ $\boxed{\text{Don't cross multiply!}}$ $\Leftrightarrow$ $\dfrac{2x-1}{3x+1} - \dfrac{x+2}{x-2} \geq 0$

$\boxed{\text{common denominator}}$ $\Leftrightarrow$ $\dfrac{(2x-1)(x-2)-(x+2)(3x+1)}{(3x+1)(x-2)} \geq 0$ $\boxed{\text{Expand...}}$ $\Leftrightarrow$ $\dfrac{2x^2-5x+2-(3x^2+7x+2)}{(3x+1)(x-2)} \geq 0$

$\boxed{\text{...and simplify.}}$ $\Leftrightarrow$ $\dfrac{-x^2-12x}{(3x+1)(x-2)} \geq 0$ $\boxed{\text{Multiply both sides by –1.}}$ $\Leftrightarrow$ $\dfrac{x^2+12x}{(3x+1)(x-2)} \leq 0$ $\boxed{\text{Factor just a little more.}}$ $\Leftrightarrow$ $\dfrac{x(x+12)}{3\left(x+\dfrac{1}{3}\right)(x-2)} \leq 0$

$$\begin{array}{ccccccccc}
(-)(-)(-)(-) & & (+)(-)(-)(-) & & (+)(+)(-)(-) & & (+)(+)(+)(-) & & (+)(+)(+)(+) \\
\hline
+ & -12 & - & -\dfrac{1}{3} & + & 0 & - & 2 & +
\end{array}$$

Therefore, $x \in \left[-12, -\dfrac{1}{3}\right) \cup [0, 2)$.

65

Two for you.

Solve: 1) $\dfrac{5}{x+7} \geq \dfrac{2}{x-5}$ 2) $\dfrac{x-1}{x+1} \leq \dfrac{3x-1}{3x+1}$

Answers 1) $(-7,5) \cup [13,\infty)$ 2) $\left(-1,-\dfrac{1}{3}\right) \cup [0,\infty)$

The Basics of Absolute Value

Remember, absolute value is **ALWAYS NON-NEGATIVE!**

This step is THE KEY STEP for understanding absolute value!

$|3| = 3, \quad |-3| = 3 \quad = \quad -(-3)$ and so $|x| = \begin{cases} -x, & \text{if } x < 0 \\ x, & \text{if } x \geq 0 \end{cases}$

Here is the part that people find so confusing.

WHY PUT "−" IN FRONT OF THE x?

Why not just make it positive as we did with -3?

BECAUSE ONE OF THE "−" SIGNS IS **INSIDE** THE x, **so you can't get rid of it!**

$f(x) = |x| = \begin{cases} -x, & \text{if } x < 0 \\ x, & \text{if } x \geq 0 \end{cases}$

Domain $= \mathbb{R}$, Range $= [0, \infty)$

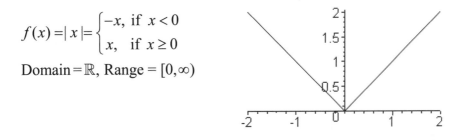

Example 1) Write (a) $|x - 1|$ (b) $|x + 1|$ without using absolute value notation.

Solution (a) $|x-1| = \begin{cases} -(x-1), & \text{if } x < 1 \\ x-1, & \text{if } x \geq 1 \end{cases}$ (b) $|x+1| = \begin{cases} -(x+1), & \text{if } x < -1 \\ x+1, & \text{if } x \geq -1 \end{cases}$

Example 2) Graph: (a) $y = |x - 1|$ (b) $y = |x + 1|$.

Solution

(a) $y = |x - 1|$

(b) $y = |x + 1|$

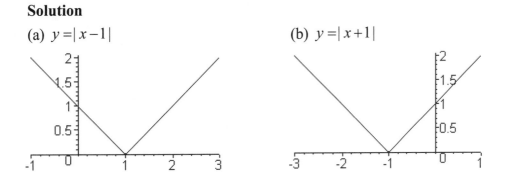

Two for you.

1) Write $|2x-3|$ without absolute value signs.

2) Graph $y = |2x-3|$.

Answers 1) $|2x-3| = \begin{cases} -(2x-3), & \text{if } x < \dfrac{3}{2} \\ (2x-3), & \text{if } x \geq \dfrac{3}{2} \end{cases}$

2)

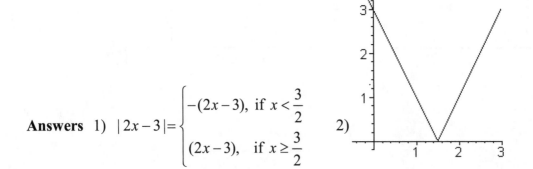

Solving Absolute Value Equations

Remember, absolute value is **ALWAYS NON-NEGATIVE**

Example 1) Solve the following absolute value equations.

(a) $|x|=4$ (b) $|x|=-3$ (c) $|2x-5|=7$

(d) $|x+5|=2x-3$ (e) $|2x+1|=|x-7|$

Solution (a) $x=4$ or $x=-4$

(b) No solution since $|x|$ is positive.

(c) Either $2x-5=7$ in which case $2x=12$ and $x=6$

or

$2x-5=-7$ in which case $2x=-2$ and $x=-1$.

(Remember, x can be negative; it is the absolute value of x that must be positive.)

(d) Easiest method here is to use cases.

Case 1) $x+5\geq0$ so $x\geq-5$. In this case, $|x+5|=x+5$. So we solve:

$x+5=2x-3 \Leftrightarrow -x=-8 \Leftrightarrow x=8$. Since $8\geq-5$, $x=8$ is a solution.

Case 2) $x+5<0$ so $x<-5$. In this case, $|x+5|=-(x+5)$. So we solve:

$-(x+5)=2x-3 \Leftrightarrow -x-5=2x-3 \Leftrightarrow -3x=2 \Leftrightarrow x=-\dfrac{2}{3}$

Since $-\dfrac{2}{3}$ **IS NOT LESS THAN** -5, $x=-\dfrac{2}{3}$ is **NOT** a solution.

(e) Since $|a|=|b| \Leftrightarrow a^2=b^2$, the easiest method here is to **square both sides**.

$|2x+1|=|x-7| \Leftrightarrow (2x+1)^2=(x-7)^2 \Leftrightarrow 4x^2+4x+1=x^2-14x+49$

$\Leftrightarrow 3x^2+18x-48=0 \Leftrightarrow x^2+6x-16=0 \Leftrightarrow (x-2)(x+8)=0 \Leftrightarrow x=2$ or $x=-8$

We **DON'T** have to check our answers in this example because of "$\Leftrightarrow$"! Not only does each step follow from the previous step, each step is **REVERSIBLE**!

In example (d), if you use the method of squaring both sides, **YOU DO HAVE TO CHECK BECAUSE THE SQUARING IN THAT EXAMPLE IS NOT REVERSIBLE!**

Three for you.

Solve: 1) $|x^3| = 1000$ 2) $2x + 1 = |3x - 2|$ 3) $|3x + 2| = |x - 6|$

Answers 1) $x = 10$ or $x = -10$ 2) $x = 3$ 3) $x = -4$ or $x = 1$

Solving Easy Absolute Value Inequalities

Keep in mind that for $a > 0$:

$$|x| < a \Leftrightarrow -a < x < a \quad \text{and} \quad |x| > a \Leftrightarrow x < -a \ \text{OR} \ x > a$$

Example 1) Solve the following absolute value inequalities.

(a) $|x| < 1$ (b) $|x| \geq 4$ (c) $|x| < -1$ (d) $|x| > -2$

Solution (a) $|x| < 1 \Leftrightarrow -1 < x < 1$

(b) $|x| \geq 4 \Leftrightarrow x \leq -4 \text{ or } x \geq 4$

(c) $|x| < -1$ is **ALWAYS FALSE**, since $|x| \geq 0$.

(d) $|x| > -2 \Leftrightarrow x \in (-\infty, \infty)$, that is, $|x| > -2$ is **ALWAYS TRUE!**

Example 2) Solve: a) $|2x - 4| < 6$ (b) $|x - 3| \geq 7$

Solution (a) $|2x - 4| < 6 \Leftrightarrow -6 < 2x - 4 < 6$
$$\Leftrightarrow -2 < 2x < 10$$
$$\Leftrightarrow -1 < x < 5, \text{ that is, } x \in (-1, 5)$$

(b) $|x - 3| \geq 7 \Leftrightarrow x - 3 \leq -7 \text{ or } x - 3 \geq 7$
$$\Leftrightarrow x \leq -4 \text{ or } x \geq 10, \text{ that is, } x \in (-\infty, -4] \cup [10, \infty)$$

Two for you.

1) Solve: (a) $|x| \leq 0.1$ (b) $|x| > 3.2$

2) Solve: (a) $|x+3| \leq 2$ (b) $1 < |3x-5|$

Answers 1)(a) $[-0.1, 0.1]$ (b) $(-\infty, -3.2) \cup (3.2, \infty)$

2)(a) $[-5, -1]$ (b) $\left(-\infty, \dfrac{4}{3}\right) \cup (2, \infty)$

Solving Less Easy Absolute Value Inequalities

There are two basic methods to use when solving more complicated absolute value inequalities (and equations as well): **"cases"** or **"squaring both sides"**. The key difference:

The implication goes in only one direction!

$$|a| < b \quad \Rightarrow \quad a^2 < b^2.$$

Note that here, since $|a| \geq 0$, b **MUST BE POSITIVE!**

When you square, you **could** introduce solutions for $a^2 < b^2$ that don't work for $|a| < b$. That's why you use cases in this type of problem.

The implication goes in both directions!

However, $|a| < |b| \quad \Leftrightarrow \quad a^2 < b^2.$ Squaring both sides is faster than cases and solutions work both ways! **BUT...**

BE CAREFUL! $a < |b| \not\Rightarrow a^2 < b^2$: a^2 can be less than b^2, **but doesn't have to be!**

Example 1) Solve $|x + 3| < 2x$.

Solution Use cases since squaring both sides can lead to "extraneous" solutions.

Case 1) $x + 3 \geq 0$ so that $x \geq -3$. In this case, $|x + 3| = x + 3$

The inequality becomes $x + 3 < 2x$ and so $3 < x$. The solution in this case is $x > 3$.

Case 2) $x + 3 < 0$ so that $x < -3$. In this case, $|x + 3| = -(x + 3)$

The inequality becomes $-x - 3 < 2x$. Therefore, $-3 < 3x$ and so $-1 < x$.

Since $x > -1$ and $x < -3$ are incompatible, there are no solutions in this case.

Combining the two cases, the solution of $|x + 3| < 2x$ is $x \in (3, \infty)$.

Example 2) Solve $|x + 4| < |2x - 6|$.

Solution In this example, squaring both sides is the best method.

(Note that there would be four separate cases if we used the case method!)

$$|x + 4| < |2x - 6| \Leftrightarrow x^2 + 8x + 16 < 4x^2 - 24x + 36 \Leftrightarrow 0 < 3x^2 - 32x + 20$$

Personal preference:
I like having the expression on the left and 0 on the right.

$$\Leftrightarrow \quad 3x^2 - 32x + 20 > 0 \Leftrightarrow (3x - 2)(x - 10) > 0 \Leftrightarrow \left(x - \frac{2}{3}\right)(x - 10) > 0$$

$$(-)(-) \qquad (+)(-) \qquad (+)(+) \qquad \therefore \quad x \in \left(-\infty, \frac{2}{3}\right) \cup (10, \infty)$$

$$\underline{ + \quad \frac{2}{3} \quad - \quad 10 \quad + }$$

Three for you.

Solve: 1) $5x - 8 \geq |4 - x|$ (Hint: use $|4 - x| = |x - 4|$.)   2) $|3x - 2| < |2x - 3|$

3) Given an example showing that $a^2 < b^2 \not\Rightarrow |a| < b$.

Answers 1) $[2, \infty)$ 2) $(-1, 1)$

3) Let $a = 3$ and $b = -5$. Then $9 = a^2 < b^2 = 25$ but $3 = a \not< b = -5$.

The Basics of $\sqrt{}$ and the Reason $\sqrt{x^2} = |x|$

Example 1) State the domain and range of the function $y = \sqrt{x}$ and draw the graph.

Solution The domain and range are both $[0, \infty)$.

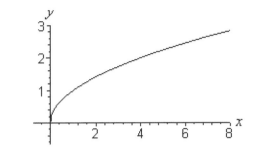

Example 2) Solve: (a) $x = \sqrt{9}$ (b) $x = -\sqrt{9}$ (c) $x^2 = 9$

Solution (a) $x = \sqrt{9} = 3$ (b) $x = -\sqrt{9} = -3$ (c) $x^2 = 9 \iff x = 3$ or $x = -3$

Example 3) Evaluate $\sqrt{(3)^2}$, $\sqrt{(-3)^2}$, $|3|$, and $|-3|$. What does this tell you about $\sqrt{x^2}$?

Solution $\sqrt{(3)^2} = \sqrt{9} = 3$, $\sqrt{(-3)^2} = \sqrt{9} = 3$, $|3| = 3$, and $|-3| = 3$.

$\therefore$ $\sqrt{x^2} = |x|$, for both $x > 0$ and $x < 0$. Put another way:

$$\sqrt{x^2} = |x| = \begin{cases} -x, & \text{if } x < 0 \\ x, & \text{if } x \geq 0 \end{cases}$$

For example:

when $x = 3$, we have $\sqrt{(3)^2} \overset{\boxed{\substack{x > 0 \text{ and so} \\ \sqrt{x^2} = x}}}{=} 3 = |3|$

when $x = -3$, we have $\sqrt{(-3)^2} = \sqrt{9} = 3 \overset{\boxed{\substack{x < 0 \text{ and so} \\ \sqrt{x^2} = -x}}}{=} -(-3) = |-3|$

Two for you.

1) State the domain and range of $f(x) = \sqrt{x+1} + 1$ and draw the graph.

2) Write $y = \sqrt{(x-4)^2}$ using first absolute value and then a "branch" definition.

Answers

1) Domain $= [-1, \infty)$, Range $= [1, \infty)$

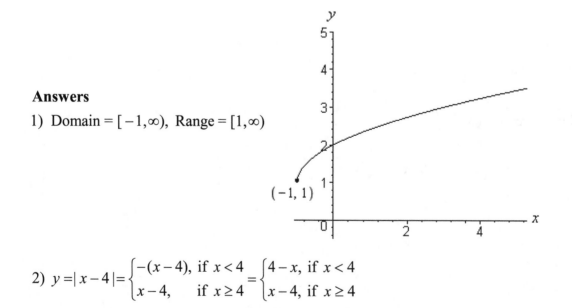

2) $y = |x-4| = \begin{cases} -(x-4), & \text{if } x < 4 \\ x-4, & \text{if } x \geq 4 \end{cases} = \begin{cases} 4-x, & \text{if } x < 4 \\ x-4, & \text{if } x \geq 4 \end{cases}$

Solving Equations Involving Square Roots

Here, as with the more complicated absolute value questions, squaring both sides works. BUT while $x = y \Rightarrow x^2 = y^2$, the converse is false: $x^2 = y^2 \not\Rightarrow x = y$. For example, $(4)^2 = (-4)^2$ but $4 \neq -4$! When we square both sides, we can introduce "**extraneous**" roots. We **must check** our possible solutions in the **original** equations!

Example 1) Solve $\sqrt{x+5} = x - 7$.

Solution $\sqrt{x+5} = x - 7 \Rightarrow x + 5 = x^2 - 14x + 49 \Rightarrow x^2 - 15x + 44 = 0$
$\Rightarrow (x-11)(x-4) = 0 \Rightarrow x = 11$ or $x = 4$.

Check $x = 11$ in the original equation:
Left Side $= \sqrt{11+5} = \sqrt{16} = 4 \qquad$ Right Side $= 11 - 7 = 4$

Check $x = 4$ in the original equation:
Left Side $= \sqrt{4+5} = \sqrt{9} = 3 \qquad$ Right Side $= 4 - 7 = -3$
Therefore, the only solution is $x = 11$.

Example 2) Solve $\sqrt{2x-7} - \sqrt{x-4} = 1$

Solution $\sqrt{2x-7} - \sqrt{x-4} = 1$

$\boxed{\text{Isolate one of the square roots.}}$
$\Rightarrow \qquad \sqrt{2x-7} = \sqrt{x-4} + 1 \quad \boxed{\text{Square both sides.}} \Rightarrow \quad 2x - 7 = x - 4 + 2\sqrt{x-4} + 1$

$\boxed{\text{Isolate the remaining square root.}}$
$\Rightarrow \qquad x - 4 = 2\sqrt{x-4}$

$\boxed{\text{Square both sides.}}$
$\Rightarrow \qquad x^2 - 8x + 16 = 4x - 16 \Rightarrow x^2 - 12x + 32 = 0$
$\Rightarrow (x-4)(x-8) = 0 \Rightarrow x = 4$ or $x = 8$

Check $x = 4$ in the original equation:
Left Side $= \sqrt{2(4) - 7} - \sqrt{4-4} = 1 \qquad$ Right Side $= 1$

Check $x = 8$ in the original equation:
Left Side $= \sqrt{2(8) - 7} - \sqrt{8-4} = 1 \qquad$ Right Side $= 1$
Therefore, both 4 and 8 are solutions.

Two for you.

1) Solve: $\sqrt{2x-7} = x-3$

2) Solve: $\sqrt{x-3} - \sqrt{2x+1} = -2$ (Hint: first isolate the $\sqrt{2x+1}$ term.)

Answers 1) 4   2) 4, 12

Rationalizing Denominators that Have $\sqrt{}$

Often you run into problems where there is either a single term with a square root in the denominator or a binomial with one or two square roots. In the first case, a simple $\dfrac{\sqrt{}}{\sqrt{}}$ solves the problem. In the second, **DIFFERENCE OF SQUARES** comes to the rescue.

Example 1) Rationalize the denominators: (a) $\dfrac{3}{\sqrt{2}}$ (b) $\dfrac{\sqrt{7}}{2\sqrt{21}}$ (c) $\dfrac{xy}{\sqrt{2x}}$

Solution (a) $\dfrac{3}{\sqrt{2}} = \dfrac{3}{\sqrt{2}} \cdot \dfrac{\sqrt{2}}{\sqrt{2}} = \dfrac{3\sqrt{2}}{2}$

(b) $\dfrac{\sqrt{7}}{2\sqrt{21}} \overset{\boxed{\text{Only the } \sqrt{21} \text{ is important!}}}{=} \dfrac{\sqrt{7}}{2\sqrt{21}} \cdot \dfrac{\sqrt{21}}{\sqrt{21}} \overset{\boxed{\sqrt{7}\sqrt{21}=\sqrt{7}\sqrt{7}\sqrt{3}}}{=} \dfrac{\overset{1}{\cancel{7}}\sqrt{3}}{2(\underset{3}{\cancel{21}})} = \dfrac{\sqrt{3}}{6}$

(c) $\dfrac{xy}{\sqrt{2x}} = \dfrac{xy}{\sqrt{2x}} \cdot \dfrac{\sqrt{2x}}{\sqrt{2x}} = \dfrac{\sqrt{2x}\,xy}{2x} = \dfrac{y\sqrt{2x}}{2}$

Example 2) Rationalize the denominators:

(a) $\dfrac{1}{\sqrt{x}-3}$ (b) $\dfrac{x}{\sqrt{x}+y}$ (c) $\dfrac{x}{\sqrt{2x+1}-3\sqrt{x-3}}$

Solution (a) $\dfrac{1}{\sqrt{x}-3} \overset{\boxed{\begin{array}{c}(a-b)(a+b)=a^2-b^2\\ \text{Here, } a=\sqrt{x} \text{ and } b=3.\end{array}}}{=} \left(\dfrac{1}{\sqrt{x}-3}\right)\left(\dfrac{\sqrt{x}+3}{\sqrt{x}+3}\right) = \dfrac{\sqrt{x}+3}{x-9}$

(b) $\dfrac{x}{\sqrt{x}+y} = \left(\dfrac{x}{\sqrt{x}+y}\right)\left(\dfrac{\sqrt{x}-y}{\sqrt{x}-y}\right) = \dfrac{x\sqrt{x}-xy}{x-y^2}$

(c) $\dfrac{x}{\sqrt{2x+1}-3\sqrt{x-3}} \overset{\boxed{\begin{array}{c}a=\sqrt{2x+1} \text{ and}\\ b=3\sqrt{x-3}\end{array}}}{=} \left(\dfrac{x}{\sqrt{2x+1}-3\sqrt{x-3}}\right)\left(\dfrac{\sqrt{2x+1}+3\sqrt{x-3}}{\sqrt{2x+1}+3\sqrt{x-3}}\right)$

$= \dfrac{x\left(\sqrt{2x+1}+3\sqrt{x-3}\right)}{2x+1-9(x-3)} = \dfrac{x\left(\sqrt{2x+1}+3\sqrt{x-3}\right)}{-7x+28}$

Two for you.

Rationalize the denominators: 1)(a) $\dfrac{\sqrt{3}}{\sqrt{45}}$ (b) $\dfrac{x-1}{\sqrt{x+4}}$ 2) $\dfrac{1}{\sqrt{x+h}-\sqrt{x}}$

Answers 1)(a) $\dfrac{\sqrt{15}}{15}$ (b) $\dfrac{(x-1)\sqrt{x+4}}{x+4}$ 2) $\dfrac{\sqrt{x+h}+\sqrt{x}}{h}$

Graphs of Basic Quadratic Relations

Four fundamental quadratic relations in variables x and y are the parabola, circle, ellipse, and hyperbola.

Example 1) Draw the graphs of the following relations.

(a) Parabola: $y = x^2$ (b) Circle: $x^2 + y^2 = 1$

(c) Ellipse: $\dfrac{x^2}{9} + \dfrac{y^2}{25} = 1$ (d) Hyperbola: $x^2 - y^2 = 1$

Solution

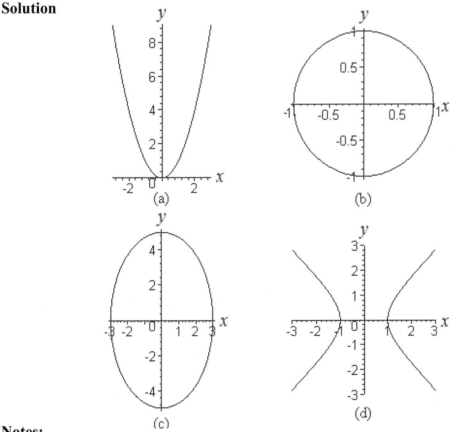

Notes:

(a) This parabola has vertex $(0,0)$ and opens upward.

(b) This circle has centre $(0,0)$ and radius 1.

(c) This ellipse has centre $(0,0)$ with x intercepts ± 3 and y intercepts ± 5.

(d) This hyperbola opens on the x axis with x intercepts ± 1. For comparison, note that the hyperbola $y^2 - x^2 = 1$ opens on the y axis with y intercepts ± 1.

One for you.

1) Graph each of the following quadratic relations and identify it as a parabola, circle, ellipse, or hyperbola.

(a) $y^2 - x^2 = 4$ (b) $y = 3 - 2x^2$ (c) $x^2 + y^2 = 9$ (d) $\dfrac{x^2}{4} + y^2 = 1$

Answer

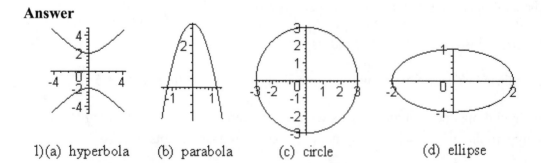

1)(a) hyperbola   (b) parabola   (c) circle   (d) ellipse

Basic $y = x^n$ Graphs, where $n \in \mathbb{N}$ and Why Even and Odd Functions Are Called Even and Odd Functions

Graphs with equations of the form $y = x^n$, where $n \in \mathbb{N}$, come up so often that they deserve a special page. This is it!

Example 1) Draw the graphs of $y = x^3$ and $y = x^5$ on the same axes.

Solution

For **odd** natural numbers n:

1) $\lim\limits_{x \to \pm\infty} x^n = \pm\infty$ and the expression approaches $\pm\infty$ faster as n increases.

2) The graphs are symmetric in the **origin**, that is, $(-x)^n = -x^n$. This is the reason functions that satisfy $f(-x) = -f(x)$ are called **ODD** functions!

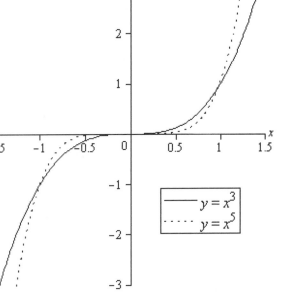

Example 2) Draw the graphs of $y = x^2$ and $y = x^4$ on the same axes.

Solution

For **even** natural numbers n:

1) $\lim\limits_{x \to \pm\infty} x^n = \infty$ and the expression approaches ∞ faster as n increases.

2) The graphs are symmetric in the y axis, that is, $(-x)^n = x^n$. This is the reason functions that satisfy $f(-x) = f(x)$ are called **EVEN** functions!

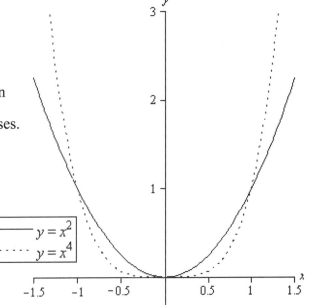

Two for you.

1) As $x \to \pm\infty$, which of these functions approach ∞ faster: $y = x^4$ or $y = x^6$?

2) As $x \to \pm\infty$, which of these functions approach $\pm\infty$ faster: $y = x^{11}$ or $y = x^9$?

Answers 1) $y = x^6$ 2) $y = x^{11}$

Basic $y = \dfrac{1}{x^n} = x^{-n}$ Graphs, where $n \in \mathbb{N}$

Graphs with equations of the form $y = \dfrac{1}{x^n}$, where $n \in \mathbb{N}$, come up so often that they deserve a special page. This is it!

Example 1) Draw the graphs of $y = \dfrac{1}{x}$ and $y = \dfrac{1}{x^3}$ on the same axes.

Solution

For **odd** natural numbers n:

1) $\displaystyle\lim_{x \to \pm\infty} \dfrac{1}{x^n} = 0$ and the expression approaches 0 faster as n increases.

2) $\displaystyle\lim_{x \to 0} \dfrac{1}{x^n} = \begin{cases} -\infty, & \text{if } x \to 0^- \\ \infty, & \text{if } x \to 0^+ \end{cases}$
and approaches $\pm\infty$ faster as n increases.

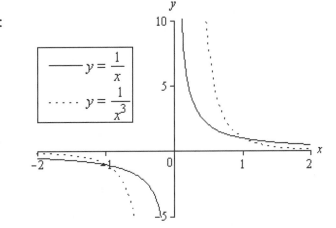

Example 2) Draw the graphs of $y = \dfrac{1}{x^2}$ and $y = \dfrac{1}{x^4}$ on the same axes.

Solution

For **even** natural numbers n:

1) $\displaystyle\lim_{x \to \pm\infty} \dfrac{1}{x^n} = 0$ and the expression approaches 0 faster as n increases.

2) $\displaystyle\lim_{x \to 0} \dfrac{1}{x^n} = \infty$ and approaches ∞ faster as n increases.

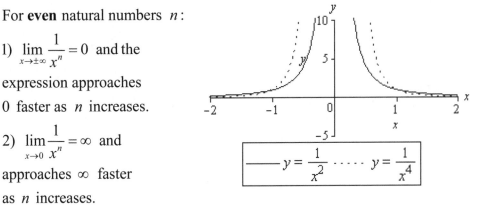

Two for you.

1) As $x \to \pm\infty$, which of these functions approach 0 faster: $y = x^{-4}$ or $y = x^{-5}$?

2) As $x \to 0^{-}$, which of these functions approach $-\infty$ faster: $y = x^{-11}$ or $y = x^{-9}$?

Answers 1) $y = x^{-5}$ 2) $y = x^{-11}$

Basic $y = x^{\frac{1}{n}}$ Graphs, where $n \in \mathbb{N}$

Graphs with equations of the form $y = x^{\frac{1}{n}}$, where $n \in \mathbb{N}$, come up so often that they deserve a special page. This is it!

Example 1) Draw the graphs of $y = x^{\frac{1}{3}}$ and $y = x^{\frac{1}{5}}$ on the same axes.

Solution

For **odd** natural numbers n:

1) $\lim\limits_{x \to \pm\infty} x^{\frac{1}{n}} = \pm\infty$ and the expression approaches $\pm\infty$ **more slowly** as n increases.

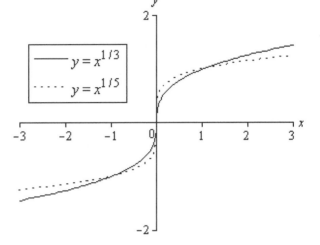

2) $\lim\limits_{x \to 0} x^{\frac{1}{n}} = 0$ and approaches 0 **more slowly** as n increases.

$$\left(\text{eg.,} \quad \left(\frac{1}{64}\right)^{\frac{1}{3}} = \frac{1}{4} < \left(\frac{1}{64}\right)^{\frac{1}{6}} = \frac{1}{2} \right)$$

Example 2) Draw the graphs of $y = x^{\frac{1}{2}}$ and $y = x^{\frac{1}{4}}$ on the same axes.

Solution For **even** natural numbers n:

1) The domain is $[0, \infty)$.

2) $\lim\limits_{x \to \infty} x^{\frac{1}{n}} = \infty$ and the expression approaches ∞ **more slowly** as n increases.

3) $\lim\limits_{x \to 0^+} x^{\frac{1}{n}} = 0$ and approaches 0 **more slowly** as n increases.

Two for you.

1) As $x \to \infty$, which of these functions approach ∞ fastest:

$y = x^{1/4}$, $y = x^{1/5}$, or $y = x^{1/6}$?

2) As $x \to 0^-$, which of these functions approach 0 faster:

$y = x^{1/11}$ or $y = x^{1/9}$?

Answers 1) $y = x^{1/4}$ 2) $y = x^{1/9}$

Shifting or Rescaling a Given Graph ($a > 0$)
$f(x+a), f(x-a), f(ax), af(x), f(x)+a, f(x)-a$

No matter what function $y = f(x)$ we begin with, the effect of each operation is **ALWAYS** the same.

Example 1) Let $y = f(x) = x^2$. Graph and describe these functions relative to $f(x)$.

(a) $y = f(x+2) = (x+2)^2$ (b) $y = f(x-2) = (x-2)^2$ (c) $y = f(2x) = (2x)^2 = 4x^2$

(d) $y = 2f(x) = 2x^2$ (e) $y = f(x)+2 = x^2+2$ (f) $y = f(x)-2 = x^2-2$

Solution

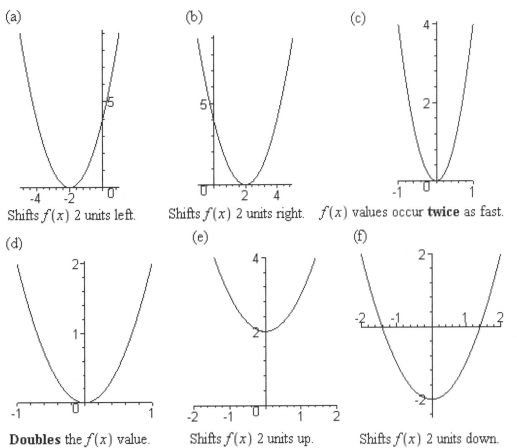

(a) Shifts $f(x)$ 2 units left.   (b) Shifts $f(x)$ 2 units right.   (c) $f(x)$ values occur **twice** as fast.

(d) **Doubles** the $f(x)$ value.   (e) Shifts $f(x)$ 2 units up.   (f) Shifts $f(x)$ 2 units down.

Note: I had to choose from one of two ways to present these graphs. First: keep the scaling the same on all. This would clearly illustrate the changing shapes in (c) and (d). However, it would make it more difficult to see how the translations in (a), (b), (e), and (f) change the original graph, since I would have had to take x from –4 to 4. Second: adjust the scaling while keeping the graphs the same size. This works well for translations but not so well for shape. I decided rescaling was the better solution overall.

One for you.

To the right is the graph of $y = f(x)$ but **I WON'T** tell you the actual function. Sketch: (a) $y = f(x+0.5)$ (b) $y = f(x-0.5)$

(c) $y = f(0.5x)$ (d) $y = 0.5f(x)$

Answer

(a)   (b)   (c)   (d)

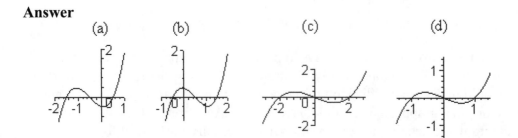

Tests for Symmetry

Symmetry in the y axis: both (x, y) and $(-x, y)$ are on the graph.

Replace x with $-x$ and see if you obtain the same y value.

Symmetry in the x axis: both (x, y) and $(x, -y)$ are on the graph.

Replace y with $-y$ and see if you obtain the same x value.

Symmetry in the origin: both (x, y) and $(-x, -y)$ are on the graph.

Replace both x with $-x$ and y with $-y$ and see if you obtain the same x and y values.

Example 1) Test for symmetry in the following relations.

(a) $y = x^2$ (b) $y = x^3 + x$ (c) $x = \cos(y)$ (d) $x^2 + y^2 = 25$

Solution (a) y axis (replace x with $-x$): $(-x)^2 = x^2$; **symmetry in the y axis? YES!**

x axis (replace y with $-y$): $-y = -x^2 \neq x^2$ for $x \neq 0$; **symmetry in the x axis? NO!**

There is **no symmetry in the origin! WHY? BECAUSE...**

**...you can have NO symmetry, ONE kind of symmetry, or ALL THREE.
But you <u>CANNOT</u> have exactly TWO KINDS OF SYMMETRY!***

(b) y axis: $(-x)^3 + (-x) = -x^3 - x \neq x^3 + x$, for $x \neq 0$. **NO!**

x axis: $-y = -(x^3 + x) \neq x^3 + x$. **NO!**

Origin: $(-x)^3 + (-x) = -x^3 - x = -(x^3 + x) = -y$, and so $x^3 + x = y$. **YES!**

(c) y axis: $-x = -\cos y$. **NO!**

x axis: $\cos(-y) = \cos y = x$. **YES!**

Origin: **NO!**

(d) y axis: $(-x)^2 + y^2 = x^2 + y^2 = 25$. **YES!**

x axis: $x^2 + (-y)^2 = x^2 + y^2 = 25$. **YES!**

Origin: **YES!**

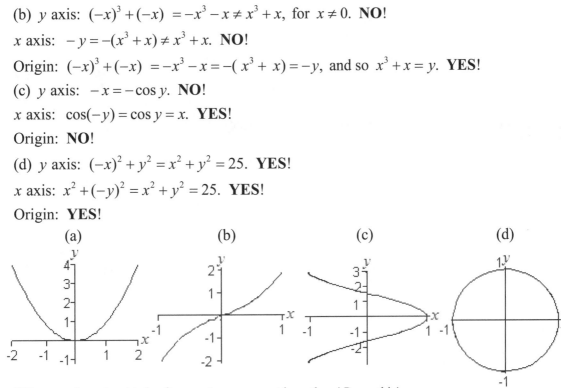

(a)   (b)   (c)   (d)

*When you have two kinds of symmetry, you **must** have three! Prove this!

Two for you.

Discuss the symmetry for the following relations: 1) $y = x\, e^{|x|}$ 2) $x^3 + y^3 = x$

Answers 1) origin   2) origin

Graphing Polynomials without Calculus

Calculus tells us exactly where to find maximum and minimum points, the subtle changes at inflection points, and more. But with a little experience, we can tell a lot about the graph of a polynomial just from its equation.

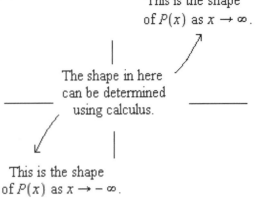

This is the shape of $P(x)$ as $x \to \infty$.

The shape in here can be determined using calculus.

This is the shape of $P(x)$ as $x \to -\infty$.

Example 1) Determine the shape of the polynomial $P(x) = 3x^5 - x^4 + 2x - 5$, as x approaches ∞ and $-\infty$.

Solution $P(x)$ does what its "leading term", "$3x^5$", tells it to do when x is **BIG** in magnitude. So, no matter what is happening "in the middle"..............

If the polynomial is factored, we know its roots

$$\boxed{x - r \text{ is a factor} \Leftrightarrow x = r \text{ is a root}}$$

and how it "behaves" near the roots. If the exponent on the factor is **even**, the graph **doesn't change sign** as it passes through 0, that is, as it crosses the x axis at the root r. If the exponent is **odd**, **it does change sign**.

Example 2) Sketch the graph of $P(x) = x^2(x-1)^3$.

Solution The only roots are 0 and 1. From the exponents on the factors, we know $P(x) \leq 0$ for $x \leq 1$ and $P(x) \geq 0$ for $x \geq 1$. (The sign doesn't change at $x = 0$!) The leading term of $P(x)$, when expanded, is x^5. So, except for the "subtleties" of the curve, $P(x)$ looks like...

...this:

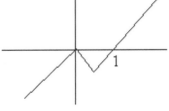

1

The graph, like $y = x^5$, comes up from $-\infty$ as x does. It hits 0 at $x = 0$, heads down to a minimum (which we can find using CALCULUS!), comes back up to 0 at $x = 1$, and finally follows x^5 to ∞! The graph is curved but I used straight lines to show the tendencies. We find the **exact** shape of the curve (extremes, concavity) using derivatives.

Two for you.

Sketch the graphs without calculus:

1) $P(x) = (x-1)x^3(x+1)^2$ 2) $P(x) = -(x-1)^2 x^2 (x+1)^2$

Answers

1)

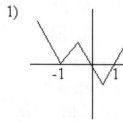

2)

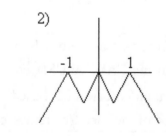

Note that
$$P(x) = -(x-1)^2 x^2 (x+1)^2$$
is symmetric in the y axis!

Vertical and Horizontal Asymptotes

A **vertical asymptote** is a **finite** x value $\boxed{x = \textbf{constant}}$ where $y \to \infty$ or $-\infty$. So, look for x values that make y "blow up": division by 0 or functions that have "built in" vertical asymptotes such as ln, tan, cot, sec, and csc.

A **horizontal asymptote** is a **finite** y value $\boxed{y = \textbf{constant}}$ where $x \to \infty$ or $-\infty$. Take the limit as $x \to \pm\infty$ to see if you obtain a finite y.

Example 1) Find the vertical and horizontal asymptotes for the function

$$y = \frac{1}{(x-5)(x+1)} + \ln(x-1)$$

Solution $x = 5$ is a vertical asymptote. Also,

$$\lim_{x \to 1^+} \left(\frac{1}{(x-5)(x+1)} + \ln(x-1) \right) = -\frac{1}{8} + \lim_{x \to 1^+} \ln(x-1) \overset{\boxed{\lim_{x \to 1^+} \ln(x-1) = -\infty}}{=} -\infty,$$

so $x = 1$ is a vertical asymptote. Note that the function is only defined for $x > 1$, and so $x = -1$ **is not a vertical asymptote**!

$$\lim_{x \to \infty} \left(\frac{1}{(x-5)(x+1)} + \ln(x-1) \right) = 0 + \lim_{x \to \infty} \ln(x-1) = \infty,$$

and so there are no horizontal asymptotes.

Example 2) Find the vertical and horizontal asymptotes for $y = \dfrac{3x^2}{(x-2)(x+1)}$.

Solution The vertical asymptotes are $x = 2$ and $x = -1$. For horizontal, consider:

$$\lim_{x \to \pm\infty} \frac{3x^2}{(x-2)(x+1)} \overset{\boxed{\text{Divide top and bottom by } x^2.}}{=} \lim_{x \to \pm\infty} \frac{\left(\dfrac{3x^2}{x^2} \right)}{\left(\dfrac{(x-2)(x+1)}{x^2} \right)} = \lim_{x \to \pm\infty} \frac{3}{\left(1 - \dfrac{2}{x} \right)\left(1 + \dfrac{1}{x} \right)} = 3$$

Therefore, the horizontal asymptote is $x = 3$.

> **Note :** There can be more than one vertical asymptote. BUT because y is a FUNCTION, there can be only one horizontal asymptote (or none) as x approaches ∞ and one (or none) as x approaches $-\infty$.
>
> **Note :** YOU must decide whether you need to check the limits as x approaches $+\infty$ and $-\infty$ separately!

Two for you.

For the following, find the horizontal and vertical asymptotes:

1) $y = \dfrac{x^3}{(x-1)(x-2)}$ 2) $y = \dfrac{5x}{3x+4} + \dfrac{1}{e^x - 1}$

Answers 1) vertical asymptotes: $x = 1$, $x = 2$; no horizontal asymptote

2) vertical asymptotes: $x = -\dfrac{4}{3}$, $x = 0$

horizontal asymptotes: $y = \dfrac{5}{3}$ as $x \to \infty$ and $y = \dfrac{2}{3}$ as $x \to -\infty$

Slant Asymptotes

A **slant asymptote** is a straight line that a function "asymptotically" (**what a word!**) approaches as x approaches ∞ or $-\infty$ or both. All you have to do is check $\lim\limits_{x\to\pm\infty} f(x)$.

Example 1) Find the slant asymptote(s) of the function $f(x) = 2x + \dfrac{1}{x+1}$.

Solution $\lim\limits_{x\to\pm\infty} f(x)$

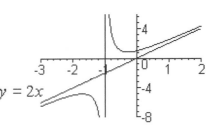

$$= \lim_{x\to\pm\infty}\left(2x + \frac{1}{x+1}\right) \overset{\boxed{\lim\limits_{x\to\pm\infty}\left(\frac{1}{x+1}\right)=0}}{=} \lim_{x\to\pm\infty} 2x.$$

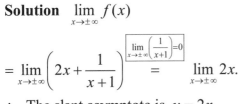
$$y = 2x$$

$\therefore$ The slant asymptote is $y = 2x$.

Just for interest, $x = -1$ is a vertical asymptote.

Example 2) Find the slant asymptotes, if any, of the function

$$g(x) = \frac{1 - x + x^3}{3x^2 + 1} + e^x.$$

Solution Remember that $\lim\limits_{x\to\infty} e^x = \infty$ while $\lim\limits_{x\to-\infty} e^x = 0$.

It would therefore be prudent to check $+\infty$ and $-\infty$ separately!

$$\lim_{x\to\infty} g(x) = \lim_{x\to\infty}\left(\frac{1-x+x^3}{3x^2+1} + e^x\right) \overset{\boxed{\text{Divide top and bottom by } x^2.}}{=} \lim_{x\to\infty}\left(\frac{\frac{1}{x^2}-\frac{1}{x}+x}{3+\frac{1}{x^2}} + e^x\right) = \lim_{x\to\infty}\left(\frac{x}{3} + e^x\right)$$

$$\lim_{x\to-\infty} g(x) = \lim_{x\to-\infty}\left(\frac{1-x+x^3}{3x^2+1} + e^x\right) \overset{\boxed{\text{Divide top and bottom by } x^2.}}{=} \lim_{x\to-\infty}\left(\frac{\frac{1}{x^2}-\frac{1}{x}+x}{3+\frac{1}{x^2}} + e^x\right) \overset{\boxed{\lim\limits_{x\to-\infty} e^x=0}}{=} \lim_{x\to-\infty}\frac{x}{3}$$

$\therefore$ There is a slant asymptote of $y = \dfrac{x}{3}$ as $x \to -\infty$ (but not $+\infty$!).

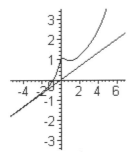

Two for you.

Find the slant asymptotes, if any, for these functions:

1) $f(x) = \dfrac{-x^5 - 2x + 7}{2x - 5x^4}$
　　　2) $g(x) = \dfrac{e^{-x} + 4x^2}{x - 3}$

Answers 1) $y = \dfrac{1}{5}x$ as $x \to \pm\infty$　　　2) $y = 4x$ as $x \to \infty$

Intersection of Two Curves

When finding the intersection of $y = f(x)$ and $y = g(x)$ you

1) set $f(x) = g(x)$ and solve for x;
2) substitute each value of x into **either** $f(x)$ or $g(x)$ to find the corresponding y;
3) if it is fairly straightforward, sketch the graphs of the two curves so you have an idea of how many intersection points there are and approximately where to find them. **Use this as a guide but be prepared on occasion to be surprised if your guess doesn't tally with the math.**

Example 1) Find the intersection of the curves given by

$y = f(x) = x^2$ and $y = g(x) = x + 6$.

Solution Set $x^2 = x + 6$. $\therefore$ $x^2 - x - 6 = 0$. Factoring, $(x-3)(x+2) = 6$ and so $x = 3$ or $x = -2$. Since $f(3) = 9$ and $f(-2) = 4$, the intersection points are $(3, 9)$ and $(-2, 4)$.

Note 1: We often forget we want the intersection points and stop once we find the x values. **Go back to ONE of the original curves to find y.**

Note 2: It doesn't matter whether you go back to f or g to find the y values. For example, here $g(3) = 9$ and $g(-2) = 4$.

Example 2) Find the intersection of $y = \sin x$ and $y = \cos x$, for $0 \le x \le 2\pi$.

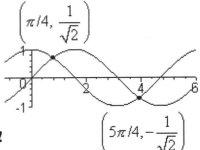

Solution Set $\sin x = \cos x$. The easiest way to tackle this one: divide both sides by $\cos x$, giving $\tan x = 1$. Now you don't need your calculator to solve this! **I hope!** In fact, if you do, your calculator would lead you astray. The calculator would give you, in radian mode, $\pi/4 \doteq 0.785$ radians. But **YOU** must realize that **tan is also positive in the third quadrant!** Don't ignore this since $0 \le x \le 2\pi$. The corresponding third quadrant angle is $5\pi/4$. And let's not

forget: $\sin\left(\dfrac{\pi}{4}\right) = \dfrac{1}{\sqrt{2}}$ and $\sin\left(\dfrac{5\pi}{4}\right) = -\dfrac{1}{\sqrt{2}}$.

The interesection points are $\left(\dfrac{\pi}{4}, \dfrac{1}{\sqrt{2}}\right)$ and $\left(\dfrac{5\pi}{4}, -\dfrac{1}{\sqrt{2}}\right)$.

Two for you.

Find the intersection of the two curves:

1) $y = x^3$ and $y = x^2 + x - 1$ 2) $y = \sin x$ and $y = -\cos x,\ -\pi \le x \le \pi$

Answers 1) $(1, 1)$ and $(-1, -1)$ 2) $\left(\dfrac{3\pi}{4}, \dfrac{1}{\sqrt{2}}\right)$ and $\left(-\dfrac{\pi}{4}, -\dfrac{1}{\sqrt{2}}\right)$

The Greatest Integer (or Floor) Function

The greatest integer function, also called the floor function, is usually denoted by $[[x]]$. **Every number** is either **an integer** or **lies between two integers, one above, one below**. The greatest integer function inputs a number.

If the number IS an integer, that's your answer: $[[4]] = 4$.

If not, your answer is the integer just below the number: $[[4.2]] = 4$.

Got it? Let's see.

Example 1) Evaluate each of the following:
(a) $[[1.7]]$ (b) $[[-2.3]]$ (c) $[[8]]$ (d) $[[-6]]$

Solution (a) 1   (b) -3 (c) 8   (d) -6

Example 2) Let $f(x) = [[x]]$, for $-2 \le x \le 3$.
Write $f(x)$ without using greatest integer
notation and draw its graph.

Solution $f(x) = \begin{cases} -2, \text{ if } -2 \le x < -1 \\ -1, \text{ if } -1 \le x < 0 \\ 0, \text{ if } 0 \le x < 1 \\ 1, \text{ if } 1 \le x < 2 \\ 2, \text{ if } x = 2 \end{cases}$

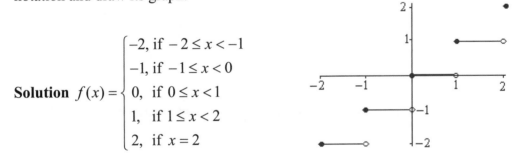

Example 3) Solve $[[2x+1]] = 6$.

| $2x+1$ must be at least 6 but less than 7. |

Solution $[[2x+1]] = 6 \quad \Leftrightarrow \quad 6 \le 2x+1 < 7 \Leftrightarrow 5 \le 2x < 6 \Leftrightarrow 2.5 \le x < 3$.

Two for you.

1) Evaluate each of the following: (a) $[[7]]$ (b) $[[-2.2]]$ (c) $[[-0.0001]]$

2)(a) Solve: $[[x^2]] = 1$ (Hint: $1 \le x^2 < 2$)   (b) $[[x^3 - 1]] = -4$

Answers 1)(a) 7   (b) -3 (c) -1

2)(a) $-\sqrt{2} < x \le -1$ or $1 \le x < \sqrt{2}$ (b) $-3^{1/3} \le x < -2^{1/3}$

Graphs with the Greatest Integer Function

The key here is to find the equations explicitly using the appropriate intervals.

Example 1) Let $f(x) = [[2x]]$, for $-1 \leq x \leq 1$.
Write $f(x)$ without using greatest integer notation
and draw its graph.

Solution $f(x) = \begin{cases} -2, \text{ if } -1 \leq x < -0.5 \\ -1, \text{ if } -0.5 \leq x < 0 \\ 0, \text{ if } 0 \leq x < 0.5 \\ 1, \text{ if } 0.5 \leq x < 1 \\ 2, \text{ if } x = 1 \end{cases}$

Example 2) Let $f(x) = x - [[x]]$, for $-2 \leq x \leq 2$.
Write $f(x)$ without using greatest integer notation
and draw its graph.

Solution $f(x) = \begin{cases} x+2, \text{ if } -2 \leq x < -1 \\ x+1, \text{ if } -1 \leq x < 0 \\ x, \quad \text{ if } 0 \leq x < 0 \\ x-1, \text{ if } 1 \leq x < 2 \\ 0, \quad \text{ if } x = 2 \end{cases}$

Example 3) Let $f(x) = [[x^2]]$, for $0 \leq x \leq 2$.
Write $f(x)$ without using greatest integer notation
and draw its graph.

Solution $f(x) = \begin{cases} 0, \quad \text{ if } 0 \leq x < 1 \\ 1, \text{ if } 1 \leq x < \sqrt{2} \\ 2, \text{ if } \sqrt{2} \leq x < \sqrt{3} \\ 3, \text{ if } \sqrt{3} \leq x < 2 \\ 4, \text{ if } x = 2 \end{cases}$

103

Two for you.

1) Let $f(x) = 2x - [[x]]$, for $-2 \le x \le 1$.

Write $f(x)$ without using greatest integer notation and draw its graph.

2) Let $f(x) = [[x^2]]$, for $-2 \le x \le 0$. Write $f(x)$ without using $[[\ ]]$.

Answer 1) $f(x) = \begin{cases} 2x + 2, & \text{if } -2 \le x < -1 \\ 2x + 1, & \text{if } -1 \le x < 0 \\ 2x, & \text{if } 0 \le x < 1 \\ 1, & \text{if } x = 1 \end{cases}$

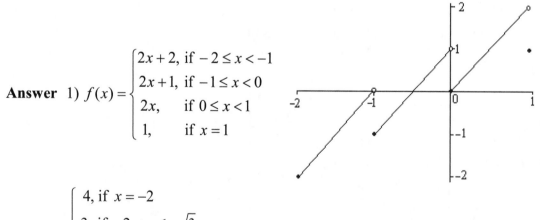

2) $f(x) = \begin{cases} 4, & \text{if } x = -2 \\ 3, & \text{if } -2 < x \le -\sqrt{3} \\ 2, & \text{if } -\sqrt{3} < x \le -\sqrt{2} \\ 1, & \text{if } -\sqrt{2} < x \le -1 \\ 0, & \text{if } -1 < x \le 0 \end{cases}$

Properties of Exponents

Just as multiplication is a **short form for repeated addition** of the same number, exponentiation is a **short form for repeated multiplication** of the same number. For example, $5 \times 4 = 5 + 5 + 5 + 5$ and $5^4 = 5 \times 5 \times 5 \times 5$.

Here are the basic rules for exponents.

$$a^x a^y = a^{x+y} \qquad \frac{a^x}{a^y} = a^{x-y} \qquad (a^x)^y = a^{xy}$$

$$a^0 = 1 \qquad a^1 = a \qquad a^{-1} = \frac{1}{a}$$

$$a^{-x} = \frac{1}{a^x} \qquad \frac{1}{a^{-x}} = a^x$$

$$(ab)^x = a^x b^x \qquad \left(\frac{a}{b}\right)^x = \frac{a^x}{b^x}$$

Example 1) Evaluate each of the following:

(a) 4^3 　　(b) 0.1^0 　　(c) 5^{-1} 　　(d) 0.1^{-3} 　　(e) $\dfrac{12}{3^{-2}}$

Solution (a) 64 　　(b) 1 　　(c) $\dfrac{1}{5}$

(d) $0.1^{-3} = \left(\dfrac{1}{10}\right)^{-3} = 10^3 = 1000$ 　　(e) $\dfrac{12}{3^{-2}} = 12 \cdot 9 = 108$

Example 2) Simplify each of the following:

(a) $x^3 x^7$ 　　(b) $\dfrac{z^4 z^{-2}}{z^7}$ 　　(c) $\left(\dfrac{2^{12} 3^4}{2^{-2} 3^{11}}\right)^{-2}$

Solution (a) $x^3 x^7 = x^{10}$ 　　(b) $\dfrac{z^4 z^{-2}}{z^7} = z^{4-2-7} = z^{-5} = \dfrac{1}{z^5}$

(c) $\left(\dfrac{2^{12} 3^4}{2^{-2} 3^{11}}\right)^{-2} = \left(\dfrac{2^{14}}{3^7}\right)^{-2} = \dfrac{2^{-28}}{3^{-14}} = \dfrac{3^{14}}{2^{28}}$

Two for you.

1) Evaluate: (a) -7^0 (b) $(-3)^3$ (c) $\dfrac{1}{3^{-4}}$

2) Simplify: (a) $x^{1/2}x^5$ (b) $\left(\dfrac{x^6 y^7}{x^{-4} y^6}\right)^5$

Answers 1)(a) -1 (b) -27 (c) 81 2)(a) $x^{11/2}$ (b) $x^{50} y^5$

Logarithms (Log Means "FIND THE EXPONENT!")

Logs cause headaches. I have to admit it. Students find logs hard. Why? I think in part it's because of the word "log". It seems to have no connection with what it represents in math. Then again, students seem to find exponents easy. So when you see "log", think, even read, **"FIND THE EXPONENT!"**

For example, $\log_2 16$: **Find the exponent** you need with base 2 to get a value of 16. Hmm... 2 times 2 times 2 times 2 ... **FOUR!** You see, that's not so hard! It's not like beating your head against a log. Sorry. Here are the rules.

$$\log_a(xy) = \log_a x + \log_a y \qquad \log_a\left(\frac{x}{y}\right) = \log_a x - \log_a y \qquad \log_a\left(x^y\right) = y\log_a x$$

$$\log_a 1 = 0 \qquad \log_a a = 1 \qquad \log_a a^{-1} = -1 \qquad \log_a\left(a^x\right) = x$$

DON'T confuse $\log_a\left(x^y\right)$ with $(\log_a x)^y$. For example,

$$\log_2\left(4^3\right) = \log_2\left(\left(2^2\right)^3\right) = \log_2\left(2^6\right) = 6$$

while $\left(\log_2 4\right)^3 = \log_2\left(2^2\right) \cdot \log_2\left(2^2\right) \cdot \log_2\left(2^2\right) = 2^3 = 8$.

Change of base formula: $\log_a x = \dfrac{\log_b x}{\log_b a}$ and in particular, $\log_a b = \dfrac{1}{\log_b a}$

Special bases: $\log x$ **MEANS** $\log_{10} x$ $\qquad$ $\ln x$ **MEANS** $\log_e x$

Example 1) Evaluate: (a) $\log 1000$ $\quad$ (b) $\log_2 \dfrac{1}{16}$ $\quad$ (c) $\log_3\left(27^4\right)$ $\quad$ (d) $\left(\log_3 27\right)^4$

Solution (a) $\log 1000 = 3$ $\quad$ (b) $\log_2 \dfrac{1}{16} = -4$ $\quad$ (c) $\log_3\left(27^4\right) = 4(3) = 12$

(d) $\left(\log_3 27\right)^4 = 3^4 = 81$

Example 2) Expand using log properties: (a) $\log_3\left(\dfrac{x^3 y^4}{z^5}\right)$ $\quad$ (b) $\log\left((x^2+1)(x^2-1)\right)$

Solution (a) $\log_3\left(\dfrac{x^3 y^4}{z^5}\right) = 3\log_3 x + 4\log_3 y - 5\log_3 z$

(b) $\log\left((x^2+1)(x^2-1)\right) = \log(x^2+1) + \log(x^2-1) \overset{\boxed{or}}{=} \log(x^2+1) + \log(x-1) + \log(x+1)$

Example 3) Change $\log_9 x$ to log base 4, log base 10, and log base e.

Solution $\log_9 x = \dfrac{\log_4 x}{\log_4 9} = \dfrac{\log x}{\log 9} = \dfrac{\ln x}{\ln 9}$

Two for you.

1)(a) Expand using properties of logs: $\log\left(a^{-2}b\sqrt{c}\right)^3$ (Hint: rewrite $\sqrt{c}$ as $c^{1/2}$.)

(b) Combine using properties of logs: $3\ln x - 4\ln y + 1$ (Hint: use $1 = \ln e$.)

2) Change $\log e$ (that is $\log_{10} e$) to base e.

Answers 1)(a) $-6\log a + 3\log b + \dfrac{3}{2}\log c$ (b) $\ln\left(\dfrac{ex^3}{y^4}\right)$ 2) $\log e = \dfrac{1}{\ln 10}$

Basic Exponential Graphs

> Graphs with equations of the form $y = a^x$, where $a > 1$, are **really really really important**.

Example 1) Draw the graphs of $y = 2^x$ and $y = 3^x$ on the same axes.

Solution For bases $a > 1$:

1) $\lim\limits_{x \to \infty} a^x = \infty$ and the expression approaches ∞ **faster** as a increases.

2) $\lim\limits_{x \to -\infty} a^x = 0$ and the expression approaches 0 **faster** as a increases.

3) !!!! a^x **IS ALWAYS > 0** !!!!

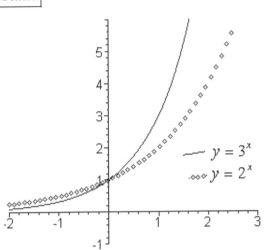

> Graphs with equations of the form $y = a^x$, where $0 < a < 1$, are **really really really almost as important**.

Example 2) Draw on the same axes the graphs of $y = \left(\dfrac{1}{2}\right)^x = 2^{-x}$ and $y = \left(\dfrac{1}{3}\right)^x = 3^{-x}$.

Solution

For bases $0 < a < 1$:

1) $\lim\limits_{x \to \infty} a^x = 0$ and the expression approaches 0 **faster** as a increases.

2) $\lim\limits_{x \to -\infty} a^x = \infty$ and the expression approaches ∞ **faster** as a increases.

3) !!!! a^x **IS STILL ALWAYS > 0** !!!!

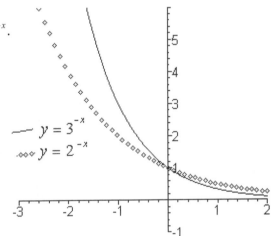

Two for you.

1)(a) As $x \to \infty$, which of these functions approaches ∞ faster: $y = e^x$ or $y = 10^x$?

(b) As $x \to -\infty$, which of these functions approaches 0 faster: $y = e^x$ or $y = 10^x$?

2)(a) As $x \to \infty$, which of these functions approaches 0 faster: $y = e^{-x}$ or $y = 10^{-x}$?

(b) As $x \to -\infty$, which of these functions approaches ∞ faster: $y = e^{-x}$ or $y = 10^{-x}$?

Answers 1)(a) $y = 10^x$ (b) $y = 10^x$ 2)(a) $y = 10^{-x}$ (b) $y = 10^{-x}$

Basic Logarithm Graphs

Graphs with equations of the form $y = \log_a x$, where $a > 1$, are **really really really important**.

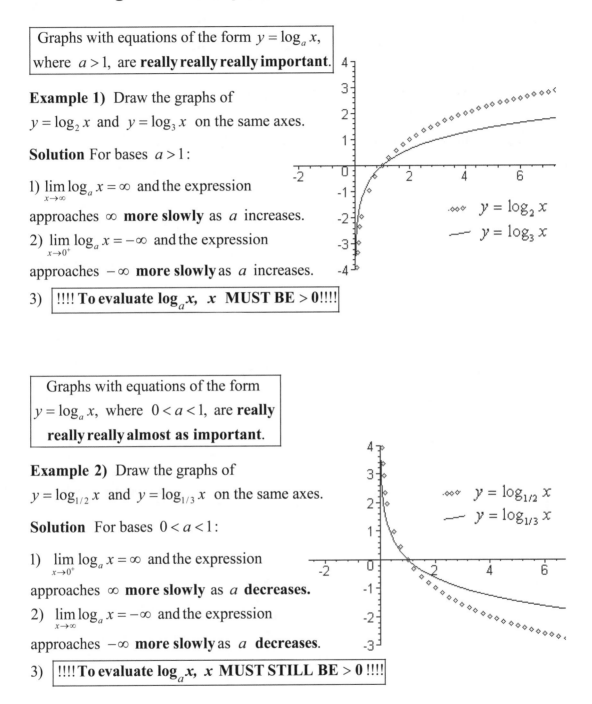

Example 1) Draw the graphs of $y = \log_2 x$ and $y = \log_3 x$ on the same axes.

Solution For bases $a > 1$:

1) $\lim\limits_{x \to \infty} \log_a x = \infty$ and the expression approaches ∞ **more slowly** as a increases.

2) $\lim\limits_{x \to 0^+} \log_a x = -\infty$ and the expression approaches $-\infty$ **more slowly** as a increases.

3) !!!! **To evaluate $\log_a x$, x MUST BE > 0**!!!!

Graphs with equations of the form $y = \log_a x$, where $0 < a < 1$, are **really really really almost as important**.

Example 2) Draw the graphs of $y = \log_{1/2} x$ and $y = \log_{1/3} x$ on the same axes.

Solution For bases $0 < a < 1$:

1) $\lim\limits_{x \to 0^+} \log_a x = \infty$ and the expression approaches ∞ **more slowly** as a **decreases.**

2) $\lim\limits_{x \to \infty} \log_a x = -\infty$ and the expression approaches $-\infty$ **more slowly** as a **decreases.**

3) !!!! **To evaluate $\log_a x$, x MUST STILL BE > 0** !!!!

111

Two for you.

1)(a) As $x \to \infty$, which of these functions approaches ∞ faster:

$y = \ln x$ or $y = \log x$?

(b) As $x \to 0^+$, which of these functions approaches $-\infty$ faster:

$y = \ln x$ or $y = \log x$?

2)(a) As $x \to \infty$, which of these functions approaches $-\infty$ faster:

$y = \log_{1/e} x$ or $y = \log_{1/10} x$?

(b) As $x \to 0^+$, which of these functions approaches ∞ faster:

$y = \log_{1/e} x$ or $y = \log_{1/10} x$?

Answers 1)(a) $y = \ln x$ (b) $y = \ln x$ 2)(a) $y = \log_{1/e} x$ (b) $y = \log_{1/e} x$

Inverse Formulas for Exponents and Logarithms

Remember: Log means "FIND THE EXPONENT!"

First, a review of the basics:

$$\log_a(xy) = \log_a x + \log_a y \qquad \log_a\left(\frac{x}{y}\right) = \log_a x - \log_a y \qquad \log_a(x^y) = y\log_a x$$

$$\log_a 1 = 0 \qquad \log_a a = 1 \qquad \log_a a^{-1} = -1 \qquad \log_a a^x = x$$

Change of base formula: $\log_a x = \dfrac{\log_b x}{\log_b a}$ and in particular, $\log_a b = \dfrac{1}{\log_b a}$

Special bases: $\log x$ **MEANS** $\log_{10} x$ $\ln x$ **MEANS** $\log_e x$. **And now, the...**

Inverse Formulas: $a^{\log_a x} = x$ $10^{\log x} = x$ $e^{\ln x} = x$

$$\log_a(a^x) = x \qquad \log(10^x) = x \qquad \ln(e^x) = x$$

Example 1) Simplify the following:

(a) $\log_3(3^{23})$ (b) $\log(10^{\sin x})$ (c) $\ln(e^{-2.37})$ (d) $\log_2(3^x)$

Solution (a) $\log_3(3^{23}) = 23$ (b) $\log(10^{\sin x}) = \sin x$ (c) $\ln(e^{-2.37}) = -2.37$

(d) $\log_2(3^x) = x\log_2 3$ We can't simplify further because **the bases don't match!**

Example 2) Simplify the following:

(a) $5^{\log_5 \pi}$ (b) $10^{\log(x+5)}$ (c) $e^{\ln(\ln x)}$ (d) $7^{\log_9 x}$

Solution (a) $5^{\log_5 \pi} = \pi$ (b) $10^{\log(x+5)} = x+5$ (c) $e^{\ln(\ln x)} = \ln x$

(d) $7^{\log_9 x}$ We can't make this simpler because **the bases don't match**!

Example 3) Simplify the following:

(a) $7\log_4(4^{2x+5})$ (b) $5\ln(e^{x^2})$ (c) $10^{3\log 2}$ (d) $e^{7\ln x}$ (e) $\log_2 4^x$

Solution (a) $7\log_4(4^{2x+5}) = 7(2x+5) = 14x+35$ (b) $5\ln(e^{x^2}) = 5x^2$

(c) $10^{3\log 2} = 10^{\log(2^3)} = 10^{\log 8} = 8$ (d) $e^{7\ln x} = e^{\ln(x^7)} = x^7$

(e) $\log_2 4^x = \log_2(2^2)^x = \log_2(2^{2x}) = 2x$

Two for you.

Simplify: 1)(a) $\log_7\left(7^{3x}\right)$ (b) $\ln(e^{4x+e^x})$ (c) $\log_2(8^t)$

2)(a) $10^{\log 7}$ (b) $e^{4\ln(\sin x)}$ (c) $4^{\log_9 x}$

Answers 1)(a) $3x$ (b) $4x+e^x$ (c) $3t$

2)(a) 7 (b) $\sin^4(x)$ (c) No **easy** simplification since the bases are different.

Solving Exponential Equations

To solve exponential and logarithm equations, you must be completely comfortable with:

$$a = b^x \Leftrightarrow x = log_b\, a$$

b is the **base** x is the **exponent** a is, well, we will call it the **value**.

(Actually, a is the "power" but millions and millions of people confuse "power" with "exponent"! So, let's call it the value. Humour me!)

Example 1) Find x in each of the following:

(a) $81 = 3^x$ (b) $5^{2x} = 12$ (c) $e^{x^2} = 9$ (d) $10^{4x+3} = 10^{2x-1}$ (e) $6^{3x+2} = -1$

Solution (a) $81 = 3^x \Leftrightarrow x = log_3 81 = 4$

(b) $5^{2x} = 12 \Leftrightarrow 2x = log_5 12 \underset{\substack{\text{optional, using the} \\ \text{change of base formula}}}{=} \dfrac{\ln 12}{\ln 5} \overset{\text{calculator}}{\doteq} 1.544$ and so $x \doteq 0.772$

(c) $e^{x^2} = 9 \Leftrightarrow x^2 = \ln 9 \Leftrightarrow x = \pm\sqrt{\ln 9} \overset{\text{optional}}{\doteq} \pm 1.482$

(d) $10^{4x+3} = 10^{2x-1} \Leftrightarrow 4x+3 = 2x-1 \Leftrightarrow 2x = -4 \Leftrightarrow x = -2$

(e) $6^{3x+2} = -1$ has no solution since, as long as a is positive, then $a^x > 0$ **ALWAYS!**

Example 2) Solve for x: $e^{2x} - 2e^x - 1 = 0$

Solution Treat this as a quadratic equation with variable e^x: $\left(e^x\right)^2 - 2e^x - 1 = 0$

Now use the quadratic formula for $aX^2 + bX + c = 0$ with $a = 1$, $b = -2$, $c = -1$, and $X = e^x$:

$$e^x = \overset{\frac{-b \pm \sqrt{b^2 - 4ac}}{2a}}{\dfrac{-(-2) \pm \sqrt{(-2)^2 - 4(1)(-1)}}{2(1)}} = \dfrac{2 \pm \sqrt{8}}{2} \overset{\sqrt{8} = \sqrt{4 \cdot 2} = 2\sqrt{2}}{=} \dfrac{2 \pm 2\sqrt{2}}{2} = 1 \pm \sqrt{2}$$

BUT $1 - \sqrt{2} < 0$ and $e^x > 0$!

$\therefore\ e^x = 1 + \sqrt{2}$ and so $x = \ln\left(1 + \sqrt{2}\right) \doteq 0.881$

Two for you.

1) Find x in each of the following:

(a) $2^x = 128$ (b) $7^{3x+1} = 49$ (c) $e^{e^x} = e$ (d) $10^{\sin x} = 1$ (e) $(-6)^{3x+6} = -216$

2) Solve for x: $10^{2x} + 2(10^x) - 1 = 0$

Answers 1)(a) $x = 7$ (b) $x = \dfrac{1}{3}$ (c) $x = 0$ (d) $x = k\pi,\, k \in \mathbb{Z}$ (e) $x = -1$

2) $x = \log\left(-1 + \sqrt{2}\right)$ $\left(\because 10^x > 0 \quad \therefore 10^x \ne -1 - \sqrt{2}. \right)$

Solving Logarithm Equations

To solve exponential and logarithm equations, you must be completely comfortable with:

$$a = b^x \Leftrightarrow x = \log_b a$$

b is the **base** x is the **exponent** a is, well, we will call it the **value**.

(Actually, a is the "power" but millions and millions of people confuse "power" with "exponent"! So, let's call it the value. Humour me!)

Example 1) Find x in each of the following:

(a) $\log_5(3x) = 2$ (b) $\ln(x^2) = -2$ (c) $\log_3(4x - 1) = \log_3(6x - 3)$

(d) $\ln(-1 - x^2) = 1$

Solution (a) $\log_5(3x) = 2 \Leftrightarrow 3x = 5^2 = 25 \Leftrightarrow x = \dfrac{25}{3}$

(b) $\ln(x^2) = -2 \Leftrightarrow x^2 = e^{-2} = \dfrac{1}{e^2} \Leftrightarrow x = \pm\dfrac{1}{e}$

> **VERY TRICKY STEP!!**
> **SINCE x CAN BE < 0, WE NEED TO INSERT "| |"!**

OR (b) $\ln(x^2) = -2 \qquad \Leftrightarrow \qquad 2\ln|x| = -2 \Leftrightarrow \ln|x| = -1 \Leftrightarrow x = \pm\dfrac{1}{e}$

(c) $\log_3(4x - 1) = \log_3(6x - 3) \Leftrightarrow 4x - 1 = 6x - 3 \Leftrightarrow 2 = 2x \Leftrightarrow x = 1$

(d) $\ln(-1 - x^2) = 1 \Leftrightarrow e = -1 - x^2$.

This has no solution since $e > 2$ while $-1 - x^2 \leq -1$.

Example 2) Solve for x: $\log x + \log(2x - 1) = \log 3$

Solution Note $x > 0$ and $x > \dfrac{1}{2}$ because of the domain of log functions!

So $x > \dfrac{1}{2}$ in this question. Using log properties:

$\log x + \log(2x - 1) = \log 3 \Leftrightarrow \log(x(2x - 1)) = \log 3 \Leftrightarrow 2x^2 - x = 3$

$\Leftrightarrow 2x^2 - x - 3 = 0 \Leftrightarrow (2x - 3)(x + 1) = 0 \Leftrightarrow x = \dfrac{3}{2}$ or $x = -1$

BUT $x > \dfrac{1}{2}$, and so $x = \dfrac{3}{2}$.

Two for you.

1) Find x in each of the following:

(a) $\log_5 x = 2$ (b) $\log_2(3x) = 4$ (c) $\ln(\ln x) = 0$ (d) $\log(3x) = \log(12 - x)$

2) Solve for x: $\ln(4x + 7) - \ln(x) = \ln 5$

Answers 1)(a) $x = 25$ (b) $\dfrac{16}{3}$ (c) $x = e$ (d) $x = 3$ 2) $x = 7$

The Derivative of $y = e^x$ and $y = a^x$

I **LOVE** this formula: $\dfrac{d(e^x)}{dx} = e^x$

> e^x **is its own derivative. At each x value, the slope equals the height.**

But enough of my obsession. We have examples to do and two for you!

Example 1) Find $\dfrac{dy}{dx}$ for each of the following:

(a) $y = x^3 e^x$ (b) $y = e^{\sin x}$ (c) $y = e^{4x}$ (d) $y = e^{x \ln 4}$ (e) $y = 4^x$

Solution (a) $y = x^3 e^x$ $\therefore$ $\dfrac{dy}{dx}$ [Product Rule] $= x^3(e^x) + e^x(3x^2)$ [a little neater...] $= x^2 e^x(x + 3)$

(b) $y = e^{\sin x}$ $\therefore$ $\dfrac{dy}{dx}$ [Chain Rule] $= e^{\sin x} \cos x$ (c) $y = e^{4x}$ $\therefore$ $\dfrac{dy}{dx}$ [Chain Rule] $= e^{4x}(4) = 4e^{4x}$

(d) $y = e^{x \ln 4}$ $\therefore$ $\dfrac{dy}{dx}$ [Chain Rule] $= e^{x \ln 4}(\ln 4)$ [Bring the "ln 4" to the left so this answer looks like the answer in (c). Remember $\ln 4$ is just a constant.] $= (\ln 4)e^{(\ln 4)x}$

(e) $y = 4^x$. | Remember a^x [$X = e^{\ln X}$. Here, $X = a^x$.] $= e^{\ln(a^x)}$ [Log Property!] $= e^{x \ln a}$. So $y = 4^x$ [Here, $a^x = 4^x$.] $= e^{\ln(4^x)} = e^{x \ln 4}$

$\therefore$ $\dfrac{dy}{dx}$ [Now this is part (d) above!] $= e^{x \ln 4}(\ln 4)$ [Don't forget: $e^{x \ln 4} = 4^x$] $= 4^x \ln 4$ [for those who like their constants at the left...] $= (\ln 4)4^x$

Part (e) gives us the rule for the derivative of $y = a^x$: $\dfrac{d(a^x)}{dx} = a^x \ln a$.

Example 2) Find $\dfrac{dy}{dx}$: (a) $y = 2^x \tan x$ (b) $y = 5^{\sec x}$ (c) $y = \dfrac{3^{x^2}}{x}$

Solution (a) $y = 2^x \tan x$

$\therefore$ $\dfrac{dy}{dx}$ [Product Rule] $= 2^x \sec^2 x + \tan x \, 2^x \ln 2$ [a little neater...] $= 2^x(\sec^2 x + \tan x \ln 2)$

(b) $y = 5^{\sec x}$ $\therefore$ $\dfrac{dy}{dx}$ [Chain Rule] $= 5^{\sec x} \sec x \tan x \ln 5$

(c) $y = \dfrac{3^{x^2}}{x}$ $\therefore$ $\dfrac{dy}{dx}$ [Quotient Rule] $= \dfrac{x3^{x^2}(2x)\ln 3 - 3^{x^2}(1)}{x^2}$ [a little neater...] $= \dfrac{3^{x^2}(2x^2 \ln 3 - 1)}{x^2}$

Two for you.

Differentiate: 1)(a) $y = e^{\cos x}$ (b) $y = \sqrt{e^{2x} + 4}$

2)(a) $y = 3^{\cos x}$ (b) $y = \sqrt{a^{2x} + 4}$, where $a > 0$

Answers 1)(a) $\dfrac{dy}{dx} = -e^{\cos x} \sin x$ (b) $\dfrac{dy}{dx} = \dfrac{e^{2x}}{\sqrt{e^{2x} + 4}}$

2)(a) $\dfrac{dy}{dx} = -3^{\cos x}(\ln 3)\sin x$ (b) $\dfrac{dy}{dx} = \dfrac{a^{2x}\ln a}{\sqrt{a^{2x} + 4}}$

The Derivative of $y = \ln x$ and $y = \log_a x$

My students are pretty comfortable with the formula $\dfrac{d(\ln x)}{dx} = \dfrac{1}{x}$. It is also true that

$\dfrac{d(\ln |x|)}{dx} = \dfrac{1}{x}$. The second formula allows $x < 0$. The good news is that the derivative is

the same! You see how the Math Gods take care of you?!

Example 1) Given $\dfrac{d(\ln x)}{dx} = \dfrac{1}{x}$, prove that $\dfrac{d(\ln |x|)}{dx} = \dfrac{1}{x}$.

Solution Case 1) Let $x > 0$ so that $|x| = x$. $\therefore \dfrac{d(\ln |x|)}{dx} = \dfrac{d(\ln x)}{dx} = \dfrac{1}{x}$

Case 2) Let $x < 0$ so that $|x| = -x$. $\therefore \dfrac{d(\ln |x|)}{dx} = \dfrac{d(\ln(-x))}{dx} \overset{\boxed{\text{Chain Rule!}}}{=} \dfrac{-1}{(-x)} = \dfrac{1}{x}$

Example 2) Differentiate: (a) $y = \ln(3x)$ (b) $y = e^x \ln |1 + 3x|$ (c) $y = \ln(\ln x)$

Solution (a) $y = \ln(3x)$ $\therefore \dfrac{dy}{dx} \overset{\boxed{\text{Chain Rule!}}}{=} \dfrac{3}{3x} = \dfrac{1}{x}$ $\boxed{\text{alternate method}}$ **OR** $y = \boxed{\text{log property}}$ $\ln 3 + \ln x$ and so $\dfrac{dy}{dx} = \dfrac{1}{x}$

(b) $y = e^x \ln |1 + 3x|$ $\therefore \dfrac{dy}{dx} \overset{\boxed{\text{Product Rule!}}}{=} e^x \dfrac{3}{1 + 3x} + \ln |1 + 3x| (e^x) = e^x \left(\dfrac{3}{1 + 3x} + \ln |1 + 3x| \right)$

(c) $y = \ln(\ln x)$ $\therefore \dfrac{dy}{dx} \overset{\boxed{\text{Chain Rule!}}}{=} \dfrac{1}{\ln x} \left(\dfrac{1}{x} \right) \overset{\boxed{\text{or}}}{=} \dfrac{1}{x \ln x}$

Example 3) Find the derivative of $y = \log_2 x$.

Solution $y = \log_2 x \overset{\boxed{\substack{\text{Change} \\ \text{of Base} \\ \text{formula}}}}{=} \dfrac{\log_e x}{\log_e 2} \overset{\boxed{\log_e = \ln}}{=} \dfrac{\ln x}{\ln 2} \overset{\boxed{\substack{\text{Remember} \\ \ln 2 \text{ is a} \\ \text{constant.}}}}{=} \dfrac{1}{\ln 2} \ln x$ $\therefore \dfrac{dy}{dx} = \dfrac{1}{\ln 2} \left(\dfrac{1}{x} \right) = \dfrac{1}{x \ln 2}$

$\boxed{\text{Compare: } \dfrac{d(a^x)}{dx} = a^x \ln a \qquad \dfrac{d(\log_a x)}{dx} = \dfrac{1}{x \ln a}}$

Example 4) Differentiate: (a) $y = \log_5 |1 + 3x|$ (b) $y = \log_a(\log_a x)$

Solution (a) $y = \log_5 |1 + 3x|$ $\therefore \dfrac{dy}{dx} \overset{\boxed{\text{Chain Rule!}}}{=} \dfrac{3}{(1 + 3x) \ln 5}$

(b) $y = \log_a(\log_a x) \overset{\boxed{\substack{\text{Be careful! Here,} \\ \text{we make a change} \\ \text{of base for the} \\ \text{"outside" } \log_a !}}}{=} \dfrac{\ln(\log_a x)}{\ln a}$

$\therefore \dfrac{dy}{dx} \overset{\boxed{\text{Chain Rule!}}}{=} \dfrac{1}{(\log_a x) \ln a} \dfrac{1}{x \ln a} \overset{\boxed{\text{much neater...}}}{=} \dfrac{1}{x \log_a x (\ln a)^2}$

Two for you.

Differentiate: 1) $y = \ln |\cos x| + \ln |\sec x + \tan x|$ 2) $y = \log(\log(x))$

Answers 1) $-\tan x + \sec x$ 2) $\dfrac{1}{x \log x (\ln 10)^2}$

Logarithmic Differentiation Part I

Now this is a **fun** page. Really. Here we take TOUGH looking questions and make them easy. You see, logs aren't scary. Logs are our friends. They make tough questions easy. Okay, I hear you. Let's get on with it.

Example 1) Find $\dfrac{dy}{dx}$ if $y = \ln\left(\dfrac{x^3(4x+5)^2}{(e^x+1)^5}\right)$.

Solution This looks **very scary**! Product rule, quotient rule, chain, log...**HELP!**

But... $y = \ln\left(\dfrac{x^3(4x+5)^2}{(e^x+1)^5}\right) \overset{\boxed{\text{Log Properties!}}}{=} 3\ln x + 2\ln(4x+5) - 5\ln(e^x+1)$

and so $\dfrac{dy}{dx} \overset{\boxed{\text{Don't forget the chain rule!}}}{=} \dfrac{3}{x} + \dfrac{8}{4x+5} - \dfrac{5e^x}{e^x+1}$. **EASY!**

Example 2) Slight complication...Find $\dfrac{dy}{dx}$ if $y = \dfrac{x^{1/3}\cos^3 x}{(x^4-x)^2}$.

Solution To use the log properties, we need to take "ln" of each side. We can only take ln of **positive numbers. So, first, take the absolute value of each side**, that is, set |Left Side| = |Right Side|. We should be concerned: does this change or restrict the original question? **NO!** Remember, $\dfrac{d\ln|x|}{dx} \overset{\boxed{\text{Say goodbye to absolute value!}}}{=} \dfrac{1}{x}$.

The absolute value disappears. We get the correct derivative with no restrictions!

$y = \dfrac{x^{1/3}\cos^3 x}{(x^4-x)^2}$ $\overset{\boxed{\text{Take the absolute value of each side.}}}{\therefore}$ $|y| = \left|\dfrac{x^{1/3}\cos^3 x}{(x^4-x)^2}\right| = \dfrac{|x|^{1/3}|\cos x|^3}{|x^4-x|^2}$ and so

$\ln|y| = \ln\left(\dfrac{|x|^{1/3}|\cos x|^3}{|x^4-x|^2}\right) \overset{\boxed{\text{Log Properties!}}}{=} \dfrac{1}{3}\ln|x| + 3\ln|\cos x| - 2\ln|x^4-x|$

$\overset{\boxed{\text{Note: we differentiate \textbf{implicitly} on the left side.}}}{\therefore}$ $\dfrac{1}{y}\dfrac{dy}{dx} = \dfrac{1}{3x} - \dfrac{3\sin x}{\cos x} - \dfrac{2(4x^3-1)}{x^4-x}$ and so

$\dfrac{dy}{dx} \overset{\boxed{\substack{\text{Cross multiply by }y.\text{ Use}\\ \frac{3\sin x}{\cos x}=3\tan x.}}}{=} y\left(\dfrac{1}{3x} - 3\tan x - \dfrac{2(4x^3-1)}{x^4-x}\right) \overset{\boxed{\substack{\text{Optional:}\\ \text{replace }y\text{ with the}\\ \text{original expression.}}}}{=} \dfrac{x^{1/3}\cos^3 x}{(x^4-x)^2}\left(\dfrac{1}{3x} - 3\tan x - \dfrac{2(4x^3-1)}{x^4-x}\right)$

Two for you.

Find $\dfrac{dy}{dx}$ in the following: 1) $y = \ln\left(\dfrac{x^5 \ln x}{\tan x}\right)$ 2) $y = \left(\dfrac{(5x-1)\sin^5 x}{e^x + 5}\right)^3$

Answers 1) $\dfrac{5}{x} + \dfrac{1}{x \ln x} - \dfrac{\sec^2 x}{\tan x}$ 2) $3y\left(\dfrac{5}{5x-1} + 5\cot x - \dfrac{e^x}{e^x + 5}\right)$

Logarithmic Differentiation Part II: $\dfrac{d}{dx}\left(f(x)^{g(x)}\right)$

You can find $\dfrac{dy}{dx}$ if $y=\left(f(x)\right)^{3}$: $\dfrac{dy}{dx}=3\left(f(x)\right)^{2}f'(x)$. This is "variable^{constant}".

You can find $\dfrac{dy}{dx}$ if $y=3^{f(x)}$: $\dfrac{dy}{dx}=3^{f(x)}f'(x)\ln 3$. This is "constant^{variable}".

But what about $\dfrac{dy}{dx}$ if $y=f(x)^{g(x)}$, that is, "variable^{variable}"?

Example 1) Differentiate $y=(2x+1)^{\sin x}$.

Solution Here we use the same method as Log Differentiation Part I. But because exponential functions are defined only when the base is positive...

> We allow the **arithmetic** expression $(-3)^{3}$ but not* the **function** $y=(-3)^{x}$!

...we don't need to take the absolute value of each side first.

$y=(2x+1)^{\sin x}$ $\therefore$ $\ln y=\ln\left((2x+1)^{\sin x}\right)$ $\boxed{\text{Use } \ln(a^{b})=b\ln(a),\text{ with } a=2x+1 \text{ and } b=\sin x.}$ $=\sin x\ln(2x+1)$.

$\therefore$ $\dfrac{1}{y}\dfrac{dy}{dx}$ $\boxed{\text{Product Rule}}$ $=\sin x\left(\dfrac{2}{2x+1}\right)+\ln(2x+1)(\cos x)$ and so

$\dfrac{dy}{dx}=y\left(\left(\dfrac{2\sin x}{2x+1}\right)+\ln(2x+1)(\cos x)\right)$ $\boxed{\substack{\text{Optional:}\\ \text{replace } y.}}$ $=(2x+1)^{\sin x}\left(\left(\dfrac{2\sin x}{2x+1}\right)+\ln(2x+1)(\cos x)\right)$

$\boxed{\substack{\text{Get a common}\\ \text{denominator.}}}$ $=(2x+1)^{\sin x}\left(\dfrac{2\sin x+(2x+1)\ln(2x+1)(\cos x)}{2x+1}\right)$

$\boxed{\substack{\text{Notice on the previous line that}\\ \text{the exponential base is } 2x+1:\\ \text{the exponent on the top is}\\ \sin x \text{ and on the bottom is } 1.}}$ $=(2x+1)^{\sin x-1}\left(2\sin x+(2x+1)\ln(2x+1)(\cos x)\right)$

Example 2) Find $\dfrac{dy}{dx}$ if $y=(x^{2}+1)^{\cos x}$.

Solution $\ln y=\ln\left((x^{2}+1)^{\cos x}\right)=\cos x\ln(x^{2}+1)$ $\therefore$ $\dfrac{1}{y}\dfrac{dy}{dx}=\cos x\left(\dfrac{2x}{x^{2}+1}\right)+\ln(x^{2}+1)(-\sin x)$

and so $\dfrac{dy}{dx}=y\left(\left(\dfrac{2x\cos x}{x^{2}+1}\right)-\sin x\ln(x^{2}+1)\right)=(x^{2}+1)^{\cos x}\left(\left(\dfrac{2x\cos x}{x^{2}+1}\right)-\sin x\ln(x^{2}+1)\right)$

$\boxed{\text{optional}}$ $=(x^{2}+1)^{\cos x-1}\left(2x\cos x-(x^{2}+1)\sin x\ln(x^{2}+1)\right)$

*Actually, we do in the area of mathematics called "complex analysis".

Two for you.

Differentiate: 1) $y = x^{5x+1}$ 2) $y = (\tan x)^{\ln x}$

Answers 1) $\dfrac{dy}{dx} = x^{5x+1}\left(\dfrac{5x+1}{x} + 5\ln x\right) \overset{\boxed{\text{optional}}}{=} x^{5x}(5x+1+5x\ln x)$

2) $\dfrac{dy}{dx} = (\tan x)^{\ln x}\left(\dfrac{\ln x \sec^2 x}{\tan x} + \dfrac{\ln(\tan x)}{x}\right) = (\tan x)^{\ln x - 1}\left(\dfrac{\left(x\ln x \sec^2 x\right) + \tan x \ln(\tan x)}{x}\right)$

Integrals Yielding ln: $\int \frac{\left(\frac{du}{dx}\right)}{u}dx = \ln|u| + C$

Compare these three integrals:

1) $\int \frac{1}{x^2+1}dx$ 2) $\int \frac{2x}{(x^2+1)^2}dx$ 3) $\int \frac{2x}{x^2+1}dx$.

Which one fits into the pattern $\int \frac{\left(\frac{du}{dx}\right)}{u}dx$? In all three examples, $u = x^2 + 1$.

Integral 1) misses the pattern because $\frac{du}{dx} = 2x$ is nowhere to be found.

Integral 2) misses the pattern because the exponent on u in the bottom is 2.

Integral 3) is like Goldilock's choice of porridge: just right!

In fact, $\int \frac{1}{x^2+1}dx = \arctan x + C$, which you may not have yet studied!

In fact, $\int \frac{2x}{(x^2+1)^2}dx$ is the Chain Rule in Reverse with the Power Rule: $\int u^{-2}\frac{du}{dx}dx$:

$$\int \frac{2x}{(x^2+1)^2}dx = \int (x^2+1)^{-2}\,2x\,dx = \frac{(x^2+1)^{-1}}{-1} + C = \frac{-1}{x^2+1} + C$$

But $\int \frac{2x}{x^2+1}dx = \ln|x^2+1| + C$ $\boxed{\begin{array}{c}x^2+1>0 \text{ so we don't}\\ \text{need absolute value.}\end{array}}$ $= \ln(x^2+1) + C$

Example 1) Evaluate the following integrals:

(a) $\int \frac{1+\sin x}{x-\cos x}dx$ (b) $\int \frac{e^{3x}}{e^{3x}-5}dx$ (c) $\int \frac{1}{x\ln x}dx$

Solution (a) $\int \frac{1+\sin x}{x-\cos x}dx = \ln|x-\cos x| + C$

(b) $\int \frac{e^{3x}}{e^{3x}-5}dx$ $\boxed{\text{Adjust the multiplicative constant.}} = \frac{1}{3}\int \frac{3e^{3x}}{e^{3x}-5}dx = \frac{1}{3}\ln|e^{3x}-5| + C$

(c) $\int \frac{1}{x\ln x}dx$ $\boxed{\text{Here, } u = \ln x \text{ and } \frac{du}{dx} = \frac{1}{x}.} = \int \frac{\left(\frac{1}{x}\right)}{\ln x}dx = \ln|\ln x| + C$

127

Two for you.

Evaluate the following integrals: 1) $\int \dfrac{x^2}{2x^3 + 1} dx$

2) $\int \dfrac{1}{x \ln(x) \ln(\ln(x))} dx$ $\left(\text{Hint: let } u = \ln(\ln(x)).\right)$

Answers 1) $\dfrac{1}{6} \ln|2x^3 + 1| + C$ 2) $\ln|\ln(\ln x)| + C$

A Degree of Knowledge about Angles

Angle Facts! Remember that, in degree measure, we always include the degree symbol. In radian measure, we sometimes (your choice) omit "radians". Why? Don't know!

Triangles: The sum of the angles in a triangle is $180° = \pi$ radians.

If all angles are equal, each **interior** angle is $60° = \dfrac{\pi}{3}$. Also, if the angles are equal, so are the sides. (In a triangle: **equiangular $\Leftrightarrow$ equilateral**)

Quadrilaterals: The sum of the angles in a quadrilateral is $360° = 2\pi$ radians.

If the quadilateral is a square (or rectangle), each **interior** angle is $90° = \dfrac{\pi}{2}$.

(In a quadrilateral: **equiangular $\not\Leftrightarrow$ equilateral**)

Polygons: The sum of the angles in a polygon with n sides is

$\boxed{\text{In Degree Measure!}}$ $\qquad\qquad\qquad\qquad$ $\boxed{\text{In Radian Measure!}}$
$$180(n-2)° = 180n° - 360° \qquad (n-2)\pi \text{ radians} = n\pi - 2\pi \text{ radians}$$

If this is a "**regular**" polygon (**both equiangular and equilateral**), each **interior** angle is
$$\frac{(n-2)180°}{n} = 180° - \frac{360°}{n} = \pi - \frac{2\pi}{n} \text{ radians. So, for example, if } n = 4, \text{ then}$$

the interior angle $= 180° - \dfrac{360°}{4} = 90° = \dfrac{\pi}{2}$ and this is what we found for rectangles.

Parallel Lines: Given $\boxed{\text{|| is the symbol for parallel.}}$ $l_1 \| l_2$:

Alternate Angles: $a = c$ and $b = d$ (**Z rule**)

Corresponding Angles: $a = e$ and $d = f$ (**F Rule**)

Interior Angles (on the same side of the transversal):
$a + d = b + c = 180° = \pi$ radians (**C Rule**)

Circles: If d is the angle at the centre of the first circle, then $d = 2e$.
In the second (*funny looking*) circle:

$\boxed{\text{or, if we are using radian measure,}}$
$$a = b = (180-c)° \qquad = \qquad \pi - c$$

(a and b are said to be **subtended by the same arc.**)

Two for you.

1)(a) In the triangle, find x in radian measure.

(b) In the circle, find y, z, and w. Assume the angle labeled z is at the centre of the circle.

2)(a) What is the interior angle, in degrees, of a regular hexagon? (Hint: hex = six)

(b) What is the interior angle, in degrees, of a regular 180-gon? (Hint: $n = 180$)

Answers 1)(a) $\dfrac{\pi}{6}$ (b) $y = 25°$ $z = 50°$ $w = 155°$

2)(a) $120°$ (b) $178°$

The Pythagorean Theorem

Pythagoras and friends proved this famous theorem around 500 BC, although it was known long before then. In fact, it caused Pythagoras some mathematical heartburn. He believed that **all** numbers were either whole numbers or rational numbers (quotients of whole numbers.) Then he took a closer look at the $(45°, 45°, 90°)$ triangle, with two equal sides of length 1. The hypotenuse turned out to have length $\sqrt{2}$ and a little mathematical ingenuity shows that $\sqrt{2}$ is NOT a rational number, let alone a whole number. The embarrassing truth is that the "Pythagorean Society" tried to hide the existence of this fact. Can you imagine this happening today? Can you imagine a government, say, not being totally forthcoming with the truth? I digress.

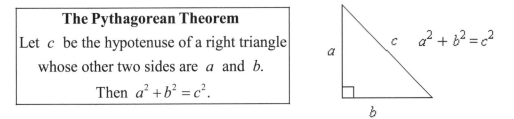

The Pythagorean Theorem

Let c be the hypotenuse of a right triangle whose other two sides are a and b.

Then $a^2 + b^2 = c^2$.

$a^2 + b^2 = c^2$

The **converse** is also true: If a triangle with sides a, b, and c satisfies $a^2 + b^2 = c^2$, then the angle opposite side c is $90°$.

Example 1) In the diagram, find x and then find y.

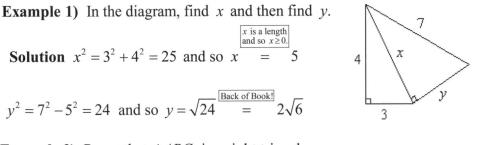

x is a length and so $x \geq 0$.

Solution $x^2 = 3^2 + 4^2 = 25$ and so $x = 5$

Back of Book!

$y^2 = 7^2 - 5^2 = 24$ and so $y = \sqrt{24} = 2\sqrt{6}$

Example 2) Prove that $\triangle ABC$ is a right triangle. Which vertex has the right angle?

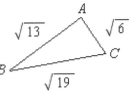

Solution Since $AB^2 + AC^2 = 13 + 6 = 19 = BC^2$, therefore, by the converse of the Pythagorean Theorem, $\triangle ABC$ is a right triangle, with $\angle A = 90°$.

Note : The Cosine Law states that in a triangle with sides a, b, and c,

$c^2 = a^2 + b^2 - 2ab\cos(\theta)$, where θ is the angle between a and b.

If $\theta = 90°$, then the cosine law becomes the Pythagorean Theorem!

Two for you.

1) A Pythagorean Triple is an ordered triple of numbers (a,b,c) satisfying $a^2 + b^2 = c^2$. Complete these Pythagorean Triples:

(a) $(5,12,c)$ 　　(b) $(\sqrt{5}, 2\sqrt{3}, c)$ 　　(c) $(1,b,2)$ 　　(d) $(a,8,7)$

2) Two friends say goodbye. One drives north averaging 100 km/h. The other drives west at an average speed of 80 km/h. How far apart are they after two hours?

Answers 1)(a) $c = 13$ 　　(b) $c = \sqrt{17}$ 　　(c) $b = \sqrt{3}$
(d) No solution since c must be greater than each of a and b!

2) $40\sqrt{41}$ *km* or about 256.1 *km*

Similar Triangles

Two triangles are similar if all three pairs of corresponding angles are equal and corresponding sides are in the same ratio. In this pair of similar triangles............ →

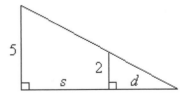

$\dfrac{A}{a} = \dfrac{B}{b} = \dfrac{C}{c}$. Note that side "$A$" in the big triangle and side "a" in the small triangle

correspond because they are both between angles x and z.

Conditions for similarity: We can conclude two triangles are similar if we know

SSS: all three pairs of corresponding sides are in the same ratio **or**

SAS: two pairs of corresponding sides are in the same ratio and the contained angles are equal **or**

AAA: all three pairs of corresponding angles are equal **or**

AA: if two pairs of angles are equal, the third pair must be as well, so the triangles are similar by AAA.

Example 1) In the diagram at the top, if $A = 10$, $B = 8$, and $a = 4$, find C, b, and c.

Solution $\dfrac{A}{a} = \dfrac{10}{4} = \dfrac{5}{2}$. Therefore, $\dfrac{B}{b} = \dfrac{8}{b} = \dfrac{5}{2}$ and so $b = \dfrac{16}{5}$. As for c and C,

we know that $\dfrac{C}{c} = \dfrac{5}{2}$ and so $C = \dfrac{5c}{2}$. However, without knowing either C or c

(or at least one of the angles), we can not find either the value of C or c!

(Don't you hate trick questions?!)

Example 2) In the picture to the right, find a formula for s in terms of d.

Solution By similar triangles (AAA), $\dfrac{s+d}{d} = \dfrac{5}{2}$. So, $2s + 2d = 5d$ and $s = \dfrac{3d}{2}$.

Two for you.

1) In the triangles at the right, suppose $A = 7$, $B = 4$, $b = 2$, and $c = 3$. Find a, and C.

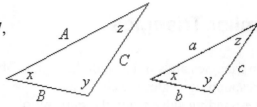

2) Use the similar triangles below to find an expression for a in terms of b.

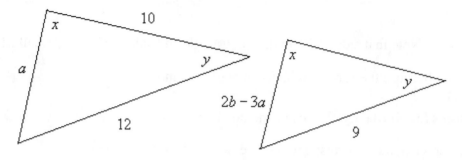

Answers 1) $a = 7/2$ and $C = 6$ 2) $a = 8b/15$

Radian Measure of an Angle

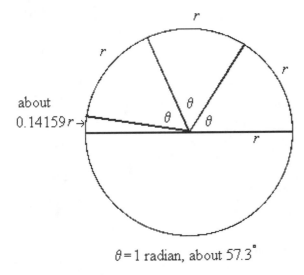

$\theta = 1$ radian, about $57.3°$

For any circle, take the circle's radius r. Wrap r around the circumference. This will create an angle just a little over 57 degrees. We call this 1 radian. If you wrap another radius around the circle starting at the end of the first wrapped r, and then another, and then another, you will find that the semi-circle will have 3 **and about 0.14159** radii wrapped around it in all. We give the number of radii wrapped around the semi-circle the name π. So
$$\pi \doteq 3.14159 \text{ and } \pi \text{ radians} = 180°.$$

It is customary (Don't ask me why!) to omit the word "radians" but not "degrees"!

Example 1) Convert the following radian measures to degrees:

(a) $\dfrac{\pi}{2}$ (b) $\dfrac{7\pi}{3}$ (c) 2

Solution $\because \pi$ radians $= 180°$ $\therefore$ 1 radian $= \left(\dfrac{180}{\pi}\right)°$. From now on, we will omit "radians"

(a) $\dfrac{\pi}{2} = \dfrac{\pi}{2}\left(\dfrac{180}{\pi}\right)° = 90°$ (b) $\dfrac{7\pi}{3} = \dfrac{7\pi}{3}\left(\dfrac{180}{\pi}\right)° = 420°$

(c) $2 = 2\left(\dfrac{180}{\pi}\right)° = \left(\dfrac{360}{\pi}\right)° \doteq 2(57.3)° = 114.6°$

Example 2) Convert the following degree measures to radians:

(a) $45°$ (b) $-40°$ (c) $\pi°$

Solution Since $180° = \pi$ radians, $\therefore 1$ degree $= \left(\dfrac{\pi}{180}\right)$ radians.

(a) $45° = 45\left(\dfrac{\pi}{180}\right) = \dfrac{\pi}{4}$ (b) $-40° = -40\left(\dfrac{\pi}{180}\right) = -\dfrac{2\pi}{9}$

(c) $\pi° = \pi\left(\dfrac{\pi}{180}\right) = \dfrac{\pi^2}{180} \doteq 0.055$

Two for you.
1) Convert to degree measure: (a) $\pi / 6$ (b) -1.8
2) Convert to radian measure: (a) $-60°$ (b) $12°$

Answers 1)(a) $30°$ (b) $\left(\dfrac{-324}{\pi}\right)° \doteq -103.1°$ 2)(a) $-\dfrac{\pi}{3}$ (b) $\dfrac{12\pi}{180} = \dfrac{\pi}{15} \doteq 0.21$

Angles in Standard Position

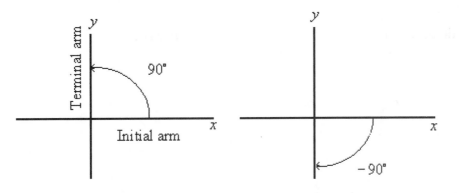

POSITIVE angles are drawn **COUNTER-CLOCKWISE** from the positive x axis.

NEGATIVE angles are drawn **CLOCKWISE** from the positive x axis.

Example 1)(a) Give, in degree measure, **all** the angles which have the same initial and terminal arms as (i) $90°$ (ii) $-90°$, and

(b) draw both $450°$ and $-450°$ in standard position.

Solution (a)(i) Let k be a **positive** integer. Then all the angles $90°$, $450°$, $810°$, and in general, $(90 + 360k)°$ have the same initial and terminal arms. Also, $90°$, $-270°$, $-630°$, and in general, $(90 - 360k)°$ have the same initial and terminal arms.

(ii) $-90°$, $-450°$, and in general, $(-90 - 360k)°$ have the same initial and terminal arms. Also, $-90°$, $270°$, and in general, $(-90 + 360k)°$ have the same initial and terminal arms.

SUMMARY
(i) $(90 + 360k)°$, for **any integer** k, has the same initial and terminal arms as $90°$.
(ii) $(-90 + 360k)°$, for **any integer** k, has the same initial and terminal arms as $-90°$.

(b)

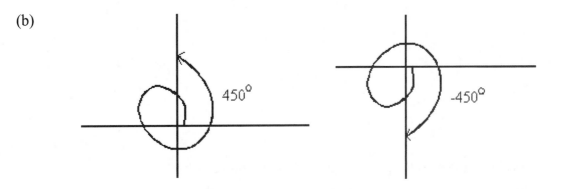

Two for you.

1) Give all angles in standard position having the same terminal arm as

(a) $45°$ (b) $-60°$.

2) Redo question 1, giving your answers in radian measure.

Answers 1)(a) $(45 + 360k)°$, for $k \in \mathbb{Z}$ (b) $(-60 + 360k)°$, for $k \in \mathbb{Z}$

2)(a) $\dfrac{\pi}{4} + 2k\pi$, for $k \in \mathbb{Z}$ (b) $-\dfrac{\pi}{3} + 2k\pi$, for $k \in \mathbb{Z}$

Related Angles in Standard Position

You will find this topic **REALLY USEFUL** when you study Trigonometric Functions!

Here, we will use the following convention for angles:

Quadrant	Angle
1	Degrees: $0 < \theta < 90°$ or Radians: $0 < \theta < \dfrac{\pi}{2}$
2	Degrees: $90° < \theta < 180°$ or Radians: $\dfrac{\pi}{2} < \theta < \pi$
3	Degrees: $180° < \theta < 270°$ or Radians: $\pi < \theta < \dfrac{3\pi}{2}$
4	Degrees: $-90° < \theta < 0°$ or Radians: $-\dfrac{\pi}{2} < \theta < 0$

Let $0 < \theta < 90°$. Draw θ in standard position and let it puncture the unit circle at $P(x, y)$. Drop a perpendicular from P to the x axis. Now you have a right triangle with hypotenuse of length 1. "Triangle Trig" gives $\cos(\theta) = x$, $\sin(\theta) = y$, and $\tan(\theta) = y/x$. Now draw three congruent triangles, one in each of the other three quadrants.

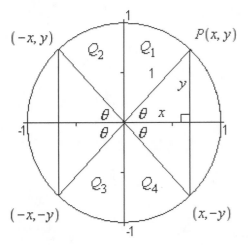

Each triangle has the angle θ at the origin.

The angle in STANDARD POSITION in quadrant TWO (Q2) that relates to θ is $180° - \theta$.

The angle in STANDARD POSITION in quadrant THREE (Q3) that relates to θ is $180° + \theta$.

The angle in STANDARD POSITION in quadrant FOUR (Q4) that relates to θ is $-\theta$.

Example 1) Find the related angles in each of the other three quadrants for

(a) $40°$　　(b) $200°$　　(c) $\dfrac{7\pi}{9}$ radians

Solution I: If θ is a first quadrant angle, use $180° - \theta$, $180° + \theta$, and $-\theta$ or the radian equivalents.

II: If the given angle is not in the first quadrant, first find the first quadrant relative, call this θ, and go back to Solution I!

(a) Quad 2: $180° - 40° = 140°$　　Quad 3: $180° + 40° = 220°$　　Quad 4: $-40°$

(b) Quad 1: $200° - 180° = 20°$　　Quad 2: $180° - 20° = 160°$　　Quad 4: $-20°$

(c) Quad 1: $\pi - \dfrac{7\pi}{9} = \dfrac{2\pi}{9}$　　　Quad 3: $\pi + \dfrac{2\pi}{9} = \dfrac{11\pi}{9}$　　　Quad 4: $-\dfrac{2\pi}{9}$

139

Two for you.

1) Find the related angles in each of the other three quadrants for (a) $10°$ (b) $-25°$.

2) Find the related angles in each of the other three quadrants for (a) $\dfrac{\pi}{12}$ (b) $\dfrac{6\pi}{5}$.

Answers 1) (a) Quad 2: $170°$ Quad 3: $190°$ Quad 4: $-10°$

(b) Quad 1: $25°$ Quad 2: $155°$ Quad 3 : $205°$

2)(a) Quad 2: $\dfrac{11\pi}{12}$ Quad 3: $\dfrac{13\pi}{12}$ Quad 4: $-\dfrac{\pi}{12}$

(b) Quad 1: $\dfrac{\pi}{5}$ Quad 2: $\dfrac{4\pi}{5}$ Quad 4: $-\dfrac{\pi}{5}$

Trig Ratios for the $(30°, 60°, 90°) \equiv (\pi/6, \pi/3, \pi/2)$ Triangle

You DON'T have to memorize these ratios. It is soooooooooooooooooooooooooo easy to take 30 seconds and redevelop them!

Draw an **equilateral** (and therefore **equiangular**) triangle. Each angle is $60° = \dfrac{\pi}{3}$ radians. Drop a perpendicular from one vertex. This divides the triangle into two congruent triangles, with angles of $30°$, $60°$, and $90°$ or, in radians, $\dfrac{\pi}{6}$, $\dfrac{\pi}{3}$, and $\dfrac{\pi}{2}$. Let each side in the original triangle have length 2. Then in each of the two congruent triangles, the sides (**using congruency and Pythagoras!**) are 2, 1, and $\sqrt{3}$.

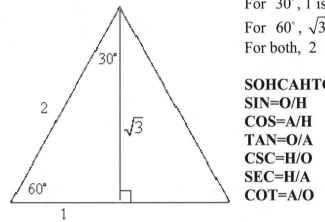

For $30°$, 1 is **opposite** and $\sqrt{3}$ is **adjacent**.
For $60°$, $\sqrt{3}$ is **opposite** and 1 is **adjacent**.
For both, 2 is the **hypotenuse**.

SOHCAHTOA!
SIN=O/H
COS=A/H
TAN=O/A
CSC=H/O
SEC=H/A
COT=A/O

(**Important! Do this construction yourself at least THREE TIMES!!**)

Example 1) State the sine, cosine and tangent ratios for $30°$ and $60°$.

Solution

$$\sin(30°) = \sin\left(\frac{\pi}{6}\right) = \frac{1}{2} \qquad \cos(30°) = \cos\left(\frac{\pi}{6}\right) = \frac{\sqrt{3}}{2} \qquad \tan(30°) = \tan\left(\frac{\pi}{6}\right) = \frac{1}{\sqrt{3}}$$

$$\sin(60°) = \sin\left(\frac{\pi}{3}\right) = \frac{\sqrt{3}}{2} \qquad \cos(60°) = \cos\left(\frac{\pi}{3}\right) = \frac{1}{2} \qquad \tan(60°) = \tan\left(\frac{\pi}{3}\right) = \sqrt{3}$$

Two for you.

1) State the cosecant, secant, and cotangent ratios for 30° and 60°.

2) Is it a coincidence that $\sin(30°) = \cos(60°)$?

Answers

1) $\csc(30°) = \csc\left(\dfrac{\pi}{6}\right) = 2 \qquad \sec(30°) = \sec\left(\dfrac{\pi}{6}\right) = \dfrac{2}{\sqrt{3}} \qquad \cot(30°) = \cot\left(\dfrac{\pi}{6}\right) = \sqrt{3}$

$\csc(60°) = \csc\left(\dfrac{\pi}{3}\right) = \dfrac{2}{\sqrt{3}} \qquad \sec(60°) = \sec\left(\dfrac{\pi}{3}\right) = 2 \qquad \cot(60°) = \cot\left(\dfrac{\pi}{3}\right) = \dfrac{1}{\sqrt{3}}$

2) **NO! Opposite** for 30° is **adjacent** for 60°! In fact, if a and b are two **complementary** angles in a triangle (that is, they add to 90°), then $\sin a = \cos b$, $\cos a = \sin b$, and $\tan a = \cot b$.

Trig Ratios for the $(45°, 45°, 90°) \equiv (\pi/4, \pi/4, \pi/2)$ Triangle

You DON'T have to memorize these ratios. It is soooooooooooooooooooooooooooo easy to take 30 seconds and redevelop them!

Draw a right isosceles triangle, that is, draw a $90°$ angle and make the two attached sides equal. Therefore, the triangle has angles of $45°$, $45°$, and $90°$ or in radians, $\dfrac{\pi}{4}$, $\dfrac{\pi}{4}$, and $\dfrac{\pi}{2}$. Let the two equal sides have length 1. Then (**using Pythagoras!**), the hypotenuse has length $\sqrt{2}$.

For $45°$, 1 is **opposite** and 1 is **adjacent**.
The **hypotenuse** is $\sqrt{2}$.

SOHCAHTOA!
SIN=O/H
COS=A/H
TAN=O/A
CSC=H/O
SEC=H/A
COT=A/O

Example 1) State the sine, cosine and tangent ratios for $45°$.

Solution $\sin(45°) = \sin\left(\dfrac{\pi}{4}\right) = \dfrac{1}{\sqrt{2}}$ $\cos(45°) = \cos\left(\dfrac{\pi}{4}\right) = \dfrac{1}{\sqrt{2}}$ $\tan(45°) = \tan\left(\dfrac{\pi}{4}\right) = 1$

Example 2) Given that $\sin^2(\theta) = \dfrac{1 - \cos(2\theta)}{2}$, find the exact value of $\sin\left(\dfrac{\pi}{8}\right)$.

Solution Taking $\theta = \dfrac{\pi}{8}$, we have $\sin^2\left(\dfrac{\pi}{8}\right) = \dfrac{1 - \cos\left(\dfrac{\pi}{4}\right)}{2} = \dfrac{1 - \dfrac{1}{\sqrt{2}}}{2}$

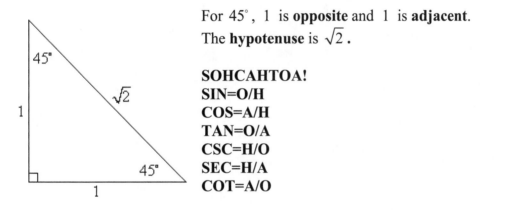

$$\boxed{\text{Get a common denominator ON THE TOP and simplify.}} = \dfrac{\sqrt{2} - 1}{2\sqrt{2}} \quad \boxed{\text{Some of us love to rationalize the bottom!}} = \dfrac{2 - \sqrt{2}}{4}$$

and so $\sin\left(\dfrac{\pi}{8}\right) \quad \boxed{\text{Take the POSITIVE root since the angle is in the first quadrant.}} = \sqrt{\dfrac{2 - \sqrt{2}}{4}} \doteq 0.383$.

143

Two for you.

1) State the cosecant, secant, and cotangent ratios for $45°$.

2) Using $\cos^2(\theta) = \dfrac{1 + \cos(2\theta)}{2}$, find the exact value of $\cos\left(\dfrac{\pi}{8}\right)$.

Answers 1) $\csc(45°) = \sec(45°) = \sqrt{2}$ $\cot(45°) = 1$ 2) $\cos\left(\dfrac{\pi}{8}\right) = \sqrt{\dfrac{2 + \sqrt{2}}{4}}$

Trig Ratios for $30°, 45°, 60°$ (and More)—A Table!

degrees	radians	sin	cos	tan	csc	sec	cot
0	0	0	1	0	undefined	1	undefined
30	$\dfrac{\pi}{6}$	$\dfrac{1}{2}$	$\dfrac{\sqrt{3}}{2}$	$\dfrac{1}{\sqrt{3}}$	2	$\dfrac{2}{\sqrt{3}}$	$\sqrt{3}$
45	$\dfrac{\pi}{4}$	$\dfrac{1}{\sqrt{2}}$	$\dfrac{1}{\sqrt{2}}$	1	$\sqrt{2}$	$\sqrt{2}$	1
60	$\dfrac{\pi}{3}$	$\dfrac{\sqrt{3}}{2}$	$\dfrac{1}{2}$	$\sqrt{3}$	$\dfrac{2}{\sqrt{3}}$	2	$\dfrac{1}{\sqrt{3}}$
90	$\dfrac{\pi}{2}$	1	0	undefined	1	undefined	0
120	$\dfrac{2\pi}{3}$	$\dfrac{\sqrt{3}}{2}$	$-\dfrac{1}{2}$	$-\sqrt{3}$	$\dfrac{2}{\sqrt{3}}$	-2	$-\dfrac{1}{\sqrt{3}}$
135	$\dfrac{3\pi}{4}$	$\dfrac{1}{\sqrt{2}}$	$-\dfrac{1}{\sqrt{2}}$	-1	$\sqrt{2}$	$-\sqrt{2}$	-1
150	$\dfrac{5\pi}{6}$	$\dfrac{1}{2}$	$-\dfrac{\sqrt{3}}{2}$	$-\dfrac{1}{\sqrt{3}}$	2	$-\dfrac{2}{\sqrt{3}}$	$-\sqrt{3}$
180	π	0	-1	0	undefined	-1	undefined
210	$\dfrac{7\pi}{6}$	$-\dfrac{1}{2}$	$-\dfrac{\sqrt{3}}{2}$	$\dfrac{1}{\sqrt{3}}$	-2	$-\dfrac{2}{\sqrt{3}}$	$\sqrt{3}$
225	$\dfrac{5\pi}{4}$	$-\dfrac{1}{\sqrt{2}}$	$-\dfrac{1}{\sqrt{2}}$	1	$-\sqrt{2}$	$-\sqrt{2}$	1
240	$\dfrac{4\pi}{3}$	$-\dfrac{\sqrt{3}}{2}$	$-\dfrac{1}{2}$	$\sqrt{3}$	$-\dfrac{2}{\sqrt{3}}$	-2	$\dfrac{1}{\sqrt{3}}$
270	$\dfrac{3\pi}{2}$	-1	0	undefined	-1	undefined	0
300	$\dfrac{5\pi}{3}$	$-\dfrac{\sqrt{3}}{2}$	$\dfrac{1}{2}$	$-\sqrt{3}$	$-\dfrac{2}{\sqrt{3}}$	2	$-\dfrac{1}{\sqrt{3}}$
315	$\dfrac{7\pi}{4}$	$-\dfrac{1}{\sqrt{2}}$	$\dfrac{1}{\sqrt{2}}$	-1	$-\sqrt{2}$	$\sqrt{2}$	-1
330	$\dfrac{11\pi}{6}$	$-\dfrac{1}{2}$	$\dfrac{\sqrt{3}}{2}$	$-\dfrac{1}{\sqrt{3}}$	-2	$\dfrac{2}{\sqrt{3}}$	$-\sqrt{3}$
360	2π	0	1	0	undefined	1	undefined

Two for you.

In **absolute value**, the numbers (or ratios) in the 1) 30° row   2) 45° row
are the same as …

Answers 1) 150°, 210°, 330° rows   2) 135°, 225°, 315° rows

Trig Ratios for $30°$, $45°$, $60°$ (and More): A (Fabulous) Picture!!

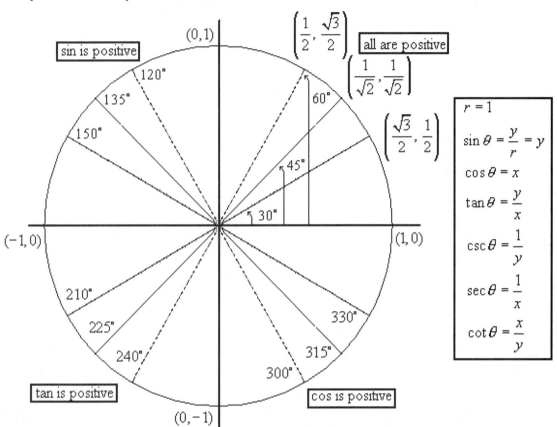

Example 1) In the above **fabulous** picture, look at the triangle formed by drawing a perpendicular from the $60°$ point to the x axis. Name the second, third, and fourth quadrant angles (between $90°$ and $360°$) that give congruent triangles by drawing perpendiculars to the x axis.

Solution second quadrant: $120°$; third quadrant: $240°$; fourth quadrant: $300°$

Example 2) Find, using the above **fabulous** picture, (a) $\sin(300°)$ (b) $\tan(180°)$.

Solution (a) $300°$ is a **fourth quadrant** angle, so the sine is **negative**.

The corresponding first quadrant point is $\left(\dfrac{1}{2}, \dfrac{\sqrt{3}}{2}\right)$. Therefore, $\sin(300°) = -\dfrac{\sqrt{3}}{2}$.

(b) Using the point $(-1, 0)$, $\tan(180°) = \dfrac{y}{x} = \dfrac{0}{-1} = 0$.

Two for you.

Find: 1) $\cos(135°)$ 2) $\cot(-180°)$

Answers 1) $-\dfrac{1}{\sqrt{2}}$ 2) undefined

Basic Trigonometric Graphs

$y = \sin x$

Domain $= \mathbb{R}$

Range $= [-1, 1]$

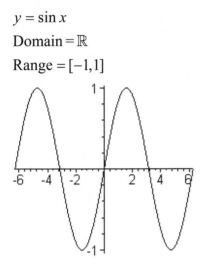

$y = \cos x$

Domain $= \mathbb{R}$

Range $= [-1, 1]$

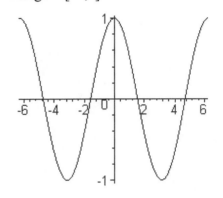

$y = \tan x$

Domain: $x \in \mathbb{R}$, $x \neq \dfrac{\pi}{2} + k\pi$, $k \in \mathbb{Z}$

Range $= \mathbb{R}$

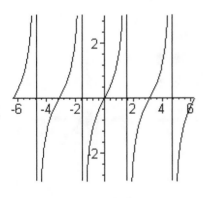

$y = \cot x$

Domain: $x \in \mathbb{R}$, $x \neq k\pi$, $k \in \mathbb{Z}$

Range $= \mathbb{R}$

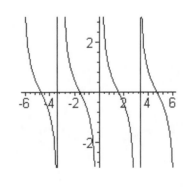

$y = \csc x$

Domain: $x \in \mathbb{R}$, $x \neq k\pi$, $k \in \mathbb{Z}$

Range $= (-\infty, -1] \cup [1, \infty)$

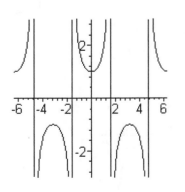

$y = \sec x$

Domain: $x \in \mathbb{R}$, $x \neq \dfrac{\pi}{2} + k\pi$, $k \in \mathbb{Z}$

Range $= (-\infty, -1] \cup [1, \infty)$

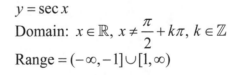

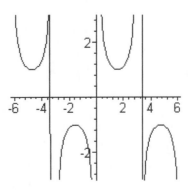

Two for you.

1) Using "...", write the restrictions on the domain for the tangent and secant functions.

2) Using "...", write the restrictions on the domain for the cotangent and cosecant functions.

Answers 1) $...-\dfrac{3\pi}{2},\ -\dfrac{\pi}{2},\ \dfrac{\pi}{2},\ \dfrac{3\pi}{2},...$ 2) $...-2\pi,\ -\pi,\ 0,\ \pi,\ 2\pi,...$

The Circle Definition of Sine and Cosine

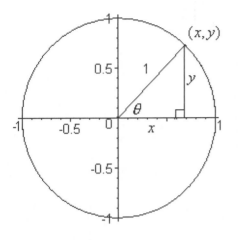

This is the circle $x^2 + y^2 = 1$. In the picture, θ is between 0 and $\pi/2$.

$$\sin\theta = \frac{y}{1} = y \quad \text{and} \quad \cos\theta = \frac{x}{1} = x$$

Mathematicians, being sensible people, said, "Let θ be any angle. Draw this angle in standard postion (counter-clockwise from the positive x axis for positive angles, clockwise for negative). The terminal arm will puncture (**OUCH!**) the circle at a point (x, y)."

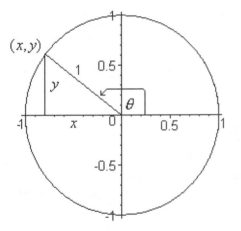

The mathematicians then said, "Let $\sin\theta = y$ and $\cos\theta = x$. The result: before, we had only sine and cosine for angles between 0 and $\pi/2$. Now, we have trig ratios for **all angles.** For any angle, the sine is the y value and the cosine is x. So, as θ goes from 0 to $\pi/2$ to π to $3\pi/2$ to 2π, the y value, that is, $\sin\theta$, goes from 0 to 1 to 0 to -1 to 0. The x value, that is, $\cos\theta$, goes from 1 to 0 to -1 to 0 to 1. From 2π to 4π, these patterns repeat. From 0 to -2π, they repeat in reverse. And that is all there really is to the sine and cosine functions."

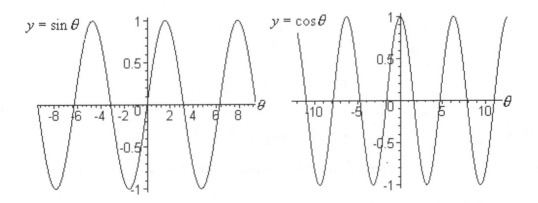

151

One for you.

1) Use the circle definition of the trigonometric functions to explain the **CAST RULE**.

$$
\begin{array}{c|c}
S & A \\
\hline
T & C
\end{array}
$$

Answer 1) For example, in the second quadrant $(\pi/2 < \theta < \pi)$ where $x < 0$ and $y > 0$, $\cos\theta = x$ is negative, $\sin\theta = y$ is positive, and $\tan\theta = \dfrac{y}{x}$ is negative. This explains the "**S**" in CA**S**T.

Solving the Trig Equation $\sin x = c$

DangerDangerDanger

If you ask your calculator (or math processor such as Maple) for help solving the equation $\sin x = c$ for x, **the calculator thinks this is the sine function!** $\rightarrow$

For each c between -1 and 1, the calculator reasons, "There is exactly **ONE** value of x between $-\pi/2$ and $\pi/2$ that makes $\sin x = c$. That value is the answer!" So your calculator gives you an answer in the **first quadrant when $c \geq 0$**, and the **fourth when $c < 0$. But you and I know that $\sin x = c$ has an infinite number of solutions.** Call the calculator answer the **principal** solution. Ask, when you solve $\sin x = c$, "Do I want the principal solution, another solution (eg., an answer in a different quadrant), or **all** possible solutions?"

Example 1) Solve, **using your knowledge of basic trig ratios (not a calculator!)**, giving, in radians, the principal solution, **a (not "the"!) solution in the other appropriate** quadrant, and the general solution: (a) $\sin x = 0.5$ (b) $\sin x = -0.5$

Solution (a) $\sin x = 0.5$ $\therefore$ $x = \dfrac{\pi}{6}$ Using the CAST rule, sine is also positive in the second quadrant. A (**not "the"**) corresponding second quadrant angle is $\pi - \dfrac{\pi}{6} = \dfrac{5\pi}{6}$. The general solution: $x = \dfrac{\pi}{6} + 2k\pi$ or $x = \dfrac{5\pi}{6} + 2k\pi$, for $k \in \mathbb{Z}$

(b) $\sin x = -0.5$ $\therefore$ $x = -\dfrac{\pi}{6}$ Using the CAST rule, sine is also negative in the third quadrant. A (**not "the"!**) corresponding third quadrant angle is $\pi + \dfrac{\pi}{6} = \dfrac{7\pi}{6}$.

The general solution: $x = -\dfrac{\pi}{6} + 2k\pi$ or $x = \dfrac{7\pi}{6} + 2k\pi$, for $k \in \mathbb{Z}$

Example 2) Find the principal solution to (a) $\sin x = 0.1$ (b) $\sin x = -0.3$.

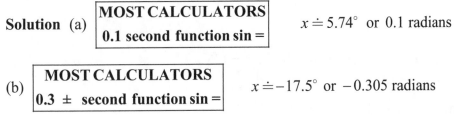

Solution (a)

MOST CALCULATORS
0.1 second function sin =

$x \doteq 5.74°$ or 0.1 radians

(b)

MOST CALCULATORS
0.3 ± second function sin =

$x \doteq -17.5°$ or -0.305 radians

Two for you.

1) Find, in degree measure, the principal, the "other quadrant", and the general solution to $\sin x = \dfrac{1}{\sqrt{2}}$.

2) Find the principal and third quadrant solutions in radians to $\sin x = -0.9$.

(Hint: for the third quadrant, use $\pi + |\text{principal solution}|$.)

Answers

1) principal solution: $x = 45°$; second quadrant: $x = 135°$;
general: $x = 45° + 360k°$ or $x = 135° + 360k°$, $k \in \mathbb{Z}$

2) principal solution: $x \doteq -1.1$; third quadrant: $x \doteq 4.3$

Solving the Trig Equation $\cos x = c$

DangerDangerDanger

If you ask your calculator (or math processor such as Maple) for help in solving the equation $\cos x = c$ for x, **the calculator thinks this is the cosine function!** $\rightarrow$

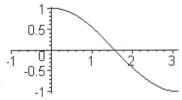

For each choice of c between -1 and 1, the calculator reasons, "There is **ONE** x between 0 and π that satisfies $\cos x = c$. **That** is the answer!" So your calculator gives you an answer in the **first quadrant when** $c \geq 0$, and the **second when** $c < 0$. **But we know** $\cos x = c$ **has an infinite number of solutions.** Call the calculator answer the **principal** solution. Ask, when you solve $\cos x = c$, "Do I want the principal solution, another solution (eg., an answer in a different quadrant), or **all** possible solutions?"

Example 1) Solve, **using your knowledge of basic trig ratios (not a calculator!)**, give the principal solution, **a (not "the"!)** solution in the **other appropriate quadrant**, and the general solution: (a) $\cos x = 0.5$ (b) $\cos x = -0.5$

Solution (a) $\cos x = 0.5$ $\therefore$ $x = \dfrac{\pi}{3}$ Using the CAST rule, cosine is also positive in the fourth quadrant. A (**not "the"!**) corresponding fourth quadrant angle is $-\dfrac{\pi}{3}$.

The general solution: $x = \dfrac{\pi}{3} + 2k\pi$ or $x = -\dfrac{\pi}{3} + 2k\pi$, for $k \in \mathbb{Z}$

(b) $\cos x = -0.5$ $\therefore$ $x = \dfrac{2\pi}{3}$ Using the CAST rule, cosine is also negative in the third quadrant. A (**not "the"!**) corresponding third quadrant angle is $2\pi - \dfrac{2\pi}{3} = \dfrac{4\pi}{3}$.

The general solution: $x = \dfrac{2\pi}{3} + 2k\pi$ or $x = \dfrac{4\pi}{3} + 2k\pi$, for $k \in \mathbb{Z}$

Example 2) Find the principal solution to (a) $\cos x = 0.1$ (b) $\cos x = -0.3$.

Solution (a) | **MOST CALCULATORS**
0.1 second function cos = | $x \doteq 84.3°$ or 1.47 radians

(b) | **MOST CALCULATORS**
0.3 $\pm$ second function cos = | $x \doteq 107.5°$ or 1.88 radians

155

Two for you.

1) Find, in degrees, the principal, the "other quadrant", and the general solution to $\cos x = \dfrac{1}{\sqrt{2}}$.

2) Find the principal and third quadrant solutions in radians to $\cos x = -0.9$.

(Hint: for the third quadrant, use $2\pi - |\text{principal solution}|$.)

Answers

1) principal solution: $x = 45°$; fourth quadrant: $x = -45°$;

general: $x = 45° + 360k$ or $x = -45° + 360k,\ k \in \mathbb{Z}$

2) principal solution: $x \doteq 2.69$; third quadrant: $x \doteq 3.59$

The Sine Law

According to the Sine Law, in the triangle at the right,

$$\frac{a}{\sin A} = \frac{b}{\sin B} = \frac{c}{\sin C}.$$

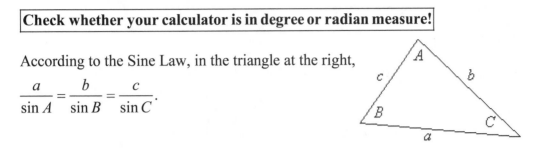

To use the Sine Law, you need two sides and a **non-contained angle** or any two angles and one side. (Remember: if you have two angles, you have three!) In the case of two sides and the contained angle, you can use the Cosine Law. So life is good!

Example 1) If in the above triangle, $a = 12$, $b = 10$, and $A = \dfrac{\pi}{3}$, find B (in radians).

Solution $\dfrac{\sin B}{b} = \dfrac{\sin A}{a} \boxed{\scriptstyle A=\frac{\pi}{3} \text{ and } a=12} = \dfrac{\left(\dfrac{\sqrt{3}}{2}\right)}{12}$ and so $\sin B \boxed{\scriptstyle b=10} = \dfrac{10\sqrt{3}}{24} \doteq 0.722$

Therefore, $B \overset{\boxed{\substack{\text{MOST CALCULATORS}\\ \text{0.722 second funtion sin}}}}{\doteq} 0.81$ radians.

Example 2) There are two possible triangles where $b = 11$, $c = 6$, and $C = 30°$, as illustrated at right. Find, in degrees, the **acute** and **obtuse** values of B.

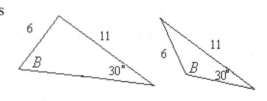

Solution $\dfrac{\sin B}{11} = \dfrac{\sin 30°}{6}$ and so $\sin B = \dfrac{(1/2)(11)}{6} = \dfrac{11}{12}.$

Therefore, $B \overset{\boxed{\text{If } B \text{ is acute!}}}{\doteq} 66.4°$ **OR** $B \overset{\boxed{\text{If } B \text{ is obtuse!}}}{\doteq} 180° - 66.4° = 113.6°.$

One for you.

1) In the triangle below, $a = 3$, $c = 5$, and $A = 30°$.

Find in degrees the two possible values of C.

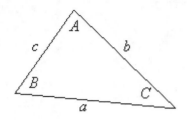

Answer 1) $C \doteq$ 56.44° **OR** $C \doteq$ 123.56°

If C is acute!   If C is obtuse!

158

The Cosine Law

According to the Cosine Law, in the triangle at the right,

$a^2 = b^2 + c^2 - 2bc \cos A,$

with similar formulas for b and c. Also,

$\cos A = \dfrac{b^2 + c^2 - a^2}{2bc}$, again with similar

formulas for $\cos B$ and $\cos C$.

So, using the Cosine Law, to find a side you need the other two sides and the contained angle. (Compare the Sine Law). To find an angle, you need all three sides.

Example 1) In the above triangle, $a = 10$, $b = 12$, and $C = \dfrac{\pi}{7}$. Find c.

Solution $c^2 = 10^2 + 12^2 - 2(10)(12)\cos\left(\dfrac{\pi}{7}\right) \doteq 244 - 240(0.901) = 27.77$

and so $c \doteq 5.27$.

Example 2) Find, in degree measure, A in this triangle.

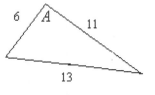

Solution $\cos A = \dfrac{11^2 + 6^2 - 13^2}{2 \cdot 11 \cdot 6} \doteq -0.0909.$

Therefore, A ⎡MOST CALCULATORS: 0.0909 ± second function cos⎤ $\doteq$ $95.2°$.

Note: with the Cosine Law, if the required angle is obtuse (that is, between $90°$ and $180°$), the calculator gives us the correct value. There is no possible ambiguity as can happen with the Sine Law. (See The Sine Law, Example 2, on page 157.)

One for you.

1) In this triangle, use the Cosine Law
to find side b and then, in degrees, A.

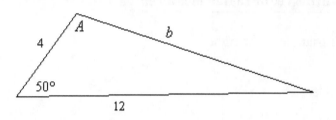

Answer 1) $b \doteq 9.9$ and $A \doteq 112°$

Commonly Used Trigonometric Formulas Including Derivatives and Integrals

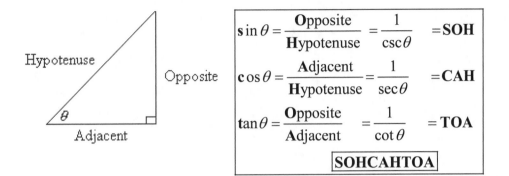

$$\sin \theta = \frac{\mathbf{Opposite}}{\mathbf{Hypotenuse}} = \frac{1}{\csc \theta} = \mathbf{SOH}$$

$$\cos \theta = \frac{\mathbf{Adjacent}}{\mathbf{Hypotenuse}} = \frac{1}{\sec \theta} = \mathbf{CAH}$$

$$\tan \theta = \frac{\mathbf{Opposite}}{\mathbf{Adjacent}} = \frac{1}{\cot \theta} = \mathbf{TOA}$$

$$\boxed{\mathbf{SOHCAHTOA}}$$

$$\sin(-\theta) = -\sin \theta \qquad \cos(-\theta) = \cos \theta \qquad \tan(-\theta) = -\tan \theta$$

$$\cos^2 \theta + \sin^2 \theta = 1 \qquad 1 + \tan^2 \theta = \sec^2 \theta \qquad \cot^2 \theta + 1 = \csc^2 \theta$$

$$\sin(A \pm B) = \sin A \cos B \pm \cos A \sin B \qquad \cos(A \pm B) = \cos A \cos B \mp \sin A \sin B$$

$$\sin(2A) = 2 \sin A \cos A \qquad \cos(2A) = \cos^2 A - \sin^2 A$$

$$\tan(A \pm B) = \frac{\tan A \pm \tan B}{1 \mp \tan A \tan B} \qquad \tan(2A) = \frac{2 \tan A}{1 - \tan^2 A}$$

$$\sin^2 \theta = \frac{1 - \cos(2\theta)}{2} \qquad \cos^2 \theta = \frac{1 + \cos(2\theta)}{2}$$

$$\frac{d(\sin \theta)}{d\theta} = \cos \theta \qquad \int \sin \theta \, d\theta = -\cos \theta + C \qquad \text{(where } C \text{ is a constant)}$$

$$\frac{d(\cos \theta)}{d\theta} = -\sin \theta \qquad \int \cos \theta \, d\theta = \sin \theta + C$$

$$\frac{d(\tan \theta)}{d\theta} = \sec^2 \theta \qquad \int \tan \theta \, d\theta = -\ln|\cos \theta| + C$$

$$\frac{d(\csc \theta)}{d\theta} = -\csc \theta \cot \theta \qquad \int \csc \theta \, d\theta = \ln|\csc \theta - \cot \theta| + C$$

$$\frac{d(\sec \theta)}{d\theta} = \sec \theta \tan \theta \qquad \int \sec \theta \, d\theta = \ln|\sec \theta + \tan \theta| + C$$

$$\frac{d(\cot \theta)}{d\theta} = -\csc^2 \theta \qquad \int \cot \theta \, d\theta = \ln|\sin \theta| + C$$

Two for you.

How can you derive the formulas 1) $1 + \tan^2 \theta = \sec^2 \theta$ and 2) $\cot^2 \theta + 1 = \csc^2 \theta$ from $\cos^2 \theta + \sin^2 \theta = 1$?

Answers 1) Divide the formula $\cos^2 \theta + \sin^2 \theta = 1$ by $\cos^2 \theta$.

2) Divide the formula $\cos^2 \theta + \sin^2 \theta = 1$ by $\sin^2 \theta$.

Easy Limits: "No Problem" Problems

When evaluating $\lim_{x \to a} f(x)$, **YOU MUST NOT LET** x **EQUAL** a. You consider instead the "behaviour" of the function $f(x)$ as x gets closer and closer to a. However, we all know that as long as the function is "well-behaved", we do, in practice, just substitute a in for x in $f(x)$.

Example 1) Evaluate the following limits:

(a) $\lim_{x \to 3} x^2$ (b) $\lim_{x \to \frac{\pi}{4}} \sin x$ (c) $\lim_{x \to 3} \left(\dfrac{x^2 - 1}{\ln x} \right)$

Solution

(a) $\lim_{x \to 3} x^2 = 9$ (b) $\lim_{x \to \frac{\pi}{4}} \sin x = \sin\left(\dfrac{\pi}{4}\right) = \dfrac{1}{\sqrt{2}}$ (c) $\lim_{x \to 3} \left(\dfrac{x^2 - 1}{\ln x} \right) = \dfrac{8}{\ln 3}$

Example 2) Let $g(x) = \begin{cases} x^2 - 1, & \text{if } x < -4 \\ x^3, & \text{if } x \geq -4 \end{cases}$.

Evaluate: (a) $\lim_{x \to -6} g(x)$ (b) $\lim_{x \to -2} g(x)$ (c) $\lim_{x \to -4.01} g(x)$ (d) $\lim_{x \to -3.99} g(x)$

Solution (a) $\lim_{x \to -6} g(x) \overset{\boxed{x < -4}}{=} 35$ (b) $\lim_{x \to -2} g(x) \overset{\boxed{x > -4}}{=} -8$

(c) $\lim_{x \to -4.01} g(x) \overset{\boxed{x \text{ is still LESS than } -4.}}{=} (-4.01)^2 - 1 = 15.0801$

(d) $\lim_{x \to -3.99} g(x) \overset{\boxed{x \text{ is still GREATER than } -4.}}{=} (-3.99)^3 = 63.521199$

We have to be careful with $g(x)$ only with the limit as x approaches **EXACTLY** -4.

Example 3) Evaluate: (a) $\lim_{x \to 2.3} [[x]]$ (b) $\lim_{x \to -3.1} [[x]]$

Solution (a) $\lim_{x \to 2.3} [[x]] = [[2.3]] = 2$ (b) $\lim_{x \to -3.1} [[x]] = [[-3.1]] = -4$

We must be careful with the greatest integer function $[[x]]$ only when x is approaching an integer.

163

Two for you.

1) Evaluate the following limits:

(a) $\lim_{x \to \pi} \cos(2x)$

(b) $\lim_{x \to -4.2} [[x]]$

(c) $\lim_{x \to 3} \dfrac{|x-5|}{x-5}$

2) Let $f(x) = \begin{cases} e^x, & \text{if } x \neq 2 \\ 5, & \text{if } x = 2 \end{cases}$. Find $\lim_{x \to 2} f(x)$.

Answers 1)(a) 1   (b) -5 (c) -1 2) e^2

"0/0" Limits

We can't divide by 0! However, if we try to evaluate $\lim\limits_{x \to a}\left(\dfrac{f(x)}{g(x)}\right)$ by simply substituting

$x = a$ (treating the limit as a **"No Problem" Problem**—see page 163) and the result is "0/0", then, often, we can find a factor of $x - a$ in both the numerator and the denominator. It is this factor that is causing both the top and the bottom to approach 0 as $x \to a$. So factor the top, factor the bottom. If you do find a factor on both the top and the bottom of $x - a$, divide it out. Remember, $x \neq a$ and so you are **not** dividing by 0! Now, fingers crossed, you might just have a **"No Problem" Problem**!

Example 1) Evaluate the following limits:

(a) $\lim\limits_{x \to 3}\left(\dfrac{x^2 - 9}{x - 3}\right)$
(b) $\lim\limits_{x \to -1}\left(\dfrac{x^2 + 2x + 1}{x^3 + 1}\right)$
(c) $\lim\limits_{x \to 16}\left(\dfrac{\sqrt{x} - 4}{x - 16}\right)$
(d) $\lim\limits_{x \to -125}\left(\dfrac{x + 125}{x^{1/3} + 5}\right)$

Solution (a) $\lim\limits_{x \to 3}\left(\dfrac{x^2 - 9}{x - 3}\right)$

> Factor the top and then divide out the common $(x-3)$. Say **GOODBYE** to the problem "0/0"!

$= \lim\limits_{x \to 3}\left(\dfrac{(x - 3)(x + 3)}{x - 3}\right) = \lim\limits_{x \to 3}(x + 3) = 6$

(b) $\lim\limits_{x \to -1}\left(\dfrac{x^2 + 2x + 1}{x^3 + 1}\right) = \lim\limits_{x \to -1}\left(\dfrac{(x + 1)^2}{(x + 1)(x^2 - x + 1)}\right) = \lim\limits_{x \to -1}\left(\dfrac{x + 1}{x^2 - x + 1}\right) = \dfrac{0}{3} = 0$

(c) $\lim\limits_{x \to 16}\left(\dfrac{\sqrt{x} - 4}{x - 16}\right)$

> Rationalize the top using difference of squares: $(a-b)(a+b)=a^2-b^2$, where $a=\sqrt{x}$ and $b=4$.

$= \lim\limits_{x \to 16}\left(\dfrac{\sqrt{x} - 4}{x - 16}\right)\left(\dfrac{\sqrt{x} + 4}{\sqrt{x} + 4}\right)$

$= \lim\limits_{x \to 16}\left(\dfrac{x - 16}{(x - 16)(\sqrt{x} + 4)}\right) = \lim\limits_{x \to 16}\left(\dfrac{1}{\sqrt{x} + 4}\right) = \dfrac{1}{8}$

OR

(c) $\lim\limits_{x \to 16}\left(\dfrac{\sqrt{x} - 4}{x - 16}\right)$

> Factor the bottom using difference of squares.

$= \lim\limits_{x \to 16}\left(\dfrac{\sqrt{x} - 4}{(\sqrt{x} - 4)(\sqrt{x} + 4)}\right) = \lim\limits_{x \to 16}\left(\dfrac{1}{\sqrt{x} + 4}\right) = \dfrac{1}{8}$

(d) $\lim\limits_{x \to -125}\left(\dfrac{x + 125}{x^{1/3} + 5}\right)$

> Factor the top using sum of cubes: $a^3 + b^3$ where $a = x^{1/3}$ and $b = 5$.

$= \lim\limits_{x \to -125}\left(\dfrac{\left(x^{1/3} + 5\right)\left(x^{2/3} - 5x^{1/3} + 25\right)}{x^{1/3} + 5}\right)$

$= \lim\limits_{x \to -125}\left(x^{2/3} - 5x^{1/3} + 25\right) = 75$

Three for you.

Evaluate the following limits:

1) $\lim\limits_{x\to 10}\left(\dfrac{x^2-100}{x-10}\right)$ 2) $\lim\limits_{x\to -2}\left(\dfrac{x^3+8}{x^2-4}\right)$ 3) $\lim\limits_{x\to -27}\left(\dfrac{x^{1/3}+3}{x+27}\right)$

Answers 1)(a) 20   2) -3 3) $\dfrac{1}{27}$

One-Sided Limits

If a function changes its definition at a point, we must check the limits from the left and the right separately.

Example 1) Let $f(x) = \begin{cases} 3, & \text{if } x < 1 \\ 0, & \text{if } x = 1 \\ x + 2, & \text{if } x > 1 \end{cases}$ and $g(x) = \begin{cases} \cos(\pi x), & \text{if } x < 1 \\ 5, & \text{if } x = 1 \\ \sin(\pi x), & \text{if } x > 1 \end{cases}$.

Evaluate: (a) $\displaystyle\lim_{x \to 1^-} f(x)$ (b) $\displaystyle\lim_{x \to 1^+} f(x)$ (c) $\displaystyle\lim_{x \to 1} f(x)$ d) $\displaystyle\lim_{x \to 1^-} g(x)$

(e) $\displaystyle\lim_{x \to 1^+} g(x)$ (f) $\displaystyle\lim_{x \to 1} g(x)$

Solution (a) $\displaystyle\lim_{x \to 1^-} f(x) \overset{\boxed{x<1}}{=} \lim_{x \to 1^-}(3) = 3$

(b) $\displaystyle\lim_{x \to 1^+} f(x) \overset{\boxed{x>1}}{=} \lim_{x \to 1^+}(x + 2) = 3$

(c) $\displaystyle\lim_{x \to 1} f(x) = 3$ since the left-hand limit and the right-hand limit are both equal to 3.

(d) $\displaystyle\lim_{x \to 1^-} g(x) \overset{\boxed{x<1}}{=} \lim_{x \to 1^-}\cos(\pi x) = \cos(\pi) = -1$

(e) $\displaystyle\lim_{x \to 1^+} g(x) \overset{\boxed{x>1}}{=} \lim_{x \to 1^+}\sin(\pi x) = \sin(\pi) = 0$

(f) $\displaystyle\lim_{x \to 1} g(x)$ does not exist since the left-hand limit $\neq$ the right-hand limit.

Note that $f(1) = 0$ and $g(1) = 5$ and **neither plays ANY part in the limits!**
Sometimes, YOU must realize that one-sided limits are necessary!

Example 2) Evaluate the following limits:

(a) $\displaystyle\lim_{x \to 2} \frac{|x-2|}{x-2}$ (b) $\displaystyle\lim_{x \to 4}(x + [[x]])$

Solution (a) $\displaystyle\lim_{x \to 2^+} \frac{|x-2|}{x-2} \overset{\boxed{\substack{x>2 \text{ so } x-2>0 \\ \therefore |x-2|=x-2}}}{=} \lim_{x \to 2^+} \frac{x-2}{x-2} = \lim_{x \to 2^+} 1 = 1$

$\displaystyle\lim_{x \to 2^-} \frac{|x-2|}{x-2} \overset{\boxed{\substack{x<2 \text{ so } x-2<0 \\ \therefore |x-2|=-(x-2)}}}{=} \lim_{x \to 2^-} \frac{-(x-2)}{x-2} = \lim_{x \to 2^-}(-1) = -1$ $\therefore$ $\displaystyle\lim_{x \to 2} \frac{|x-2|}{x-2}$ does not exist.

(b) $\displaystyle\lim_{x \to 4^+}(x + [[x]]) \overset{\boxed{\substack{4<x<5 \text{ so} \\ [[x]]=4}}}{=} \lim_{x \to 4^+}(x+4) = 8$ $\displaystyle\lim_{x \to 4^-}(x + [[x]]) \overset{\boxed{\substack{3<x<4 \text{ so} \\ [[x]]=3}}}{=} \lim_{x \to 4^-}(x+3) = 7$

$\therefore$ $\displaystyle\lim_{x \to 4}(x + [[x]])$ does not exist.

Two for you.

1) Let $f(x) = \begin{cases} x^2, & \text{if } x < -4 \\ x^3, & \text{if } x \geq -4 \end{cases}$. Find $\lim_{x \to -4^-} f(x)$.

2) Evaluate: (a) $\lim_{x \to -3^+} \dfrac{x+3}{|x+3|}$ (b) $\lim_{x \to -5^-} (x[[x]])$

Answers 1) 16   2)(a) 1   (b) 30

Limits Which Approach $\pm\infty$

Whenever a limit yields the form $\dfrac{\text{"constant"}}{0}$ where the constant **IS NOT 0**, the answer

WILL BE INFINITE. We just need to determine if it is $+\infty$ or $-\infty$.

Keep these basic infinite limits in mind: $\boxed{\displaystyle\lim_{x\to 0^+}\frac{1}{x}=+\infty \text{ and } \lim_{x\to 0^-}\frac{1}{x}=-\infty}$

Also, remember that some functions have infinite limits "built in".

For example, $\displaystyle\lim_{x\to 0^+}\ln x = -\infty$.

Example 1) Evaluate (a) $\displaystyle\lim_{x\to 3^+}\left(\frac{x^2+1}{x-3}\right)$ (b) $\displaystyle\lim_{x\to 3^-}\left(\frac{x^2+1}{x-3}\right)$

Solution (a) Note that just substituting yields $\dfrac{\text{"}10\text{"}}{0}$. Since x is **greater than**

and approaching 3, therefore $x-3$ is **POSITIVE** and **SMALL**.

$\therefore\ \displaystyle\lim_{x\to 3^+}\left(\frac{x^2+1}{x-3}\right)\overset{\boxed{\substack{\text{See the personal note}\\\text{below to explain where}\\\text{the "10" comes from!}}}}{=}10\lim_{x\to 3^+}\left(\frac{1}{x-3}\right)=+\infty$

$\boxed{\textbf{A personal note : in these questions, } \underset{\boxed{\text{The Author!}}}{\overset{\boxed{\text{Me!}}}{\textbf{I}}} \textbf{ like to evaluate everything except}\\ \textbf{the factor causing the "0 denominator" and pull the result OUTSIDE the limit.}}$

(b) $\displaystyle\lim_{x\to 3^-}\left(\frac{x^2+1}{x-3}\right)=10\lim_{x\to 3^-}\left(\frac{1}{x-3}\right)=-\infty$

Example 2) Evaluate $\displaystyle\lim_{x\to 4^-}\left(\frac{1-x^2}{(4-x)(x+1)}\right)$.

Solution $\displaystyle\lim_{x\to 4^-}\left(\frac{1-x^2}{(4-x)(x+1)}\right)\overset{\boxed{\substack{\text{Evaluate everything}\\\text{but the }4-x\text{ term and}\\\text{rewrite it as }-(x-4).}}}{=}\frac{-15}{5}\lim_{x\to 4^-}\left(\frac{1}{-(x-4)}\right)$

$\overset{\boxed{\substack{\text{Why? It's easier to look}\\\text{at }x-4\text{ than }4-x\text{ as }x\to 4^-.}}}{=}3\lim_{x\to 4^-}\left(\frac{1}{x-4}\right)^{\boxed{\substack{\because x<4\\\therefore x-4<0}}}=-\infty$

Two for you.

Find the following limits: 1)(a) $\lim\limits_{x \to 1^+} \ln(x-1)$ (b) $\lim\limits_{x \to \frac{\pi}{2}^-} \tan x$

2) $\lim\limits_{x \to 5^-} \left(\dfrac{x^2 - 25}{(x-5)^2} \right)$ (Hint: factor and simplify first.)

Answers 1)(a) $-\infty$ (b) $+\infty$ 2) $-\infty$

Limits At Infinity

Keep the basic limits "at infinity" (ie., limits where x approaches $+\infty$ or $-\infty$) in mind:

$$\lim_{x \to +\infty} \frac{1}{x} = 0 \quad \text{and} \quad \lim_{x \to -\infty} \frac{1}{x} = 0$$

Some functions have limits at infinity "built in". For example, $\lim_{x \to -\infty} 2^x = 0$.

Often, these kinds of questions arise when you have $\dfrac{\text{(almost) a polynomial}}{\text{(almost) another polynomial}}$.

In these examples, the **EASIEST** method is to divide the top and the bottom by the **HIGHEST POWER OF x IN THE <u>DENOMINATOR</u>!**

Example 1) Evaluate:

(a) $\lim_{x \to \infty} \left(\dfrac{x+1}{3x+2} \right)$
(b) $\lim_{x \to -\infty} \left(\dfrac{x^2 + \sin x}{x^3 + 2x} \right)$
(c) $\lim_{x \to -\infty} \left(\dfrac{x^3 - x + \cos x}{x^2 + 1 + \sin x} \right)$

Solution (a) $\lim_{x \to \infty} \left(\dfrac{x+1}{3x+2} \right) \overset{\boxed{\text{Divide top and bottom by } x.}}{=} \lim_{x \to \infty} \dfrac{\left(\dfrac{x+1}{x} \right)}{\left(\dfrac{3x+2}{x} \right)} = \lim_{x \to \infty} \left(\dfrac{1 + \dfrac{1}{x}}{3 + \dfrac{2}{x}} \right) = \dfrac{1+0}{3+0} = \dfrac{1}{3}$

(b) $\lim_{x \to -\infty} \left(\dfrac{x^2 + \sin x}{x^3 + 2x} \right) \overset{\boxed{\text{Divide top and bottom by } x^3.}}{=} \lim_{x \to -\infty} \left(\dfrac{\dfrac{1}{x} + \dfrac{\sin x}{x^3}}{1 + \dfrac{2}{x^2}} \right) \overset{\boxed{\begin{array}{c}\text{Remember } -1 \leq \sin x \leq 1, \text{ so } \frac{\sin x}{x^3} \\ \text{is, in magnitude, } \frac{\text{small number}}{\text{BIG NUMBER}} \\ \text{and will therefore approach 0!}\end{array}}}{=} \dfrac{0+0}{1+0} = \dfrac{0}{1} = 0$

(c) $\lim_{x \to -\infty} \left(\dfrac{x^3 - x + \cos x}{x^2 + 1 + \sin x} \right) \overset{\boxed{\begin{array}{c}\text{Divide top} \\ \text{and bottom} \\ \text{by } x^2, \\ \text{NOT } x^3!\end{array}}}{=} \lim_{x \to -\infty} \left(\dfrac{x - \dfrac{1}{x} + \dfrac{\cos x}{x^2}}{1 + \dfrac{1}{x^2} + \dfrac{\sin x}{x^2}} \right)$

$\overset{\boxed{\begin{array}{c}\text{Watch the special way} \\ \text{we handle the } x \text{ on top!} \\ \text{Evaluate each limit} \\ \text{except the one that} \\ \text{still goes to } \pm\infty.\end{array}}}{=} \dfrac{\lim_{x \to -\infty} x - 0 + 0}{1 + 0 + 0} = -\infty$

171

Two for you.

Evaluate the limits:

1) $\displaystyle\lim_{x \to -\infty} \left(\frac{4x^3 - 2x + e^x}{3x^3 - 5x^2 + \sin x} \right)$

2) $\displaystyle\lim_{x \to \infty} \left(\frac{x+1}{\sqrt{4x^2 + x} + 5x} \right)$

Hint: the highest power of x in the bottom is x, because of the "$\sqrt{}$".

Another hint: $\dfrac{\sqrt{4x^2 + x}}{x} \overset{\boxed{\begin{array}{c}\because x \to \infty \ \therefore x > 0 \\ \text{and so } x = \sqrt{x^2}\end{array}}}{=} \dfrac{\sqrt{4x^2 + x}}{\sqrt{x^2}} = \sqrt{\dfrac{\text{you get}}{\text{the idea!}}}$

Answers 1) $\dfrac{4}{3}$ 2) $\dfrac{1}{7}$

An "$\infty - \infty$" Limit: $\lim\limits_{x \to \infty} \left(\sqrt{x^2 + 8x} - x \right)$

You might think "$\infty - \infty$" has to be 0. Not necessarily. In fact, anything can happen, depending on how the first term approaches ∞ compared to the second term.

For example, $\lim\limits_{x \to \infty}(x^2 - x) = \infty$ $\lim\limits_{x \to \infty}(x - x) = 0$ $\lim\limits_{x \to \infty}(x - x^2) = -\infty$

Example 1) Evaluate $\lim\limits_{x \to \infty} \left(\sqrt{x^2 + 8x} - x \right)$.

Solution $\lim\limits_{x \to \infty} \left(\sqrt{x^2 + 8x} - x \right) \overset{\boxed{\begin{array}{l}\text{Rationalize the numerator}\\ \text{using } (a-b)(a+b)=a^2-b^2,\\ \text{with } a=\sqrt{x^2+8x} \text{ and } b=x.\end{array}}}{=} \lim\limits_{x \to \infty} \left(\sqrt{x^2 + 8x} - x \right)\left(\dfrac{\sqrt{x^2 + 8x} + x}{\sqrt{x^2 + 8x} + x} \right)$

$= \lim\limits_{x \to \infty} \left(\dfrac{x^2 + 8x - x^2}{\sqrt{x^2 + 8x} + x} \right) = \lim\limits_{x \to \infty} \left(\dfrac{8x}{\sqrt{x^2 + 8x} + x} \right) \overset{\boxed{\begin{array}{l}\text{Divide the top and the}\\ \text{bottom by } x. \text{ Use } x=\sqrt{x^2}\\ \text{(which is true when } x>0)^*\\ \text{to divide } x \text{ into } \sqrt{x^2+8x}.\end{array}}}{=} \lim\limits_{x \to \infty} \left(\dfrac{8}{\sqrt{1 + \dfrac{8}{x}} + 1} \right) = \dfrac{8}{2} = 4$

BUT...

Example 2) Evaluate $\lim\limits_{x \to \infty} \left(\sqrt{x^2 + 8} - x \right)$

Solution $\lim\limits_{x \to \infty} \left(\sqrt{x^2 + 8} - x \right) \overset{\boxed{\begin{array}{l}\text{Rationalize the numerator}\\ \text{using } (a-b)(a+b)=a^2-b^2.\end{array}}}{=} \lim\limits_{x \to \infty} \left(\sqrt{x^2 + 8} - x \right)\left(\dfrac{\sqrt{x^2 + 8} + x}{\sqrt{x^2 + 8} + x} \right)$

$= \lim\limits_{x \to \infty} \left(\dfrac{x^2 + 8 - x^2}{\sqrt{x^2 + 8} + x} \right) = \lim\limits_{x \to \infty} \left(\dfrac{8}{\sqrt{x^2 + 8} + x} \right) \overset{\boxed{\begin{array}{l}\text{Divide the top and the}\\ \text{bottom by } x. \text{ Use } x=\sqrt{x^2}\\ \text{(which is true when } x>0.)^*\end{array}}}{=} \lim\limits_{x \to \infty} \left(\dfrac{\dfrac{8}{x}}{\sqrt{1 + \dfrac{8}{x}} + 1} \right) = \dfrac{0}{2} = 0$

$* \, |x| = \sqrt{x^2} = \begin{cases} -x, & x < 0 \\ x, & x \geq 0 \end{cases}$

When $x \to \infty$, we can certainly say $x > 0$ and so $\sqrt{x^2} = x$.

173

Two for you.

1) Evaluate: $\displaystyle\lim_{x\to\infty}\left(\sqrt{x^2-x+1}-x\right)$

2) Evaluate: $\displaystyle\lim_{x\to-\infty}\left(\sqrt{x^2-3x}+x\right)$

Hint: For $x<0$, $\sqrt{x^2}=-x$. For example, if $x=-10$,

then $\sqrt{(-10)^2}=\sqrt{100}=10=-(-10)$.

Another hint: $\dfrac{\sqrt{x^2-3x}}{x}\overset{\boxed{\text{For } x<0,\; x=-\sqrt{x^2}.}}{=}\dfrac{\sqrt{x^2-3x}}{-\sqrt{x^2}}=-\sqrt{\dfrac{x^2-3x}{x^2}}=-\sqrt{1-\dfrac{3}{x}}$

Answers 1) $-\dfrac{1}{2}$ 2) $\dfrac{3}{2}$

174

Limits: A Summary

This is a non-standard Survival Kit page but my students find this summary of limit questions **hugely** useful. Almost every limit question you encounter will look like one of these!

Case 1) "No Problem" Problems. Letting x get close to a leads to a clear answer.

Example 1) $\lim\limits_{x \to 6}\left(\dfrac{x^2 - 25}{x + 5}\right) = \dfrac{11}{11} = 1$

Case 2) "$\dfrac{c}{0}$", where $c \neq 0$. Here, the answer will be $+\infty$ or $-\infty$, or possibly both,

in which case you need to consider one-sided limits.

Example 2) $\lim\limits_{x \to -5^+}\left(\dfrac{x^2}{x + 5}\right) = 25 \lim\limits_{x \to -5^+}\left(\dfrac{1}{x + 5}\right)^{\boxed{x+5\,>\,0}} = +\infty$

Case 3) "$\dfrac{0}{0}$" when $x = a$. Divide out $\dfrac{x - a}{x - a}$, possibly more than once, and the

problem should reduce to case 1 or 2.

Example 3) $\lim\limits_{x \to -5}\left(\dfrac{x^2 - 25}{x + 5}\right) = \lim\limits_{x \to -5}\left(\dfrac{(x - 5)\,\cancel{(x+5)}}{\cancel{x+5}}\right) = -10$

Case 4) One-sided limits. Any of cases 1, 2, and 3 can come in the form of one-sided limits. These can be either explicit or require you to consider separate cases.

Example 4) Explicit: $\lim\limits_{x \to 2^-}[[x]] = 1$;

Implicit: $\lim\limits_{x \to 2}[[x]] \quad \because \lim\limits_{x \to 2^-}[[x]] = 1 \neq \lim\limits_{x \to 2^+}[[x]] = 2, \quad \therefore \lim\limits_{x \to 2}[[x]]$ does not exist.

Case 5) x approaches $+\infty$ or $-\infty$ in a $\dfrac{\text{polynomial}}{\text{polynomial}}$. Divide the top and bottom by

the highest power of x in the bottom, to obtain one of these outcomes:

(i) $\dfrac{0}{c}$ (ii) $\dfrac{b}{c}$ (iii) "$\pm\dfrac{\infty}{c}$", where $b, c \neq 0$.

Then the answer is (i) 0 (ii) $\dfrac{b}{c}$ (iii) $+\infty$ or $-\infty$

Example 5) $\lim\limits_{x \to \infty}\left(\dfrac{x^5 + 1}{x^4 + x^3}\right) \overset{\boxed{\text{Divide top and bottom by } x^4.}}{=} \lim\limits_{x \to \infty}\left(\dfrac{x + \dfrac{1}{x^4}}{1 + \dfrac{1}{x}}\right) = \dfrac{\lim\limits_{x \to \infty} x + 0}{1 + 0} = +\infty$

Two for you.

Evaluate: 1) $\displaystyle\lim_{x\to 3^-}\left(\frac{3-4x}{x-3}\right)$ 2) $\displaystyle\lim_{x\to -\infty}\left(\frac{x^5+1}{x^4+x^3}\right)$

Answers 1) ∞ 2) $-\infty$

Variations on $\lim\limits_{\theta\to 0}\left(\dfrac{\sin\theta}{\theta}\right)=1$

Lots of trigonometric $\dfrac{\text{``}0\text{''}}{0}$ limits are

evaluated with a little clever use of $\lim\limits_{\theta\to 0}\dfrac{\sin\theta}{\theta}=1$.

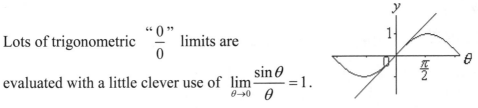

(By the way, the interpretation of this limit is very intuitive: when θ is small, $\sin\theta$ and θ are nearly equal. Therefore, this ratio approaches 1.)

Example 1) Evaluate the following limits:

(a) $\lim\limits_{\theta\to 0}\dfrac{\theta}{\sin\theta}$ 　　(b) $\lim\limits_{\theta\to 0}\dfrac{\sin 3\theta}{\theta}$ 　　(c) $\lim\limits_{\theta\to 0}\dfrac{\tan 2\theta}{\sin\theta}$ 　　(d) $\lim\limits_{\theta\to 0}\dfrac{1-\cos\theta}{\theta}$

Solution (a) $\lim\limits_{\theta\to 0}\dfrac{\theta}{\sin\theta}=\lim\limits_{\theta\to 0}\dfrac{1}{\left(\dfrac{\sin\theta}{\theta}\right)}=\dfrac{1}{1}=1$

(b) $\lim\limits_{\theta\to 0}\dfrac{\sin 3\theta}{\theta}$
　　"3θ" is playing the role of "θ" here! Put 3 in the bottom and compensate with 3 on top to keep things equal!
　　$=\lim\limits_{\theta\to 0}\dfrac{3\sin 3\theta}{3\theta}$
　　3θ approaches 0 as θ approaches 0.
　　$=\lim\limits_{3\theta\to 0}\dfrac{3\sin 3\theta}{3\theta}=3(1)=3$

(c) $\lim\limits_{\theta\to 0}\dfrac{\tan 2\theta}{\sin\theta}$　Use $\tan 2\theta=\dfrac{\sin 2\theta}{\cos 2\theta}$.　$=\lim\limits_{\theta\to 0}\dfrac{\sin 2\theta}{\sin\theta\cos 2\theta}$

Throw in some "θ's" to make the variables MATCH!
$=\lim\limits_{\theta\to 0}\left(\dfrac{\sin 2\theta}{2\theta}\right)\left(\dfrac{\theta}{\sin\theta}\right)\left(\dfrac{2}{\cos 2\theta}\right)=(1)(1)(2)=2$

(d) $\lim\limits_{\theta\to 0}\dfrac{1-\cos\theta}{\theta}$　Use $\sin^2\theta=1-\cos^2\theta$.　$=\lim\limits_{\theta\to 0}\left(\dfrac{1-\cos\theta}{\theta}\right)\left(\dfrac{1+\cos\theta}{1+\cos\theta}\right)=\lim\limits_{\theta\to 0}\left(\dfrac{1-\cos^2\theta}{\theta(1+\cos\theta)}\right)$

$=\lim\limits_{\theta\to 0}\left(\dfrac{\sin^2\theta}{\theta(1+\cos\theta)}\right)=\lim\limits_{\theta\to 0}\left(\dfrac{\sin\theta}{\theta}\right)\left(\dfrac{\sin\theta}{1+\cos\theta}\right)=(1)\left(\dfrac{0}{2}\right)=0$

Two for you.

Evaluate the following limits:

1) $\displaystyle\lim_{\theta \to 0}\left(\frac{\sin 5\theta}{\sin 3\theta}\right)$

2) $\displaystyle\lim_{h \to 0}\left(\frac{\sin(x+h) - \sin x}{h}\right)$ (Hint: use $\sin(x+h) = \sin x \cos h + \cos x \sin h$.)

Answers 1) $\dfrac{5}{3}$

2) $\cos x$ (Here, you have just shown the derivative of $\sin x$ is $\cos x$!)

Domain (Food for a Function!)

Compare these two problems:

1) Find the domain of the function $y = \sqrt{x-1}$ and then graph the function.

2) Graph the function $y = \sqrt{x-1}$.

While the second question doesn't explicitly ask for the domain, you still need to know it in order to draw the graph.

DOMAIN CATALOG

Expression	Domain
$\sqrt{x}$, $\sqrt[4]{x}$, $\sqrt[6]{x}$, etc.	$x \geq 0$
$\dfrac{1}{x}$	$x \neq 0$
$\log_a(x)$, including $\log(x)$ and $\ln(x)$	$x > 0$
$\tan(x)$, $\sec(x)$	$x \neq \pm\dfrac{\pi}{2}, \pm\dfrac{3\pi}{2}, \pm\dfrac{5\pi}{2}, \ldots$
$\cot(x)$, $\csc(x)$	$x \neq \pm\pi, \pm2\pi, \pm3\pi, \ldots$
When you learn a new function…	…you will learn the restrictions that come with it.

Example 1) Find the domain for each of the following functions.

(a) $y = \sqrt{x-6}$ (b) $y = \sqrt{9-x^2}$ (c) $y = \dfrac{1}{\sqrt{x^2-9}}$ (d) $y = \sqrt[3]{x-4} = (x-4)^{\frac{1}{3}}$

Solution

Set Notation

Interval Notation
Square bracket: **include** the end point.
Round bracket: **exclude** the end point.

(a) $x - 6 \geq 0 \Leftrightarrow x \geq 6$ $\therefore$ Domain $= \{x \in \mathbb{R} \mid x \geq 6\} = [6, \infty)$

(b) $9 - x^2 \geq 0 \Leftrightarrow 9 \geq x^2 \Leftrightarrow x^2 \leq 9 \Leftrightarrow -3 \leq x \leq 3$ $\therefore$ Domain $= [-3, 3]$

(c) $x^2 - 9 > 0 \Leftrightarrow x^2 > 9 \Leftrightarrow |x| > 3 \Leftrightarrow x < -3$ or $x > 3$ $\therefore$ Domain $= (-\infty - 3) \cup (3, \infty)$

(d) There is no restriction. We CAN take the cube root (or the fifth root or the seventh root) of any number, $-$ or $+$, so we don't need $x - 4 \geq 0$! $\therefore$ Domain $= \mathbb{R}$

Example 2) Find the domain for each: (a) $y = \ln(6 + 5x)$ (b) $y = \tan(2x)$

We divided by a "$-$" and therefore, reversed the inequality!

Solution (a) $6 + 5x > 0 \Leftrightarrow 6 > -5x \Leftrightarrow -\dfrac{6}{5} < x$ $\therefore$ Domain $= \left(-\dfrac{6}{5}, \infty\right)$

(b) $2x \neq \pm\dfrac{\pi}{2}, \pm\dfrac{3\pi}{2}, \pm\dfrac{5\pi}{2}, \ldots$ and so $x \neq \pm\dfrac{\pi}{4}, \pm\dfrac{3\pi}{4}, \pm\dfrac{5\pi}{4}, \ldots$

So, to be concise, Domain $= \left\{ x \in \mathbb{R} \mid x \neq \dfrac{\pi}{4} + \dfrac{k\pi}{2}, \text{ where } k \in \mathbb{Z} \right\}$!

Two for you.

1) State the domain and range of $f(x) = \sqrt{x+1} + 1$ and draw the graph.

2) Write $y = \sqrt{(x-4)^2}$ using first absolute value and then a "branch" definition.

Answers

1) Domain $= [-1, \infty)$, Range $= [1, \infty)$

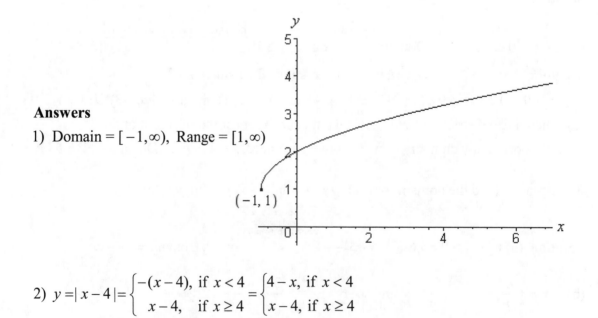

2) $y = |x-4| = \begin{cases} -(x-4), & \text{if } x < 4 \\ x-4, & \text{if } x \geq 4 \end{cases} = \begin{cases} 4-x, & \text{if } x < 4 \\ x-4, & \text{if } x \geq 4 \end{cases}$

Continuity and Discontinuity at a Point

f is continuous at $x = a$ if $\lim\limits_{x \to a} f(x) = f(a)$.

Continuous functions have no holes or breaks or vertical asymptotes. You have to have a **limit**, you have to have a **function value**, and they must be **equal**.

Example 1) Explain why each function is discontinuous at the indicated value:

(a) $f(x) = \dfrac{x^2 - 16}{x - 4}$ at $x = 4$
(b) $f(x) = \dfrac{x}{|x|}$ at $x = 0$

(c) $f(x) = \begin{cases} x^2, & \text{if } x \neq 0 \\ 2, & \text{if } x = 0 \end{cases}$ at $x = 0$
(d) $f(x) = [[x]]$ at $x = 2$

Solution (a) $\lim\limits_{x \to 4} f(x) = \lim\limits_{x \to 4} \dfrac{(x - 4)(x + 4)}{x - 4} = 8$,

so the limit exists, but $f(4)$ does not exist.

(b) $f(x) = \dfrac{x}{|x|} = \begin{cases} -1, & \text{if } x < 0 \\ 1, & \text{if } x > 0 \end{cases}$

$\therefore \lim\limits_{x \to 0^-} f(x) = \lim\limits_{x \to 0^-} (-1) = -1$ and $\lim\limits_{x \to 0^+} f(x) = \lim\limits_{x \to 0^+} 1 = 1$ and so $\lim\limits_{x \to 0} f(x)$ does not exist.

(c) $\lim\limits_{x \to 0} f(x) = \lim\limits_{x \to 0} x^2 = 0$ so the limit exists. But $f(0) = 2 \neq \lim\limits_{x \to 0} f(x)$.

(d) $\lim\limits_{x \to 2^-} f(x) \overset{\boxed{\text{For } 1 \le x < 2, f(x) = 1.}}{=} \lim\limits_{x \to 2^-} (1) = 1$ and $\lim\limits_{x \to 2^+} f(x) = \lim\limits_{x \to 2^+} 2 = 2$,

and so $\lim\limits_{x \to 2} f(x)$ does not exist.

Note that $f(2) = 2$ and so f is continuous from the **right**.

Example 2) For the function at the right, give a reason why it is discontinuous at each of a, b, and c. State whether it is continuous from the left or right.

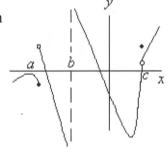

Solution The function is discontinuous at a and b because the limit does not exist. It is discontinuous at c because the limit and value are unequal. The function is continuous from the **left** at a but from neither side at b and c.

181

Two for you.

For each of the following, give a reason why the function is not continuous at the indicated value:

1) $f(x) = \dfrac{1}{x-3}$ at $x = 3$

2) $f(x) = \begin{cases} x+1, & \text{if } x < -2 \\ 2, & \text{if } x = -2 \\ x^2 - 5, & \text{if } x > -2 \end{cases}$ at $x = -2$

Answers 1) $\lim\limits_{x \to 3} f(x)$ does not exist **OR** $f(3)$ does not exist (either answer).

2) $\lim\limits_{x \to -2} f(x) = -1 \neq f(-2)$

Continuous Functions (Intervals of Continuity)

Continuous functions have no holes. When you draw a continuous function, your pen never leaves the paper. When is a function **not continuous**? Basically, you have to check **domain restrictions**, **division by 0**, and "**branches**" (which we look at geometrically in Example 2 and using function definitions in the next section!) When you add, subtract, and multiply continuous functions, you get continuous functions. Same for division, as long as you don't have 0 in the bottom!

Example 1)(a) Based on your mathematical experience, which of the following are continuous: polynomials, trigonometric functions, $y = a^x$, $y = \log_a x$?

(b) If f and g are continuous, discuss the continuity of $f + g$, $f - g$, fg, f/g.

Solution

(a) Polynomials, $y = \sin x$, $y = \cos x$, and $y = a^x$ are continuous for $x \in \mathbb{R}$.

$y = \log_a x$ is continuous for $x > 0$.

$y = \tan x$ and $y = \sec x$ are continuous for $x \neq \pi/2 + k\pi$, where $k \in \mathbb{Z}$.

$y = \cot x$ and $y = \csc x$ are continuous for $x \neq \pi + k\pi$, where $k \in \mathbb{Z}$.

(b) $f + g$, $f - g$, and fg are all continuous whenever f and g are.

f/g is continuous as long as f and g are and $g(x) \neq 0$.

Example 2) State the intervals of continuity

for this function....... $\rightarrow$

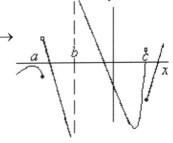

Solution The function is continuous on the intervals $(-\infty, a]$, (a, b), (b, c), and $[c, \infty)$.

Note that the function is continuous from the **left** at $x = a$ and from the **right** at $x = c$.

Example 3) State the intervals on which the following are continuous:

(a) $f(x) = \sqrt{x - 3}$ (b) $g(x) = \ln(|x|)$ (c) $h(x) = \dfrac{x^{1/4}}{(x-5)(x+3)}$

Solution

(a) Since $x - 3 \geq 0$, therefore $x \geq 3$ and so f is continuous on the interval $[3, \infty)$.

(b) Since $|x| \geq 0$, we only have to exclude $x = 0$ and so g is continuous on $(-\infty, 0)$ and $(0, \infty)$.

(c) $x \neq 5$ or -3. But $x^{1/4}$ is only defined for $x \geq 0$, so -3 is already gone. Therefore h is continuous on $[0, 5)$ and $(5, \infty)$.

Two for you.

State the intervals of continuity for f and g.

1) $f(x) = \dfrac{\sqrt{3x-9}}{x-5}$

2) $g(x) = [[x]]$, where $-2 \le x \le 2$

(g is "the greatest integer less than or equal to x" or "floor" function.)

Answers 1) $[3,5)$, $(5,\infty)$ 2) $[-2,-1)$, $[-1,0)$, $[0,1)$, $[1, 2)$

Continuity and Branch Functions

There are two kinds of branch functions: explicit and implicit. Apart from the usual continuity concerns (division by 0, positive domain for logs, etc.) you have to be careful **at the values of x where the function branches.** Remember:

> f is continuous at $x = a$ if $\lim\limits_{x \to a} f(x) = f(a)$.

Example 1) Discuss the continuity of

the function $f(x) = \begin{cases} x, & \text{if } x < 0 \\ 2, & \text{if } x = 0 \\ x^2, & \text{if } 0 < x < 2 \\ x+2, & \text{if } x \geq 2 \end{cases}$

Solution The only possible problems are at $x = 0$ and $x = 2$.

$$\lim_{x \to 0^-} f(x) = \lim_{x \to 0^-} x = 0 \qquad \lim_{x \to 0^+} f(x) = \lim_{x \to 0^+} x^2 = 0$$

Since the left- and right-hand limits are equal, $\lim\limits_{x \to 0} f(x) = 0$.

But $f(0) = 2$ and so f **is not** continuous at $x = 0$.

$$\lim_{x \to 2^-} f(x) = \lim_{x \to 2^-} x^2 = 4 \qquad \lim_{x \to 2^+} f(x) = \lim_{x \to 2^+} (x+2) = 4.$$

The left-hand and right-hand limits are equal, so $\lim\limits_{x \to 2} f(x) = 4$. Also, $f(2) = 4$

and so f **is** continuous at $x = 2$. f is continuous on the intervals $(-\infty, 0)$ and $(0, \infty)$.

Example 2) Discuss the continuity of the function $g(x) = \dfrac{|x|}{x}$.

Solution The only possible problem here is at $x = 0$.
Writing g explicitly as a branch function,

we have $g(x) = \begin{cases} \dfrac{-x}{x}, & \text{if } x < 0 \\ \dfrac{x}{x}, & \text{if } x > 0 \end{cases} = \begin{cases} -1, & \text{if } x < 0 \\ 1, & \text{if } x > 0 \end{cases}$

$$\lim_{x \to 0^-} g(x) = \lim_{x \to 0^-} (-1) = -1 \quad \text{and} \quad \lim_{x \to 0^+} g(x) = \lim_{x \to 0^+} 1 = 1$$

so $\lim\limits_{x \to 0} g(x)$ does not exist. Therefore, g is **not continuous**

at $x = 0$ and so g is continuous on the intervals $(-\infty, 0)$ and $(0, \infty)$.

185

Two for you.

State the intervals of continuity for f and g.

1) $f(x) = \begin{cases} \sin x, & \text{if } x < \pi \\ \cos x, & \text{if } x \geq \pi \end{cases}$

2) $g(x) = \dfrac{x+3}{|x+3|}$

Answers 1) $(-\infty, \pi)$, $[\pi, \infty)$ 2) $(-\infty, -3)$, $(-3, \infty)$

186

Essential versus Removable Discontinuities

This is easy!

The discontinuity is **removable** if it is a "hole" in the function. In this case, there is a limit and there is a function value, and they are different **or** there is no function value.

The discontinuity is **essential** if it is **any other type of discontinuity**. In this case, there is definitely **NO** limit, though this can happen for a variety of reasons.

Example 1) Each of the following functions has a discontinuity at one point. Classify it as either essential or removable. If essential, give the reason. If removable, redefine the function to make it continuous at the point.

(a) $f(x) = \begin{cases} \sin x, & \text{if } x < 0 \\ 1, & \text{if } x = 0 \\ x, & \text{if } x > 0 \end{cases}$ (b) $g(x) = \dfrac{x^2 - 9}{x - 3}$ (c) $h(x) = \dfrac{1}{x^2}$

(d) $j(x) = \begin{cases} x, & \text{if } x < 0 \\ 1, & \text{if } x = 0 \\ x+1, & \text{if } x > 0 \end{cases}$ (e) $k(x) = \sin\left(\dfrac{1}{x}\right)$

Solution

(a) Removable. Define $f(0) = 0$.

(b) Removable. The problem is at $x = 3$:

$$\lim_{x \to 3} g(x) = \lim_{x \to 3} \frac{(x-3)(x+3)}{x-3} = 6, \text{ but } g(3) \text{ is not defined. Define } g(3) = 6.$$

(c) Essential. $\lim_{x \to 0} h(x) = \infty$

(d) Essential. $\lim_{x \to 0^-} j(x) = \lim_{x \to 0^-} x = 0$ while $\lim_{x \to 0^+} j(x) = \lim_{x \to 0^+} (x+1) = 1$

and so $\lim_{x \to 0} j(x)$ does not exist.

(e) Essential. $\lim_{x \to 0} k(x)$ does not exist. In fact, $\sin\left(\dfrac{1}{x}\right)$ **oscillates** between -1 and 1

faster and **faster** as x gets closer and closer to 0. It is actually quite "dizzying" and fun to watch!

Two for you.

Each function has a single discontinuity. State the problem x value and whether the discontinuity is essential or removable. If essential, state why. If removable, redefine the function to make it continuous.

1) $f(x) = \dfrac{|x-5|}{x-5}$ 2) $g(x) = \dfrac{\sin x}{x}$

Answers 1) Essential at $x=5$ since $\lim\limits_{x \to 5} f(x)$ does not exist.

2) Removable at $\theta = 0$. Define $g(0) = 1$.

Finding the Derivative from the Definition

$$\boxed{f \text{ is differentiable at } x = a \text{ if } \lim_{h \to 0} \frac{f(a+h) - f(a)}{h} = f'(a).}$$

The alternate form of this definition is

$$\boxed{f \text{ is differentiable at } x = a \text{ if } \lim_{x \to a} \frac{f(x) - f(a)}{x - a} = f'(a).}$$

Forgive me, but I am about to be very wordy!

The second definition is, **believe me**, the same as the first. Many of you find this hard to believe. Trust me. The **variable** in the second formulation is $x = a + h$ and so $x - a = h$. As h approaches 0, x approaches a. So, in the first definition, replace:

$$h \to 0 \text{ with } x \to a \qquad h \text{ with } x - a \qquad a + h \text{ with } x$$

Lo and behold (not by magic!), you have the second definition. Why do some students confuse these? I think it is because teachers ask you to find $f'(\boxed{x})$, rather than $f'(\boxed{a})$, from the definition when you first study derivatives. This is okay in the first definition where x takes on the role of a. **BUT** if you try to use the second definition, you would be forcing x to be both $(a + h)$ and a at the same time!

Example 1) Find the derivative for the function $f(x) = x^2 + x + 1$ at $(a, f(a))$
(a) using the first definition   (b) using the second definition.

Solution (a) $f'(a) = \lim_{h \to 0} \dfrac{f(a+h) - f(a)}{h} = \lim_{h \to 0} \dfrac{(a+h)^2 + (a+h) + 1 - (a^2 + a + 1)}{h}$

$= \lim_{h \to 0} \dfrac{a^2 + 2ah + h^2 + a + h + 1 - a^2 - a - 1}{h} = \lim_{h \to 0} \dfrac{2ah + h^2 + h}{h} = \lim_{h \to 0} \dfrac{\cancel{h}(2a + h + 1)}{\cancel{h}}$

$= 2a + 1$

(b) $f'(a) = \lim_{x \to a} \dfrac{f(x) - f(a)}{x - a} = \lim_{x \to a} \dfrac{x^2 + x + 1 - (a^2 + a + 1)}{x - a}$

$= \lim_{x \to a} \dfrac{x^2 - a^2 + x - a}{x - a} = \lim_{x \to a} \dfrac{(x - a)(x + a + 1)}{x - a} = \lim_{x \to a} \dfrac{\cancel{(x - a)}(x + a + 1)}{\cancel{x - a}} = 2a + 1$

Two for you.

Set up the first step to find $f'(a)$ for $f(x) = \dfrac{1}{\sqrt{x}}$

1) using the first definition   2) using the second definition.

Answers   1) $f'(a) = \lim\limits_{h \to 0} \dfrac{\dfrac{1}{\sqrt{a+h}} - \dfrac{1}{\sqrt{a}}}{h}$ 2) $f'(a) = \lim\limits_{x \to a} \dfrac{\dfrac{1}{\sqrt{x}} - \dfrac{1}{\sqrt{a}}}{x-a}$

Differentiable Functions (Intervals of Differentiability)

When is a **continuous** function **not differentiable**?

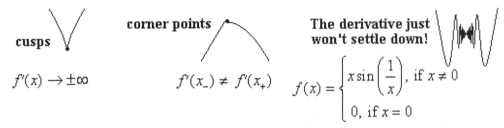

cusps

$f'(x) \to \pm\infty$

corner points

$f'(x_-) \neq f'(x_+)$

The derivative just won't settle down!

$$f(x) = \begin{cases} x\sin\left(\dfrac{1}{x}\right), & \text{if } x \neq 0 \\ 0, & \text{if } x = 0 \end{cases}$$

Also, check **domain restrictions**, **division by 0 in the derivative**, and "**branches**". When you add, subtract and multiply differentiable functions, you get differentiable functions. Same for division, as long as you don't have 0 in the bottom!

Example 1) Based on your mathematical experience, which of the following are differentiable: polynomials, trigonometric functions, $y = a^x$, $y = \log_a x$, $y = |x|$?

Solution Polynomials, $y = \sin x$, $y = \cos x$, and $y = a^x$ are differentiable for $x \in \mathbb{R}$.
$y = \log_a x$ is differentiable for $x > 0$.
$y = \tan x$ and $y = \sec x$ are differentiable for $x \neq \pi/2 + k\pi$, where $k \in \mathbb{Z}$.
$y = \cot x$ and $y = \csc x$ are differentiable for $x \neq \pi + k\pi$, where $k \in \mathbb{Z}$.

$y = |x|$ has a $\boxed{\text{corner point at } x = 0}$ and so the function is differentiable for $x \neq 0$.

> Corner Point at $x=0$: $f'(0_-) \neq f'(0_+)$

Example 2) State the intervals of differentiability for this function... →

Solution The function is differentiable on the intervals $[-1, 1]$, $[1, 2)$, and $(2, 3]$. Note that $x = 1$ is a corner point and $x = 2$ is a cusp point.

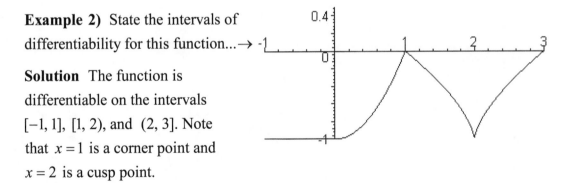

Example 3) State the intervals on which the following are differentiable.

(a) $f(x) = \sqrt{x-3}$ (b) $h(x) = \dfrac{x^{1/4}}{(x-5)(x+3)}$

Solution

(a) Since $x - 3 \geq 0$, therefore $x \geq 3$ and so f is differentiable on the interval $[3, \infty)$.

(b) $x \neq 5$ or -3. But $x^{1/4}$ is only defined for $x \geq 0$, so -3 is already gone! Therefore, h is differentiable on the intervals $[0, 5)$ and $(5, \infty)$.

Two for you.

State the intervals of differentiability:

1) $f(x) = \dfrac{\sqrt{3x-9}}{x-5}$ 2) $g(x) = [[x]]$, if $-2 \le x \le 2$

Answers 1) $[3, 5)$, $(5, \infty)$ 2) $[-2, -1)$, $[-1, 0)$, $[0, 1)$, $[1, 2)$

Differentiability and Branch Functions

There are two kinds of branch functions: explicit and implicit. Apart from the usual differentiability concerns (division by 0 in the derivative, positive domain for logs, etc.) you have to be careful **at the values of x where the function branches. Also, we will deal here only with functions that are continuous on their domains.**

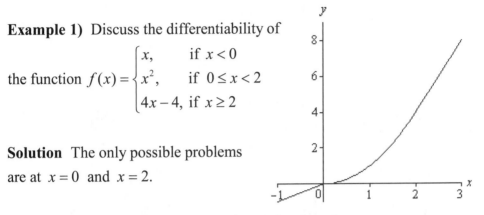

Example 1) Discuss the differentiability of the function $f(x) = \begin{cases} x, & \text{if } x < 0 \\ x^2, & \text{if } 0 \le x < 2 \\ 4x - 4, & \text{if } x \ge 2 \end{cases}$

Solution The only possible problems are at $x = 0$ and $x = 2$.

$x = 0$: $\lim\limits_{x \to 0^-} f'(x) = \lim\limits_{x \to 0^-} 1 = 1$ $\lim\limits_{x \to 0^+} f'(x) = \lim\limits_{x \to 0^+} 2x = 0$

Since the left- and right-hand limits are unequal, $f'(0)$ does not exist.

> **Note**: f **is** differentiable from both the left and the right at $x = 0$ and yet $f'(0)$ does not exist.

$x = 2$: $\lim\limits_{x \to 2^-} f'(x) = \lim\limits_{x \to 2^-} 2x = 4$ $\lim\limits_{x \to 2^+} f'(x) = \lim\limits_{x \to 2^+} 4 = 4$.

Therefore, $f'(2) = 4$ and so f is differentiable for $x \ne 0$.

> **Note continued** : If a function is discontinuous at a value of x, it can be continuous from the left or the right or neither, but not both. As this example shows, a continuous function may not be differentiable at a value of x yet still be differentiable from the left **and** the right.

Example 2) Discuss the differentiability of the function $g(x) = |x^3|$.

Solution The only possible problem here is at $x = 0$.

Writing g explicity as a branch function,

we have $g(x) = \begin{cases} -x^3, & \text{if } x < 0 \\ x^3, & \text{if } x \ge 0 \end{cases}$

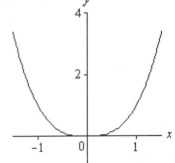

$\lim\limits_{x \to 0^-} g'(x) = \lim\limits_{x \to 0^-} (-3x^2) = 0$ and $\lim\limits_{x \to 0^+} g(x) = \lim\limits_{x \to 0^+} 3x^2 = 0$

so $g''(0) = 0$ and g is differentiable for $x \in \mathbb{R}$.

193

Two for you.

State the intervals of differentiability:

1) $f(x) = \begin{cases} \sin x - \pi, & \text{if } x < \pi \\ \cos x - x + 1, & \text{if } x \geq \pi \end{cases}$

2) $g(x) = |x + 3|$

Answers 1) $(-\infty, \infty)$ 2) $(-\infty, -3]$, $[-3, \infty)$

Critical Numbers

A **critical number** of a function $y = f(x)$ is a number c | in the domain of f |
where (i) $f'(c) = 0$ or (ii) $f'(c)$ does not exist or (iii) $(c, f(c))$ is an end point.
We all know what 0 derivatives and end points look like. If $f(x)$ is **continuous** at c
but $f'(c)$ does not exist, then one of three things must be happening:

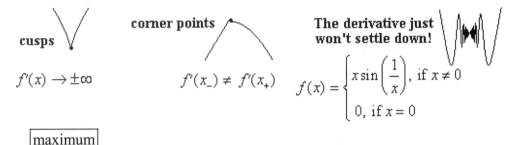

cusps $f'(x) \to \pm\infty$

corner points $f'(x_-) \neq f'(x_+)$

The derivative just won't settle down! $f(x) = \begin{cases} x\sin\left(\dfrac{1}{x}\right), & \text{if } x \neq 0 \\ 0, & \text{if } x = 0 \end{cases}$

A | maximum or minimum | point of a continuous function f **must occur** at a critical number of f!

| **The reverse is FALSE! Lots of critical points are neither maxima nor minima!** |

Example 1) Find all critical numbers of the function $f(x) = 3x^4 + 2x^3$, $-2 \leq x \leq 2$
and classify the corresponding critical points.

Solution $f'(x) = 12x^3 + 6x^2 = 12x^2\left(x + \dfrac{1}{2}\right)$

Both f and f' have domain $[-2, 2]$. The critical numbers are -2, $-\dfrac{1}{2}$, 0, and 2.

$f'(x)$

-2 $-$ -1/2 $+$ 0 $+$ 2

$(-2, 32)$ is an end point maximum;

$(-1/2, -1/16)$ is a minimum where $f' = 0$;

$(0, 0)$ is neither a max nor a min. In fact, it is a point of inflection;

$(2, 64)$ is an end point maximum.

Example 2) Find all critical numbers of the function $f(x) = 5x^{2/3} - x^{5/3}$.

Solution $f'(x) = \dfrac{10}{3}x^{-1/3} - \dfrac{5}{3}x^{2/3} = -\dfrac{5}{3}\left(\dfrac{x-2}{x^{1/3}}\right)$

The critical numbers are 0 and 2. Note that $0 \in \text{domain}(f)$ but not $\text{domain}(f')$.

Two for you.

Find the critical numbers for each of the following functions:

1) $f(x) = \dfrac{x^2}{x^2 - 4}$

2) $g(x) = (x+1)^{1/3}(x-1)^{2/3}$ $\left(\text{Hint: } g'(x) = \dfrac{x+1/3}{(x+1)^{2/3}(x-1)^{1/3}} \right)$

Answers 1) $x = 0$ 2) $x = -\dfrac{1}{3}, \ x = -1, \ x = 1$

Max and Min Points from the First Derivative

There are **four** ways a **continuous** function can have a maximum or minimum point:
1) $f'(x) = 0$ 2) $f'(x) \to \pm\infty$ 3) $f'(x_-) \neq f'(x_+)$ 4) an end point
       (a cusp)   (a corner point)

minimum points

$y' > 0$ (end point)	$y' < 0 \quad y' > 0$	$y' < 0 \bigvee y' > 0$	$y' < 0 \quad y' > 0$ $y' < 0$
end point	$f'(x) = 0$	$f'(x) \to \pm\infty$ cusp	$f'(x_-) \neq f'(x_+)$ corner	end point
$y' < 0$	$y' > 0 \quad y' < 0$	$y' > 0 \bigwedge y' < 0$	$y' > 0 \quad y' < 0$	$y' > 0$

maximum points

What all minimums have in common: the function decreases $\searrow$ and then increases $\nearrow$.

What all maximums have in common: the function increases $\nearrow$ and then decreases $\searrow$.

(For end points, "half" of each statement applies!)

Example 1) Given $f'(x) = \dfrac{(x-2)^5 (x+2)^3}{(x-1)^{1/3}}$, $-3 \leq x \leq 3$, identify the values of x where $f(x)$ has maximum and minimum points. Classify these extremes as one of the 4 types. (You may assume that $f(x)$ is defined for $x \in [-3,3]$, including $x = 1$.)

Solution Analyze the sign of $f'(x)$ on $[-3,3]$. The significant values are $x = -3, -2, 1, 2,$ and 3.

$f'(x)$
$\qquad$ (−)(−)(−) $\qquad$ (+)(−)(−) $\qquad$ (+)(+)(−) $\quad$ (+)(+)(+)

$\qquad -3 \quad\underset{\text{dec} \searrow}{-}\quad -2 \quad\underset{\text{inc} \nearrow}{+}\quad 1 \quad\underset{\text{dec} \searrow}{-}\quad 2 \quad\underset{\text{inc} \nearrow}{+}\quad 3$

$x = -3$: end point, $(-3, f(-3))$ is a maximum point.

$x = -2$: $f'(-2) = 0$, $(-2, f(-2))$ is a minimum point.

$x = 1$: $f'(1) \to \pm\infty$, cusp, $(1, f(1))$ is a maximum point.

$x = 2$: $f'(2) = 0$, $(2, f(2))$ is a minimum point.

$x = 3$: end point, $(3, f(3))$ is a maximum point.

Two for you.

For the following, identify the values of x where the function has maxima or minima and classify each extreme:

1) $f'(x) = -\dfrac{x-2}{x^{1/3}}$, where $x \geq -1$ (Hint: be careful with that extra "−"!)

2) $g'(x) = \begin{cases} -x, & \text{if } x < 0 \\ x^2, & \text{if } x \geq 0 \end{cases}$

Answers 1) $x = -1$: end point, maximum; $x = 0$, cusp, minimum; $x = 2$, $f'(x) = 0$, maximum
2) $x = 0$, corner point.

Graphing y vs y' vs y''
(Increasing/Decreasing and Concavity)

Here is a function that illustrates:

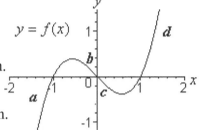

$y' > 0$ and $y'' > 0$: y is increasing and concave up.

$y' > 0$ and $y'' < 0$: y is increasing and concave down.

$y' < 0$ and $y'' > 0$: y is decreasing and concave up.

$y' < 0$ and $y'' < 0$: y is decreasing and concave down.

Example 1) Insert the letters *a, b, c,* and *d* with the correct choice of y' and y'' in the above graph.

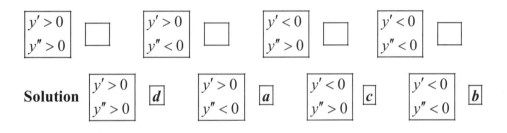

Example 2)(a) By estimating the slopes of the tangents to $y = f(x)$, sketch the graph of $y' = f'(x)$.

(b) By estimating the slopes of the tangents to $y' = f'(x)$, sketch the graph of $y'' = f''(x)$.

Solution m = slope

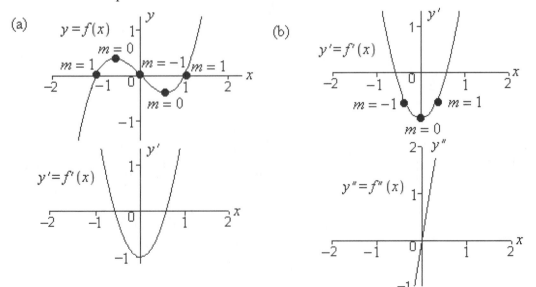

199

Two for you.

Match the shapes with the appropriate pair of derivatives as in Example 1.

1)

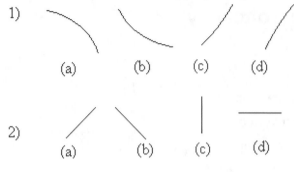

       (a)   (b)   (c)   (d)

2)

       (a)   (b)   (c)   (d)

Answers 1)(a) $\begin{array}{c} y' < 0 \\ y'' < 0 \end{array}$ (b) $\begin{array}{c} y' < 0 \\ y'' > 0 \end{array}$ (c) $\begin{array}{c} y' > 0 \\ y'' > 0 \end{array}$ (d) $\begin{array}{c} y' > 0 \\ y'' < 0 \end{array}$

2)(a) $\begin{array}{c} y' > 0 \\ y'' = 0 \end{array}$ (b) $\begin{array}{c} y' < 0 \\ y'' = 0 \end{array}$ (c) $\begin{array}{c} y', \ y'' \text{ both} \\ \text{undefined} \end{array}$ (d) $y' = y'' = 0$

Graph Sketching With Calculus

We know how to find intercepts, intervals of increasing and decreasing, intervals of concave up and concave down, extreme points, and points of inflection. **PLEASE REVIEW THE PREVIOUS THREE SECTIONS AND THEN** let's put it all together to accurately graph a function.

Example 1) The function $y = 3x^4 + 2x^3 = 3x^3(x + 2/3)$ has first and second derivatives $y' = 12x^2(x + 1/2)$ and $y'' = 36x(x + 1/3)$. Using intercepts, intervals of increasing and decreasing, intervals of concave up and concave down, extreme points, and points of inflection, create a beautiful graph!*

*When setting up your number line analysis charts, remember that $(x - a)^n$ changes sign at $x = a$ only if n is **odd**!

Solution x intercepts: $y = 0 \Rightarrow x = 0, \ x = -2/3$; y intercept: $x = 0 \Rightarrow y = 0$

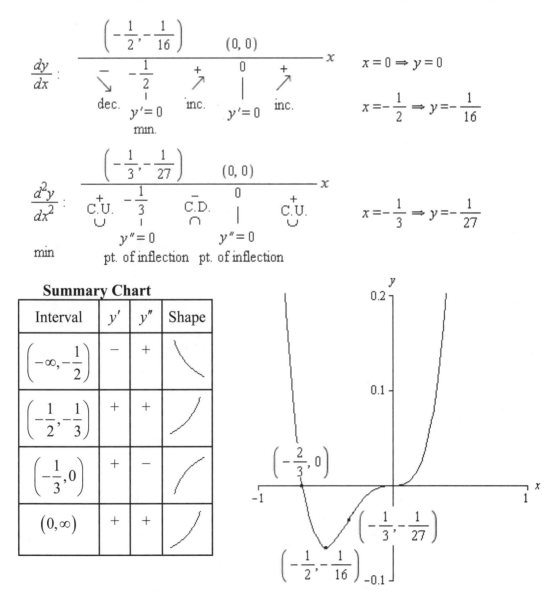

$$x = 0 \Rightarrow y = 0$$

$$x = -\frac{1}{2} \Rightarrow y = -\frac{1}{16}$$

$$x = -\frac{1}{3} \Rightarrow y = -\frac{1}{27}$$

Summary Chart

Interval	y'	y''	Shape
$\left(-\infty, -\dfrac{1}{2}\right)$	$-$	$+$	
$\left(-\dfrac{1}{2}, -\dfrac{1}{3}\right)$	$+$	$+$	
$\left(-\dfrac{1}{3}, 0\right)$	$+$	$-$	
$(0, \infty)$	$+$	$+$	

201

Two for you.

1) The function $y = x^3 - 9x$ satisfies $y' = 3x^2 - 9 = 3(x - \sqrt{3})(x + \sqrt{3})$ and $y'' = 6x$. Using intercepts, intervals of increasing and decreasing, intervals of concave up and concave down, extreme points, and points of inflection, create a beautiful graph!

2) The function $y = \dfrac{x-1}{x^2}$ satisfies $y' = \dfrac{-(x-2)}{x^3}$ and $y'' = \dfrac{2(x-3)}{x^4}$. Using intercepts, intervals of increasing and decreasing, intervals of concave up and concave down, extreme points, and points of inflection, create a beautiful graph! **Oh, and look for horizontal and vertical asymptotes too!**

Answers

1)   2)

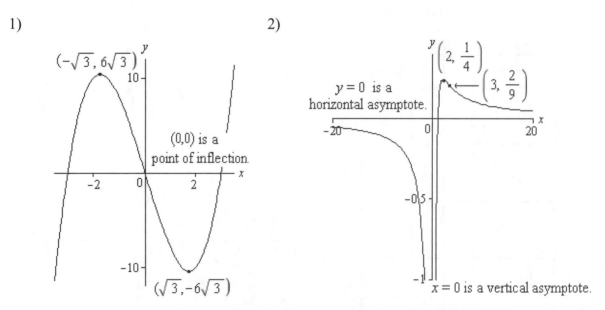

Graph Sketching With Calculus: Vertical Tangent!

FIRST, PLEASE REVIEW THE PREVIOUS FOUR SECTIONS. Let's do a graph sketching example where a **vertical tangent** makes an appearance.

Example 1) The function $y = 5x^{\frac{2}{3}} - x^{\frac{5}{3}} = -x^{\frac{2}{3}}(x-5)$ has first and second

derivatives $y' = -\dfrac{5}{3}\left(\dfrac{x-2}{x^{\frac{1}{3}}}\right)$ and $y'' = -\dfrac{10}{9}\left(\dfrac{x+1}{x^{\frac{4}{3}}}\right)$. Using intercepts, intervals of

increasing and decreasing, intervals of concave up and concave down, extreme points, and points of inflection, create a beautiful graph!*

*We are dealing with **third roots** here. When setting up your number line analysis charts,

remember that $(x-a)^{\frac{n}{3}}$ **changes sign at** $x = a$ **only if** n **is odd!**

Solution x intercepts: $y = 0 \Rightarrow x = 0,\ x = 5;$ $\quad y$ intercept: $x = 0 \Rightarrow y = 0$

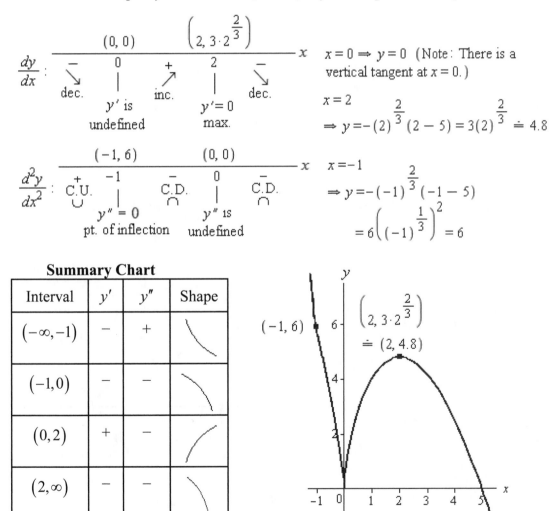

$x = 0 \Rightarrow y = 0$ (Note: There is a vertical tangent at $x = 0$.)

$x = 2$
$\Rightarrow y = -(2)^{\frac{2}{3}}(2-5) = 3(2)^{\frac{2}{3}} \doteq 4.8$

$x = -1$
$\Rightarrow y = -(-1)^{\frac{2}{3}}(-1-5)$
$= 6\left((-1)^{\frac{1}{3}}\right)^2 = 6$

Summary Chart

Interval	y'	y''	Shape
$(-\infty,-1)$	$-$	$+$	
$(-1,0)$	$-$	$-$	
$(0,2)$	$+$	$-$	
$(2,\infty)$	$-$	$-$	

203

Two for you.

1) The function $y = x^{\frac{4}{3}} + 4x^{\frac{1}{3}}$ satisfies $y' = \frac{4}{3}\left(\dfrac{x+1}{x^{\frac{2}{3}}}\right)$ and $y'' = \frac{4}{9}\left(\dfrac{x-2}{x^{\frac{5}{3}}}\right)$. Using

intercepts, intervals of increasing and decreasing, intervals of concave up and concave down, extreme points, and points of inflection, create a beautiful graph!

2) The function $y = (x+1)^{\frac{1}{3}}(x-1)^{\frac{2}{3}}$ satisfies

$$y' = \frac{x+\dfrac{1}{3}}{(x+1)^{\frac{2}{3}}(x-1)^{\frac{1}{3}}} \quad \text{and} \quad y'' = \frac{-8}{9(x+1)^{\frac{5}{3}}(x-1)^{\frac{4}{3}}}.$$ Using intercepts, intervals of increasing

and decreasing, intervals of concave up and concave down, extreme points, and points of inflection, create a beautiful graph!

Answers

1)   2)

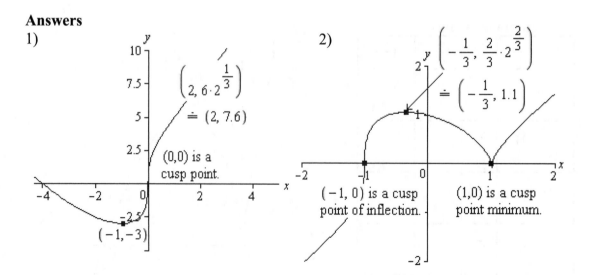

Estimating Using the Differential

Let $y = f(x)$. $\dfrac{dy}{dx} = f'(x)$ gives the slope of the tangent at the point $(x, f(x))$.

If we treat $dx\,(\neq 0)$ as the run and dy as the rise so that $\dfrac{dy}{dx} = f'(x) =$ slope of the

tangent, then $\boxed{dy \overset{\substack{\text{Cross multiply} \\ \text{by } dx!}}{=} f'(x)\,dx;}$ in words, **the rise = slope times the run.**

$(x + \Delta x, f(x + \Delta x))$

$\Delta y - dy$

$(x, f(x))$ $dx = \Delta x$ dy

slope $= f'(x)$

$\Delta y = f(x + \Delta x) - f(x)$

The key: when dx is small, dy **is very nearly equal** Δy ($\leftarrow$ **Look at the picture!**), so...

$\boxed{\text{...the new } y = f(x + \Delta x) = \text{old } y + \Delta y \overset{\substack{\text{when } dx \text{ is small!}}}{\doteq} \text{old } y + dy = f(x) + f'(x)\,dx}$

Example 1) Estimate $\sqrt{4.02}$ using the differential.

Solution We need to choose an appropriate function $f(x)$, a value of x close to 4.02 at which we can **easily** evaluate the function and a **small** dx value.

Let $f(x) = \sqrt{x}$, $x = 4$, and $dx = 0.02$. Then $\dfrac{dy}{dx} = f'(x) = \dfrac{1}{2}x^{-1/2} = \dfrac{1}{2\sqrt{x}}$.

$\therefore\ dy = f'(x)\,dx = \dfrac{dx}{2\sqrt{x}}$. In this example, $dy \overset{\substack{x=4 \\ dx=0.02}}{=} \dfrac{0.02}{2\sqrt{4}} = \dfrac{1}{200} = 0.005$

$\therefore\ \sqrt{4.02} \overset{\text{exactly}}{=} \sqrt{4} + \Delta y \doteq \sqrt{4} + dy = 2.005$.

Compare $\sqrt{4.02} \overset{\text{calculator}}{\doteq} 2.00499376558$. Pretty good!

Two for you.

1) Estimate $\sqrt{3.98}$ using the differential.

(Hint: this is just like the example above but use $dx = -0.02$.)

2) Give the best choice for $f(x)$, x, and dx in order to estimate $\dfrac{1}{26^{1/3}}$ using the differential.

Answers 1) 1.995   2) $f(x) = \dfrac{1}{x^{1/3}}$, $x = 27$, $dx = -1$

Rolle's Theorem

Suppose $y = f(x)$ is

(i) continuous on $[a, b]$

(ii) differentiable on (a, b) and

(iii) $f(a) = f(b)$.

Then there is **at least one** value

$c \in (a, b)$ such that $f'(c) = 0$.

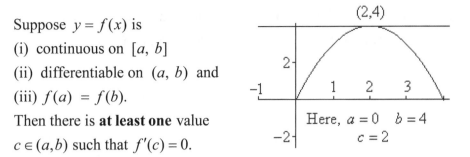

Here, $a = 0$ $b = 4$

$c = 2$

So, basically, Rolle's says that if a continuous function goes, for example, up and then turns around and comes back down to its starting value, then it must have a maximum, say at $x = c$. Since the function is differentiable, this max can't be a corner point nor a cusp. Since it certainly isn't an end point, the only other choice is $f'(c) = 0$.

Example 1) Verify Rolle's Theorem with $f(x) = x^2 - 3$, $a = -1$, and $b = 1$.

Solution f is certainly differentiable and continuous on $(-1, 1)$ and $[-1, 1]$, respectively. Also, $f(-1) = f(1) = -2$. Rolle's Theorem guarantees $c \in (-1, 1)$ satisfying $f'(c) = 0$. Since $f'(x) = 2x$, solving $2c = 0$ gives $c = 0 \in (-1, 1)$.

Example 2) Sketch the graph of a function showing

(a) how the conclusion of Rolle's Theorem **can fail** if

   (i) f is not continuous at a

   (ii) f is not differentiable for some $x \in (a, b)$ and

(b) how Rolle's Theorem **will succeed** even if f is not differentiable at $x = a$.

(This illustrates that f doesn't have to be differentiable at $x = a$ for Rolle's Theorem!)

Solution

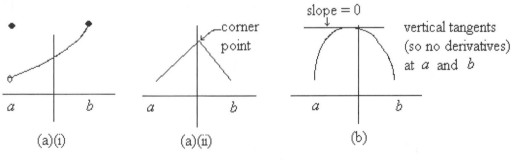

no zero slope   no zero slope   There is—**as there must be**—a zero slope!

Two for you.

1) Verify Rolle's Theorem for the function $f(x) = x^3 - x + 3$, with $a = 0$ and $b = 1$.

2) Sketch a function that illustrates how the conclusion of Rolle's Theorem **can fail**, that is, there will be no 0 derivative, if f is not continuous for some $x \in (a, b)$.

Answers 1) $f'\left(\dfrac{1}{\sqrt{3}}\right) = 0$ and $\dfrac{1}{\sqrt{3}} \in (0,1)$, as required.

2)

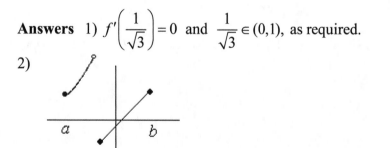

The Mean Value Theorem

Suppose $y = f(x)$ is
(i) continuous on $[a,b]$ and
(ii) differentiable on (a,b).
Then there is **at least one**
$c \in (a,b)$ such that
$$f'(c) = \frac{f(b) - f(a)}{b - a}.$$

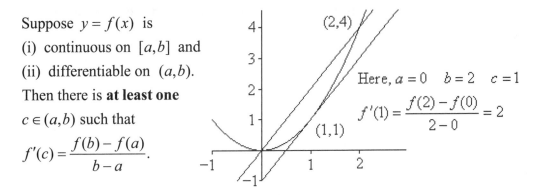

Here, $a = 0 \quad b = 2 \quad c = 1$

$$f'(1) = \frac{f(2) - f(0)}{2 - 0} = 2$$

Note : when $f(a) = f(b)$, the MVT becomes Rolle's Theorem.

Example 1) Verify The Mean Value Theorem with $f(x) = x^2 - 1$, $a = -1$, and $b = 2$.

Solution Since f is a polynomial, it is differentiable and continuous on $(-1, 2)$ and $[-1, 2]$, respectively. According to The Mean Value Theorem, we should be able to find $c \in (-1, 2)$ satisfying $f'(c) = \dfrac{f(2) - f(-1)}{2 - (-1)} = \dfrac{3 - 0}{3} = 1$.

Since $f'(x) = 2x$, solving $2c = 1$, we find $c = \dfrac{1}{2} \in (-1, 2)$.

Example 2) Sketch the graph of a function showing

(a) how the conclusion of The Mean Value Theorem **can fail** if

   (i) f is not continuous at a

   (ii) f is not differentiable for some $x \in (a,b)$ and

(b) how, if the hypothesis is satisfied, The Mean Value Theorem **will succeed** even if f is not differentiable at $x = a$. (This shows that $f'(a)$ is not necessary for The Mean Value Theorem to work!)

Solution

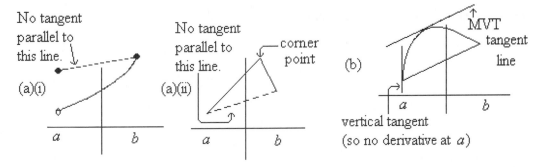

209

Two for you.

1) Verify The Mean Value Theorem with $f(x) = x^3 + 3$, $a = -1$, and $b = 2$.

2) Sketch a function **not continuous** at some $x \in (a,b)$ for which the conclusion of the MVT **fails**.

Answers 1) $f'(1) = 3$ and $1 \in (-1,2)$, as required.   2)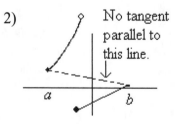

No tangent parallel to this line.

Derivatives: The Product Rule

Think of *First* and *Second*:

$$\frac{d}{dx}(FS) = FS' + SF' \quad \textbf{Note: the order is NOT important!}$$

Example 1) Find $\dfrac{dy}{dx}$ if $y = (x^3 + x)(\sin x - 4)$.

Solution $\dfrac{dy}{dx} = \overset{\boxed{F}}{(x^3 + x)}\,\overset{\boxed{S'}}{\cos x} + \overset{\boxed{S}}{(\sin x - 4)}\,\overset{\boxed{F'}}{(3x^2 + 1)}$

$$= x^3 \cos x + x \cos x + 3x^2 \sin x - 12x^2 + \sin x - 4$$

Here is the product rule combined with the **chain rule** (reviewed in the next section!)

Example 2) Find $\dfrac{dy}{dx}$ if $y = x\left(e^x + \ln x\right)^5$.

Solution $\dfrac{dy}{dx} = x\left(5\left(e^x + \ln x\right)^4\left(e^x + \dfrac{1}{x}\right)\right) + \left(e^x + \ln x\right)^5 (1)$

$$= \left(e^x + \ln x\right)^4\left(5x\left(e^x + \dfrac{1}{x}\right) + \left(e^x + \ln x\right)\right)$$

$$= \left(e^x + \ln x\right)^4\left(5xe^x + 5 + e^x + \ln x\right)$$

Example 3) Find the formula for the derivative of the product of three functions,
that is, find $\dfrac{dy}{dx}$ when $y = f(x)g(x)h(x)$.

Solution Group two of the functions together and use the basic product rule.
Writing $y = \left(f(x)g(x)\right)h(x)$,

$$\frac{dy}{dx} = \left(f(x)g(x)\right)h'(x) + h(x)\left(f(x)g(x)\right)'$$

$$= \left(f(x)g(x)\right)h'(x) + h(x)\left(f(x)g'(x) + g(x)f'(x)\right)$$

$$= f(x)g(x)h'(x) + f(x)h(x)g'(x) + g(x)h(x)f'(x)$$

In short: $\boxed{(f\,g\,h)' = f'\,g\,h + f\,g'\,h + f\,g\,h'}$

Two for you.

1) Find $\dfrac{dy}{dx}$ for each of the following:

(a) $y = x^4(x^5 + 10)^6$ (b) $y = (5x + 4)(\sin x)(\ln x)$

2) Write the formula for $\dfrac{dy}{dx}$ if $y = f_1 f_2 f_3 f_4$.

Answers 1)(a) $2x^3(x^5 + 10)^5(17x^5 + 20)$

(b) $\dfrac{(5x + 4)(\sin x)}{x} + (5x + 4)(\ln x)(\cos x) + 5(\sin x)(\ln x)$

2) $f_1' f_2 f_3 f_4 + f_1 f_2' f_3 f_4 + f_1 f_2 f_3' f_4 + f_1 f_2 f_3 f_4'$

Derivatives: The Chain Rule

Example 1) Find $\dfrac{dy}{dx}$ if $y = (\sin x + x)^3$.

Solution Think of this as $y = (inside)^3$.

The chain rule tells us to take the derivative of the **outside** and multiply by the derivative of the **inside**. Keep taking the derivative until you "get to the derivative with respect to x." So…

$$\frac{dy}{dx} = \frac{d\left(inside^3\right)}{d\left(inside\right)} \frac{d(inside)}{dx} = 3(inside)^2 \frac{d(inside)}{dx} = 3(\sin x + x)^2 (\cos x + 1)$$

Now, repeating myself in my (slowly approaching **late**) middle age, we keep going and going and going until we finally get down to x. If you can do this next example, you are a chain rule pro!

Example 2) Find $\dfrac{dy}{dx}$ if $y = \sqrt{x + \sqrt{x + \sqrt{x}}}$. Here we are going to have go inside **once! twice!! three!!! times!!!!**

Solution I find it much easier to handle an example like this if I rewrite it as

$$y = \sqrt{x + \sqrt{x + \sqrt{x}}} = \left(x + \left(x + x^{1/2}\right)^{1/2}\right)^{1/2}.$$

We are going to take the derivative of the outside and then multiply by the derivative of the **FIRST** inside and then go inside again and, for the final $x^{1/2}$, a third time!

$$\frac{dy}{dx} = \frac{1}{2}\left(\underbrace{x + \left(x + x^{1/2}\right)^{1/2}}_{\text{Now take this inside derivative}}\right)^{-1/2}\left(1 + \frac{1}{2}\left(\underbrace{x + x^{1/2}}_{\text{Now take this inside derivative!}}\right)^{-1/2}\left(\underbrace{1 + \frac{1}{2}x^{-1/2}}_{\text{We are down to } x,\,\textbf{finally!}}\right)\right)$$

$$= \frac{1}{2\sqrt{x + \sqrt{x + \sqrt{x}}}}\left(1 + \frac{1}{2\sqrt{x + \sqrt{x}}}\left(1 + \frac{1}{2\sqrt{x}}\right)\right)$$

Two for you.

Find $\dfrac{dy}{dx}$ for each of the following:

1) $y = \sin(x^3 + 3x^2 + 1)$

2) $y = \dfrac{1}{(2x-1)^{3/2}}$ $\left(\text{Hint: first rewrite this as } y = (2x-1)^{-3/2}.\right)$

Answers 1) $(3x^2 + 6x)\cos(x^3 + 3x^2 + 1)$ 2) $-3(2x-1)^{-5/2}$

optional back of book answer $= \dfrac{-3}{(2x-1)^{5/2}}$

Derivatives: The Quotient Rule

Think of **Top** (numerator) and **Bottom** (denominator):

$$\boxed{\frac{d}{dx}\left(\frac{T}{B}\right) = \frac{BT' - TB'}{B^2}}$$

Note the "−". **Note** the order. **Note**, no $B' = \dfrac{dB}{dx}$ in the bottom!

Example 1) Find $\dfrac{dy}{dx}$ if $y = \dfrac{4x^2}{x^2 - \sin x} = 4\left(\dfrac{x^2}{x^2 - \sin x}\right)$.

Solution $\dfrac{dy}{dx} \overset{\boxed{\text{Keep the constant 4 outside!}}}{=} 4\left(\dfrac{\overset{\boxed{B}}{(x^2 - \sin x)}\overset{\boxed{T'}}{(2x)} - \overset{\boxed{T}}{x^2}\overset{\boxed{B'}}{(2x - \cos x)}}{\underset{\boxed{B^2}}{(x^2 - \sin x)^2}}\right)$

$= 4\left(\dfrac{2x^3 - 2x\sin x - 2x^3 + x^2\cos x}{(x^2 - \sin x)^2}\right) = \dfrac{4(x^2\cos x - 2x\sin x)}{(x^2 - \sin x)^2}$

Here is a common use of the chain and quotient rules together:

Example 2) Find $\dfrac{dy}{dx}$ if $y = \left(\dfrac{3x + 5}{4x + 7}\right)^5$.

Solution $\dfrac{dy}{dx} = 5\left(\dfrac{3x + 5}{4x + 7}\right)^4\left(\dfrac{(4x + 7)(3) - (3x + 5)(4)}{(4x + 7)^2}\right)$

$\overset{\boxed{\substack{\text{Combine the } (4x+7) \\ \text{factors in the denominator.}}}}{=} 5\left(\dfrac{(3x + 5)^4}{(4x + 7)^6}\right)(12x + 21 - 12x - 20) = \dfrac{5(3x + 5)^4}{(4x + 7)^6}$

Alternate Solution Use the product rule with the chain rule:

$y = \left(\dfrac{3x + 5}{4x + 7}\right)^5 = (3x + 5)^5(4x + 7)^{-5}$

$\dfrac{dy}{dx} = (3x + 5)^5(-5)(4x + 7)^{-6}(4) + (4x + 7)^{-5}(5)(3x + 5)^4(3)$

$\overset{\boxed{\text{Take out the common factors.}}}{=} 5(3x + 5)^4(4x + 7)^{-6}\left(-4(3x + 5) + 3(4x + 7)\right) *$

$= 5(3x + 5)^4(4x + 7)^{-6}(-12x - 20 + 12x + 21) = \dfrac{5(3x + 5)^4}{(4x + 7)^6}$

*Note that 4 was the lower of the two exponents on $(3x + 5)$ and -6 was the lower exponent of the two exponents on $(4x + 7)$.

Two for you.

Find $\dfrac{dy}{dx}$ for each of the following: 1) $y = \dfrac{x^2 + 1}{e^x + x^2}$ 2) $y = \left(\dfrac{x^4 + 1}{x^4 - 1}\right)^2$

Answers 1) $\dfrac{2xe^x - x^2 e^x - e^x - 2x}{(e^x + x^2)^2}$ 2) $\dfrac{-16x^3(x^4 + 1)}{(x^4 - 1)^3}$

Derivatives: Implicit Differentiation

Don't panic! Implicit Differentiation is just an application of the **chain rule** in disguise.

Example 1) Let $xy + \sin y = 4$.   (a) Find $\dfrac{dy}{dx}$.   (b) Find x and $\dfrac{dy}{dx}$ when $y = \pi$.

Solution It is **impossible** to rewrite this equation with y on the left side and only terms involving x on the right side. (Try to isolate y. Futile!) Instead, to find $\dfrac{dy}{dx}$, we take the derivative with respect to x directly from the equation using the **GOLDEN RULE** of math equations:

What you do to one side you do to the other!*

Note that we need the **product rule** to deal with the xy term.

$$\frac{d(Left\ Side)}{dx} = \frac{d(Right\ Side)}{dx} \quad \therefore \quad x\frac{dy}{dx} + y(1) + \cos y \frac{dy}{dx} = 0.$$

Now factor out the $\dfrac{dy}{dx}$ terms and solve: $\dfrac{dy}{dx}(x + \cos y) = -y \Rightarrow \dfrac{dy}{dx} = \dfrac{-y}{x + \cos y}$

(b) $y = \pi \Rightarrow \pi x + 0 = 4 \Rightarrow x = \dfrac{4}{\pi}.$

At the point $\left(\dfrac{4}{\pi}, \pi\right)$, $\dfrac{dy}{dx} = \dfrac{-\pi}{\dfrac{4}{\pi} + \cos(\pi)} = \dfrac{-\pi}{\dfrac{4}{\pi} - 1} \overset{\boxed{\text{Multiply the top and the bottom by } \pi.}}{=} \dfrac{-\pi^2}{4 - \pi}$

Example 2) Find $\dfrac{dy}{dx}$ if $x^2 y^3 + 2x + 3y = \sin(xy) + 4$.

Solution $x^2(3y^2)\dfrac{dy}{dx} + 2xy^3 + 2 + 3\dfrac{dy}{dx} = \cos(xy)(x\dfrac{dy}{dx} + y)$

Now bring $\dfrac{dy}{dx}$ terms to the left and factor out $\dfrac{dy}{dx}$. All other terms go to, or stay on, the right side.

$$\frac{dy}{dx}\left(3x^2 y^2 + 3 - x\cos(xy)\right) = y\cos(xy) - 2 - 2xy^3$$

$$\therefore \quad \frac{dy}{dx} = \frac{y\cos(xy) - 2 - 2xy^3}{3x^2 y^2 + 3 - x\cos(xy)}$$

*Would you consider this a precise math analog of the usual **GOLDEN RULE**?

217

Two for you.

1)(a) Find $\dfrac{dy}{dx}$ if $e^{x+y} + 5x + 2y = 1$.   (b) Find $\dfrac{dy}{dx}$ at $(0,0)$.

2) Find $\dfrac{dy}{dx}$ if $y\sin x + y = x + \tan y$.

Answers 1)(a) $\dfrac{-(e^{x+y}+5)}{e^{x+y}+2}$ (b) -2 2) $\dfrac{1 - y\cos x}{\sin x + 1 - \sec^2 y}$

Derivatives: Implicit Differentiation Second Derivative

Here the key is one simple fact: $\dfrac{d}{dx}\left(\dfrac{dy}{dx}\right)=\dfrac{d^2y}{dx^2}$, that is, the derivative with respect to x of the first derivative (with respect to x) is the second derivative (with respect to x).

Also, the second derivative may seem to get mechanically scary. It is not implicit differentiation that causes this, **but GRADE 5 fractions!**

Example 1) Find $\dfrac{dy}{dx}$ and $\dfrac{d^2y}{dx^2}$ if $e^y-xy=1$.

Solution Find the first derivative implicitly.

$$e^y\frac{dy}{dx}-x\frac{dy}{dx}-y(1)=0\Rightarrow\frac{dy}{dx}(e^y-x)=y \text{ and so } \frac{dy}{dx}=\frac{y}{e^y-x}$$

Now, we use the quotient rule to find $\dfrac{d^2y}{dx^2}$.

$$\frac{d^2y}{dx^2}=\frac{(e^y-x)\dfrac{dy}{dx}-y(e^y\dfrac{dy}{dx}-1)}{(e^y-x)^2}\boxed{\begin{array}{c}\text{Factor out }\frac{dy}{dx}\text{ and}\\\text{expand the numerator.}\end{array}}=\frac{\dfrac{dy}{dx}(e^y-x-ye^y)+y}{(e^y-x)^2}$$

$$\boxed{\text{We already know }\tfrac{dy}{dx}=\tfrac{y}{e^y-x}!}=\frac{\left(\dfrac{y}{e^y-x}\right)(e^y-x-ye^y)+y}{(e^y-x)^2}$$

$$\boxed{\begin{array}{c}\text{Get a common denominator}\\\text{in the numerator.}\end{array}}=\frac{y(e^y-x-ye^y)+y(e^y-x)}{(e^y-x)}\frac{1}{(e^y-x)^2}$$

$$\boxed{\text{Expand the numerator...}}=\frac{ye^y-xy-y^2e^y+ye^y-xy}{(e^y-x)^3}\boxed{\text{...and collect like terms.}}=\frac{2ye^y-2xy-y^2e^y}{(e^y-x)^3}\quad\textbf{Whew!*}$$

Alternate Solution Differentiate $\dfrac{dy}{dx}(e^y-x)=y$ using the Product Rule.

$$\frac{dy}{dx}(e^y\frac{dy}{dx}-1)+(e^y-x)\frac{d^2y}{dx^2}=\frac{dy}{dx} \text{ and so } (e^y-x)\frac{d^2y}{dx^2}=2\frac{dy}{dx}-e^y\left(\frac{dy}{dx}\right)^2$$

$$=2\frac{y}{e^y-x}-e^y\left(\frac{y}{e^y-x}\right)^2\boxed{\text{Common Denominator!}}=\frac{2ye^y-2xy-y^2e^y}{(e^y-x)^2}$$

and so (**whew** * once more), $\dfrac{d^2y}{dx^2}=\dfrac{2ye^y-2xy-y^2e^y}{(e^y-x)^3}$

*As promised, it's just grade five fractions making this **seem** tough, although, I admit, there is a little bit of algebra mixed in!

Two for you.

Find $\dfrac{dy}{dx}$ and $\dfrac{d^2y}{dx^2}$ for each of the following: 1) $x^3 + y^3 = 1$ 2) $y^2 + 2xy = 10$

(Hint: in each question, at the **last step**, use the original equation!)

Answers 1) $\dfrac{dy}{dx} = -\dfrac{x^2}{y^2}$, $\dfrac{d^2y}{dx^2} = \dfrac{-2x}{y^5}$ 2) $\dfrac{dy}{dx} = -\dfrac{y}{x+y}$, $\dfrac{d^2y}{dx^2} = \dfrac{10}{(x+y)^3}$

Easy Integrals/Anti-Derivatives

Okay, this page is the most basic of the basic—the anti-derivative/integral formulas you learn in your first calculus semester applied with **NO TRICKS, NO TWISTS, NO COMPLICATIONS**. The diabolical stuff, and the means to deal with it, comes later!

$$\int 0\,dx = C \qquad \int 1\,dx = x + C \qquad \int m\,dx = mx + C$$

$$\int f(x) \pm g(x)\,dx = \int f(x)\,dx \pm \int g(x)\,dx \qquad \int cf(x)\,dx = c\int f(x)\,dx$$

$$\int x^n\,dx = \frac{x^{n+1}}{n+1} + C,\ n \neq -1 \qquad \int \frac{1}{x}\,dx = \int x^{-1}\,dx = \ln|x| + C$$

$$\int \sin x\,dx = -\cos x + C \qquad \int \cos x\,dx = \sin x + C$$

$$\int \tan x\,dx = -\ln|\cos x| + C \qquad \int \cot x\,dx = \ln|\sin x| + C$$

$$\int \csc x\,dx = \ln|\csc x - \cot x| + C \qquad \int \sec x\,dx = \ln|\sec x + \tan x| + C$$

$$\int e^x\,dx = e^x + C \qquad \int a^x\,dx = \frac{a^x}{\ln a} + C$$

Example 1) Evaluate the following integrals:

(a) $\int 1 + x^2 + x^{-5/3}\,dx$ (b) $\int \sin x + 2\csc x + \frac{1}{3}e^x + 10^x\,dx$

Solution

(a) $\int 1 + x^2 + x^{-5/3}\,dx$ $\boxed{\text{for } n \neq -1,\ \int x^n\,dx = \frac{x^{n+1}}{n+1} + C}$

$= x + \dfrac{x^3}{3} + \dfrac{x^{-2/3}}{-\frac{2}{3}} + C = x + \dfrac{x^3}{3} - \dfrac{3x^{-2/3}}{2} + C$

(b) $\int \sin x + 2\csc x + \frac{1}{3}e^x + 10^x\,dx = -\cos x + 2\ln|\csc x - \cot x| + \frac{1}{3}e^x + \dfrac{10^x}{\ln 10} + C$

Example 2) If $\int f(x)\,dx = 3x^2 + C$ and $\int g(x)\,dx = 2\sin x - e^x + D$,

find $\int 3f(x) - 2g(x)\,dx$.

Solution $\int 3f(x) - 2g(x)\,dx = 3\int f(x)\,dx - 2\int g(x)\,dx = 3(3x^2 + C) - 2(2\sin x - e^x + D)$

$\boxed{\text{Replace the constant } 3C-2D \text{ with the single constant } E.}$

$= 9x^2 - 4\sin x + 2e^x + 3C - 2D \qquad = \qquad 9x^2 - 4\sin x + 2e^x + E$

Two for you.

Evaluate the following integrals:

1) $\int -1 + 4x^9 - x^{-5/3} \, dx$

2) $\int \cot x - \sec x - 2^x \ln 2 \, dx$ $\left(\text{Hint: } \int 2^x \ln 2 \, dx = \ln 2 \left(\int 2^x \, dx \right) \right)$

Answers 1) $-x + \dfrac{2x^{10}}{5} + \dfrac{3x^{-2/3}}{2} + C$ 2) $\ln |\sin x| - \ln |\sec x + \tan x| - 2^x + C$

Easy Integrals that Need a Little Tweaking

Here is a variety of really easy integrals—except you have to do something first to see why they are so easy.

Example 1) Evaluate the following integrals:

(a) $\int (x^3 + 3)^2 \, dx$
(b) $\int (x^{1/2} + 1)(2x + 5) \, dx$
(c) $\int \dfrac{x^4 - 7}{x^2} \, dx$

(d) $\int \dfrac{1}{\sec x} \, dx$
(e) $\int \dfrac{1}{e^x} \, dx$

Solution (a) **EXPAND**: $\int (x^3 + 3)^2 \, dx = \int x^6 + 6x^3 + 9 \, dx = \dfrac{x^7}{7} + \dfrac{3x^4}{2} + 9x + C$

Note how unpleasant this example would be if changed to $\int (x^3 + 3)^{20} \, dx$. Note how much MORE unpleasant it would be if changed to $\int (x^3 + 3)^{2/3} \, dx$! The first you could expand, but would you want to? The second, you **can't** expand, at least not with your current math toolkit! **But test your understanding of the Chain Rule in Reverse (CRI R, coming to an MSK page soon! See page 225.):**

both $\int \boxed{x^2}(x^3 + 3)^{20} \, dx$ and $\int \boxed{x^2}(x^3 + 3)^{2/3} \, dx$ are **easy**!

$\int x^2 (x^3 + 3)^{20} \, dx \overset{\boxed{\text{Adjust by 3.}}}{=} \dfrac{1}{3}\int 3x^2 (x^3 + 3)^{20} \, dx \overset{\boxed{\text{CRIR!}}}{=} \dfrac{1}{3}\left(\dfrac{(x^3 + 3)^{21}}{21} \right) + C = \dfrac{(x^3 + 3)^{21}}{63} + C$

$\int x^2 (x^3 + 3)^{2/3} \, dx \overset{\boxed{\text{Adjust by 3.}}}{=} \dfrac{1}{3}\int 3x^2 (x^3 + 3)^{2/3} \, dx \overset{\boxed{\text{CRIR!}}}{=} \dfrac{1}{3}\left(\dfrac{(x^3 + 3)^{5/3}}{5/3} \right) + C = \dfrac{(x^3 + 3)^{5/3}}{5} + C$

(b) $\int (x^{1/2} + 1)(2x + 5) \, dx \overset{\boxed{\text{Expand!}}}{=} \int 2x^{3/2} + 5x^{1/2} + 2x + 5 \, dx = \dfrac{4}{5}x^{5/2} + \dfrac{10}{3}x^{3/2} + x^2 + 5x + C$

(c) $\int \dfrac{x^4 - 7}{x^2} \, dx \overset{\boxed{\text{Make separate fractions!}}}{=} \int x^2 - 7x^{-2} \, dx = \dfrac{x^3}{3} - \dfrac{7x^{-1}}{-1} + C = \dfrac{x^3}{3} + \dfrac{7}{x} + C$

(d) $\int \dfrac{1}{\sec x} \, dx \overset{\boxed{\text{This is just a case of the teacher being sneaky!}}}{=} \int \cos x \, dx = \sin x + C$

(e) $\int \dfrac{1}{e^x} \, dx \overset{\boxed{\text{This is just a case of the teacher being sneaky again!}}}{=} \int e^{-x} \, dx \overset{\boxed{\text{CRIR: Adjust by } -1.}}{=} - \int -e^{-x} \, dx = -e^{-x} + C$

Two for you.

Evaluate the following integrals:

1) $\int (2x^2 - 1)^3 \, dx$ 2) $\int \dfrac{e^{3x} - 2e^x + e^{-x}}{2e^x} \, dx$

Answers 1) $\dfrac{8x^7}{7} - \dfrac{12x^5}{5} + 2x^3 - x + C$ 2) $\dfrac{1}{4}e^{2x} - x - \dfrac{1}{4e^{2x}} + C$

The Chain Rule in Reverse: No Adjustments Needed!

Many students find this **very** hard but in fact it is pretty easy. **The chain rule in reverse:**

BASIC	CHAIN RULE IN REVERSE
$\int f'(x)\,dx = f(x)+C$	$\int f'(u)\dfrac{du}{dx}\,dx = f(u)+C$

It may be gross but I tell my students that when taking the derivative of $y = f(u)$...

Please read $f(u)$ as "f **AT** u"; otherwise, we go to a whole other level of gross!

...with respect to x, the chain rule "**spits out**" du/dx. So, when taking the anti-derivative or integral with respect to x, the du/dx is "**sucked**" back inside the u!

Think **"DOUBLE S"**: **Spit** for the derivative, **Suck** for the integral. This is not to say that you are allowed to spit on your derivatives, nor that integrals s...well, let's not finish that thought. Here are all the basic formulas, modified to show the CRIR.

$$\int u^n \frac{du}{dx}\,dx \overset{\boxed{n \neq -1}}{=} \frac{u^{n+1}}{n+1}+C, \qquad \int \frac{1}{u}\frac{du}{dx}\,dx = \int u^{-1}\frac{du}{dx}\,dx = \ln|u|+C$$

$$\int \sin u \frac{du}{dx}\,dx = -\cos u + C \qquad \int \cos u \frac{du}{dx}\,dx = \sin u + C \qquad \int \tan u \frac{du}{dx}\,dx = -\ln|\cos u|+C$$

$$\int \cot u \frac{du}{dx}\,dx = \ln|\sin u|+C \qquad \int e^u \frac{du}{dx}\,dx = e^u + C \qquad \int a^u \frac{du}{dx}\,dx = \frac{a^u}{\ln a}+C$$

$$\int \csc u \frac{du}{dx}\,dx = \ln|\csc u - \cot u|+C \qquad \int \sec x \frac{du}{dx}\,dx = \ln|\sec u + \tan u|+C$$

Example 1) Evaluate, using the chain rule in reverse. Identify u and $\dfrac{du}{dx}$.

(a) $\int (x^3+1)^{10}(3x^2)\,dx$ (b) $\int e^{\tan x}\sec^2 x\,dx$ (c) $\int \cos(x^{1/2})\left(\dfrac{1}{2}x^{-1/2}\right)dx$

(d) $\int \dfrac{2x}{x^2+1}\,dx$

Solution (a) $\int (x^3+1)^{10}(3x^2)\,dx \overset{\boxed{u=x^3+1,\ \frac{du}{dx}=3x^2}}{=} \dfrac{(x^3+1)^{11}}{11}+C$

(b) $\int e^{\tan x}\sec^2 x\,dx \overset{\boxed{u=\tan x,\ \frac{du}{dx}=\sec^2 x}}{=} e^{\tan x}+C$

(c) $\int \cos(x^{1/2})\left(\dfrac{1}{2}x^{-1/2}\right)dx \overset{\boxed{u=x^{1/2},\ \frac{du}{dx}=\frac{1}{2}x^{-1/2}}}{=} \sin(x^{1/2})+C$

(d) $\int \dfrac{2x}{x^2+1}\,dx \overset{\boxed{u=x^2+1,\ \frac{du}{dx}=2x}}{=} \ln(x^2+1)+C$ (Note: $x^2+1>0$, so we don't need "$|\ |$".)

Two for you.

Evaluate using the **Chain Rule In Reverse**. For each, identify u and $\dfrac{du}{dx}$.

1) $\displaystyle\int (x^5 + 2x^2 + 1)^{2/3}(5x^4 + 4x)\, dx$ 2) $\displaystyle\int \sin(\sin x)(\cos x)\, dx$

Answers 1) $\dfrac{3}{5}(x^5 + 2x^2 + 1)^{5/3} + C$; $u = x^5 + 2x^2 + 1$, $\dfrac{du}{dx} = 5x^4 + 4x$

2) $-\cos(\sin x) + C$; $u = \sin x$, $\dfrac{du}{dx} = \cos x$

The Chain Rule in Reverse: Adjustments Needed BUT Don't Use Substitution!

Now let's use the **the chain rule in reverse** where we adjust by a "**multiplicative constant**". You can always pull a multiplicative constant outside the integral and you can adjust an integral by a multiplicative constant **providing you compensate**. The CRIR "sucks" in the du/dx. The key here is that you recognize **in advance** that you have both the u and the du/dx—at least up to the constant—in the integral. You know before you start that the CRIR will solve the problem.

Example 1) Evaluate, using the chain rule in reverse. In each, identify u and $\dfrac{du}{dx}$.

(a) $\displaystyle\int x^2 (x^3 + 1)^{10}\, dx$ (b) $\displaystyle\int \frac{\cos\sqrt{x}}{\sqrt{x}}\, dx$ (c) $\displaystyle\int 3e^{\tan x} \sec^2 x\, dx$ (d) $\displaystyle\int \frac{x}{x^2 + 1}\, dx$

Solution

(a) $\displaystyle\int x^2 (x^3 + 1)^{10}\, dx$ Here, $u = x^3 + 1$ and $\dfrac{du}{dx} = 3x^2$. We need to multiply by 3. To compensate, we divide by 3 **outside** the integral sign.

YOU CAN ALWAYS ADJUST BY A MULTIPLICATIVE CONSTANT.

$$\int x^2 (x^3 + 1)^{10}\, dx = \frac{1}{3}\int 3x^2 (x^3 + 1)^{10}\, dx = \frac{1}{3}\frac{(x^3 + 1)^{11}}{11} + C = \frac{1}{33}(x^3 + 1)^{11} + C$$

> Question: Where has the $3x^2$ gone? Answer: **SUCKED INSIDE by the chain rule!**

(b) $\displaystyle\int \frac{\cos\sqrt{x}}{\sqrt{x}}\, dx$ Here, $u = \sqrt{x} = x^{1/2}$ and $\dfrac{du}{dx} = \dfrac{1}{2}x^{-1/2} = \dfrac{1}{2\sqrt{x}}$. We need to divide by 2. To compensate, we multiply by 2 outside the integral sign.

$$\int \frac{\cos\sqrt{x}}{\sqrt{x}}\, dx = 2\int \frac{1}{2}x^{-1/2}\cos\left(x^{1/2}\right)dx = 2\sin\left(x^{1/2}\right) + C = 2\sin\sqrt{x} + C$$

(c) $\displaystyle\int 3e^{\tan x}\sec^2 x\, dx$ Here, $u = \tan x$ and $\dfrac{du}{dx} = \sec^2 x$, so no compensation needed.

But move the constant 3 outside: $\displaystyle\int 3e^{\tan x}\sec^2 x\, dx = 3\int e^{\tan x}\sec^2 x\, dx = 3e^{\tan x} + C$

(d) $\displaystyle\int \frac{x}{x^2 + 1}\, dx$ Here, $u = x^2 + 1$ and $\dfrac{du}{dx} = 2x$. Compensate with 2.

$$\int \frac{x}{x^2 + 1}\, dx = \frac{1}{2}\int \frac{2x}{x^2 + 1}\, dx \overset{\boxed{x^2 + 1 > 0 \text{ so we don't need absolute value.}}}{=} \frac{1}{2}\ln(x^2 + 1) + C$$

Two for you.

Evaluate: 1) $\int (x^4 + 1)\sin(x^5 + 5x)\,dx$ 2) $\int e^{\sec(2x+1)}\sec(2x+1)\tan(2x+1)\,dx$

Answers 1) $-\dfrac{1}{5}\cos(x^5 + 5x) + C$ 2) $\dfrac{1}{2}e^{\sec(2x+1)} + C$

The Chain Rule in Reverse:
Adjustments Needed and Using Substitution

Let's get something straight: I (**that's right, me, the teacher/author talking!**) don't like using substitution for these problems. Why? Because EVERY TIME you adjust the constant to make things work just right as we did on the preceding topic, you consolidate further your understanding of the CRIR. It is so easy! Yet students find it so hard! The real key is recognizing that the questions are **"cooked"!** The du/dx term, up to a constant, **must** be present for most problems or the integral is, in **many many many** examples, too hard or even undo-able. Even so, this page is almost exactly the same as the preceding one, except here we will (**grumble grumble**) use substitution.

Example 1) Evaluate, using the chain rule in reverse. In each, identify u and du.

(a) $\int x^2(x^3+1)^{10}\,dx$ (b) $\int \dfrac{\cos(\sqrt{x})}{\sqrt{x}}\,dx$ (c) $\int 3e^{\tan(x)}\sec^2(x)\,dx$ (d) $\int \dfrac{x}{x^2+1}\,dx$

Solution

(a) $\int x^2(x^3+1)^{10}\,dx$ Here, $u = x^3+1$ and $\dfrac{du}{dx} = 3x^2$.

$\therefore\ du = 3x^2 dx$. We need to replace $x^2 dx$. Since $x^2 dx = \dfrac{1}{3}du$,

we have $\int x^2(x^3+1)^{10}\,dx$ $\overset{\boxed{\text{Pull } \frac{1}{3} \text{ outside the integral.}}}{=} \dfrac{1}{3}\int u^{10}\,du = \dfrac{1}{3}\dfrac{u^{11}}{11} + C \overset{\boxed{u=x^3+1}}{=} \dfrac{1}{33}(x^3+1)^{11} + C$

(b) $\int \dfrac{\cos(\sqrt{x})}{\sqrt{x}}\,dx$ Here, $u = \sqrt{x} = x^{1/2}$ and $\dfrac{du}{dx} = \dfrac{1}{2}x^{-1/2} = \dfrac{1}{2\sqrt{x}}$ $\therefore\ du = \dfrac{dx}{2\sqrt{x}}$

So $2\,du = \dfrac{dx}{\sqrt{x}}$ and $\int \dfrac{\cos(\sqrt{x})}{\sqrt{x}}\,dx = 2\int \cos(u)\,du = 2\sin(u) + C = 2\sin(\sqrt{x}) + C$

(c) $\int 3e^{\tan(x)}\sec^2(x)\,dx$ Here, $u = \tan(x)$ and $\overset{\boxed{\text{Let's go right to the differential this time!}}}{du = \sec^2(x)\,dx}$

and $\int 3e^{\tan(x)}\sec^2(x)\,dx = 3\int e^u\,du = 3e^u + C = 3e^{\tan(x)} + C$

(d) $\int \dfrac{x}{x^2+1}\,dx$ Here, $u = x^2+1$ and $du = 2x\,dx$ $\therefore\ \dfrac{du}{2} = x\,dx$ and

$\int \dfrac{x}{x^2+1}\,dx = \dfrac{1}{2}\int \dfrac{du}{u} = \dfrac{1}{2}\ln|u| + C \overset{\boxed{x^2+1>0 \text{ so we don't need absolute value.}}}{=} \dfrac{1}{2}\ln(x^2+1) + C$

Three for you.

Evaluate:

1) $\displaystyle\int \frac{x^3 - \csc^2 x}{x^4 + 4\cot x}\,dx$

2) $\displaystyle\int e^{e^x + x}\,dx$ (Hint: $e^{e^x + x} = e^{e^x}e^x$)

3) $\displaystyle\int \frac{x}{(5x^2 + 1)^4}\,dx$

Answers

1) $\displaystyle\frac{1}{4}\ln|x^4 + 4\cot x| + C$

2) $e^{e^x} + C$

3) $\displaystyle -\frac{1}{30(5x^2 + 1)^3} + C$

Substitution when the CRIR Doesn't Apply

Here is a question just waiting for the Chain Rule in Reverse: $\int x^3 (x^4+1)^{1/2}\, dx$.

A simple adjustment of the multiplicative constant gives a final answer in two steps. Substitution not needed!

$$\int x^3 (x^4+1)^{1/2}\, dx = \frac{1}{4}\int 4x^3 (x^4+1)^{1/2}\, dx = \frac{1}{6}(x^4+1)^{3/2} + C$$

Now here is a question where the CRIR just doesn't apply: $\int x^2 (x+3)^{1/2}\, dx$.

We do not have $\dfrac{du}{dx}$ up to a multiplicative constant. Also, we can't just expand because of the exponent "1/2". So, we make the $x+3$ the variable by substitution.

Example 1) Evaluate $\int x^2 (x+3)^{1/2}\, dx$.

Solution Let $u = x+3$. Then $du = dx$ and $x = u-3$. Therefore,

$$\int x^2 (x+3)^{1/2}\, dx = \int (u-3)^2 u^{1/2}\, du \overset{\boxed{\text{Now expand.}}}{=} \int (u^2 - 6u + 9)u^{1/2}\, du = \int u^{5/2} - 6u^{3/2} + 9u^{1/2}\, du$$

$$= \frac{2}{7}u^{7/2} - \frac{12}{5}u^{5/2} + 6u^{3/2} + C \overset{\boxed{\substack{\text{Resubstitute for} \\ u \text{ in terms of } x.}}}{=} \frac{2}{7}(x+3)^{7/2} - \frac{12}{5}(x+3)^{5/2} + 6(x+3)^{3/2} + C$$

Example 2) Evaluate $\int \dfrac{x+3}{2x-1}\, dx$.

Solution Let $u = 2x-1$. Then $du = 2dx$ and so $dx = \dfrac{du}{2}$.

Also, $2x = u+1$ and so $x = \dfrac{u+1}{2}$. Therefore,

$$\int \frac{\frac{u+1}{2} + 3}{u} \frac{du}{2} \overset{\boxed{\substack{\text{Get a common} \\ \text{denominator} \\ \text{in the top.}}}}{=} \int \frac{\left(\frac{u+1+6}{2}\right)}{2u}\, du \overset{\boxed{\substack{\text{Simplify the fraction.} \\ \text{Remember: } \frac{\left(\frac{a}{b}\right)}{c} = \frac{a}{b} \times \frac{1}{c} = \frac{a}{bc}}}}{=} \int \frac{u+7}{4u}\, du \overset{\boxed{\substack{\text{I like to pull the} \\ \text{constant outside} \\ \text{the integral.}}}}{=} \frac{1}{4}\int \frac{u+7}{u}\, du$$

$$\overset{\boxed{\text{Make separate fractions.}}}{=} \frac{1}{4}\int 1 + \frac{7}{u}\, du = \frac{1}{4}(u + 7\ln|u|) + C \overset{\boxed{\text{Substitute } u=2x-1.}}{=} \frac{1}{4}(2x-1 + 7\ln|2x-1|) + C$$

$$\overset{\boxed{\text{optional}}}{=} \frac{x}{2} - \frac{1}{4} + \frac{7}{4}\ln|2x-1| + C \overset{\boxed{\text{optional: } D = C - \frac{1}{4}}}{=} \frac{x}{2} + \frac{7}{4}\ln|2x-1| + D$$

231

Two for you.

Evaluate the following integrals: 1) $\int (3x-1)(x+5)^{1/3}\,dx$ 2) $\int \dfrac{2x+x^2}{x+1}\,dx$

Answers 1) $\dfrac{9}{7}(x+5)^{7/3} - 12(x+5)^{4/3} + C$ 2) $\dfrac{x^2}{2} + x - \ln|x+1| + C$

Integration by Parts (I by P): $\int u\,dv = uv - \int v\,du$

This is the first "**serious** integration technique" we study in calculus. The key is the …

…Integration by Parts Strategy

Choose u so that du is an "easier" math expression than u. Choose dv so that (i) v is easy to find and (ii) v is no more difficult to work with than dv.

Example 1) Evaluate: $\int x\,e^x dx$

Solution Let $I = \int x\,e^x dx = \int u\,dv$ Choose u and dv obeying the strategy!

Let $u = x$ $\qquad\qquad$ $dv = e^x dx$

$\therefore$ $\qquad$ $\underbrace{du = dx}_{du \text{ is easier to work with than } u.}$ $\qquad$ $\underbrace{v = e^x}_{v \text{ is easy to find and is no more difficult to work with than } dv.}$ (Don't add C yet!)

$\boxed{\begin{array}{c} I = uv - \int v\,du \\ uv = xe^x,\ \int v\,du = \int e^x dx \end{array}}$

$I \qquad = \qquad xe^x - \int e^x dx \quad \overset{\boxed{\text{Now add } C.}}{=} \quad xe^x - e^x + C$

Example 2) Evaluate: $\int x^2 \cos(x)\,dx$

Solution This time we will need Integration by Parts **TWICE**!

Let $I = \int x^2 \cos(x)\,dx = \int u\,dv$. Choose u and dv!

Let $u = x^2$ $\qquad\qquad$ $dv = \cos(x)\,dx$

$\therefore$ $\qquad$ $\underbrace{du = 2x\,dx}_{du \text{ is easier to work with than } u!}$ $\qquad$ $\underbrace{v = \sin(x)}_{v \text{ is easy to find and is no more difficult to work with than } dv.}$ (Don't add C yet!)

$I = x^2 \sin(x) - \underset{\boxed{\substack{\text{Keep the constant} \\ \textbf{outside} \\ \text{the integral sign!}}}}{2} \underset{\boxed{\substack{\text{We will use "I by P" again} \\ \text{for this term!}}}}{\int x\sin(x)\,dx}$

$\qquad\qquad$ Let $u = x$ $\quad$ $dv = \sin(x)\,dx$ $\qquad$ $\boxed{\begin{array}{l}\text{(As we apply I by P again, we are} \\ \text{"recycling" the letters } u \text{ and } dv.)\end{array}}$

$\qquad\qquad$ $\therefore du = dx$ $\quad$ $v = -\cos(x)$

$\therefore I = x^2 \sin(x) - \underset{\boxed{\substack{\text{We kept this consant outside} \\ \text{the bracket to avoid clutter!}}}}{2} \left(\overset{\boxed{\text{This whole bracket replaces } \int x\sin(x)\,dx.}}{-x\cos(x) - \int -\cos(x)\,dx} \right)$

$= x^2 \sin(x) + 2x\cos(x) - 2\int \cos(x)\,dx$

$\overset{\boxed{\text{Now add } C!}}{=} \quad x^2 \sin(x) + 2x\cos(x) - 2\sin(x) + C$

Two for you.

1) Evaluate: $\int x \sin(x)\, dx$ 2) Evaluate: $\int x^2 e^x dx$

Answers 1) $\sin(x) - x\cos(x) + C$ 2) $x^2 e^x - 2xe^x + 2e^x + C \overset{\text{or}}{=} e^x(x^2 - 2x + 2) + C$

"Circular" Integration by Parts

Integration by Parts CIRCULAR Strategy

Choose u so that du is "no harder" (not necessarily easier!) to work with than u. Choose dv so that (i) v is easy to find and (ii) is no more difficult to work with than dv. Cross your fingers.

Example 1) Evaluate: $\int e^x \cos(x)\,dx$

Solution Let $I = \int e^x \cos(x)\,dx = \int u\,dv$ Choose u and dv using the modified strategy!

$$\text{Let } u = e^x \qquad\qquad dv = \cos(x)\,dx$$

$$\therefore \quad \underline{du = e^x dx} \qquad\qquad v = \sin(x) \qquad \text{(Don't add } C \text{ yet!)}$$

$\boxed{du \text{ is no harder to work with than } u.}$ $\qquad$ $\boxed{v \text{ is easy to find and is no more difficult to work with than } dv.}$

$\boxed{\begin{array}{c} I = uv - \int v\,du \\ uv = e^x \sin(x),\ \int v\,du = \int e^x \sin(x)\,dx \end{array}}$ $\qquad$ $\boxed{\begin{array}{c}\text{We will do "I by P"}\\ \text{again for this term!}\end{array}}$

$$I \qquad = \qquad e^x \sin(x) - \int e^x \sin(x)\,dx$$

$\boxed{\begin{array}{c}\text{Since we used } u=e^x \text{ the first}\\ \text{time, we use } u=e^x \text{ again. } \textbf{See}\\ \textbf{Example 2* for the reason}\\ \text{letting } u = \sin(x) \textbf{ is a BAD IDEA!}\end{array}}$

$$*\text{Let } u = e^x \qquad\qquad dv = \sin(x)\,dx \,*$$

$$\therefore \ du = e^x dx \qquad\qquad v = -\cos(x)$$

$\boxed{\begin{array}{c}\text{This is } I, \text{ the original}\\ \text{integral, reappearing. We}\\ \text{have come full } \textbf{CIRCLE!}\\ \textbf{CIRCULAR I BY P!}\end{array}}$

$$\therefore \ I = e^x \sin(x) - \left(\underbrace{-e^x \cos(x) - \int -e^x \cos(x)\,dx}_{\boxed{\text{This whole bracket replaces } \int e^x \sin(x)\,dx.}} \right) = e^x \sin(x) + e^x \cos(x) - \int e^x \cos(x)\,dx$$

So we now have $I = e^x \sin(x) + e^x \cos(x) - I$. **Solve** for I!

$$2I = e^x \sin(x) + e^x \cos(x)$$

$\boxed{\text{Solve for } I. \text{ Add } C \text{ now!}}$

$$I \qquad = \qquad \frac{1}{2}\left(e^x \sin(x) + e^x \cos(x)\right) + C = \frac{e^x}{2}\left(\sin(x) + \cos(x)\right) + C$$

Example 2) What goes wrong if we let $u = \sin(x)$ when we do "I by P" again at step *?

Solution Let's try it! Let $\ \underset{\boxed{\text{This is a bad idea!}}}{u = \sin(x)} \qquad dv = e^x dx$

$$\therefore \ du = \cos(x)\,dx \qquad v = e^x$$

$$\therefore \ I = e^x \sin(x) - \left(\underbrace{e^x \sin(x) - \int e^x \cos(x)\,dx}_{\boxed{\text{This whole bracket replaces } \int e^x \sin(x)\,dx.}} \right) = e^x \sin(x) - e^x \sin(x) + I = I$$

We now have $I = I$! The **good news**: this is TRUE! The **bad news**: we haven't integrated. This method is like tying your shoelaces and then untying them. You may not have done anything wrong but you are not ready to walk!

Two for you.

1)(a) Redo $\int e^x \cos(x)\,dx$ but this time use $u = \cos(x)$ and $dv = e^x dx$ when you apply "I by P" first and then use $u = \sin(x)$ and $dv = e^x dx$ when you "I by P" again. Show that you get the same answer as in Example 1.

(b) Redo $\int e^x \cos(x)\,dx$ but this time use $u = \cos(x)$ and $dv = e^x dx$ when you "I by P" first and then use $u = e^x$ and $dv = \sin(x)\,dx$ when you "I by P" again. Show that you get $I = I$.

2) Evaluate: $\int e^x \sin(x)\,dx$

Answers 1)(a) $\dfrac{e^x}{2}(\sin(x) + \cos(x)) + C$ (b) $I = I$

2) $\dfrac{e^x}{2}(\sin(x) - \cos(x)) + C$

Integration by Parts (I by P): The Tan—Sec Connection

Note: These are **very** popular I by P test questions! First, review page 235.

Special Toolbox for $\int \sec^3(x)\,dx$ and $\int \sec^5(x)\,dx$

$$\tan^2(x) = \sec^2(x) - 1 \qquad\qquad u = \sec(x) \Rightarrow du = \sec(x)\tan(x)\,dx;$$

$$\int \sec^2(x)\,dx = \tan(x) + C \qquad\qquad \int \sec(x)\,dx = \ln|\sec(x) + \tan(x)| + C$$

The Chain Rule!
$$\frac{d(u^3)}{dx} = 3u^2\frac{du}{dx}$$

$$u = \sec^3(x) = \big(\sec(x)\big)^3 \Rightarrow du \quad = \quad 3\big(\sec(x)\big)^2 \sec(x)\tan(x)\,dx = 3\sec^3(x)\tan(x)\,dx$$

Example 1) Evaluate: $\int \sec^3(x)\,dx$

Solution Let $I = \int \sec^3(x)\,dx = \int u\,dv$ Choose u and dv using the I by P strategy!

$$\text{Let } u = \sec(x) \qquad\qquad dv = \sec^2(x)\,dx$$

$$\therefore \quad du = \sec(x)\tan(x)\,dx \qquad\qquad v = \tan(x) \qquad \text{(Don't add } C \text{ yet!)}$$

du is maybe a little harder to work with than u. | v is easy to find and seems a little easier to work with than dv.

$$I = uv - \int v\,du$$
$uv = \sec(x)\tan(x), \quad \int v\,du = \int \sec(x)\tan^2(x)\,dx$

Now we will substitute $\tan^2(x) = \sec^2(x) - 1$.

$$I \quad = \quad \sec(x)\tan(x) - \int \sec(x) \quad \tan^2(x) \quad dx$$

$$= \sec(x)\tan(x) - \int \sec(x)(\sec^2(x) - 1)\,dx$$

$$\int f(x) - g(x)\,dx = \int f(x)\,dx - \int g(x)\,dx$$

$$= \sec(x)\tan(x) - \int \sec^3(x) - \sec(x)\,dx$$

This is I! Solve for I. | This is in our Toolbox.

$$= \sec(x)\tan(x) - \int \sec^3(x)\,dx + \int \sec(x)\,dx$$

$$\therefore 2I = \sec(x)\tan(x) + \ln|\sec(x) + \tan(x)|$$

$$\therefore \quad I = \frac{1}{2}\big(\sec(x)\tan(x) + \ln|\sec(x) + \tan(x)|\big) + C$$

Example 2) Show the first Integration by Parts steps in evaluating $\int \sec^5(x)\,dx$.

We could have used $dv = \sec^3(x)\,dx$ and used the answer from Example 1, but v would be **very** complicated! Try it and I know I'll see you back here in ten minutes!

Solution Let $u = \sec^3(x)$ $\qquad\qquad dv = \sec^2(x)\,dx$

from the toolbox

$$\therefore \quad du \quad = \quad 3\sec^3(x)\tan(x)\,dx \qquad\qquad v = \tan(x) \ \text{(Don't add } C \text{ yet!)}$$

Keep the constant outside to avoid "integral" clutter. | Now, as in Example 1, we will substitute $\tan^2(x) = \sec^2(x) - 1$.

$$I = \sec^3(x)\tan(x) - \quad 3 \quad \int \sec^3(x) \quad \tan^2(x) \quad dx$$

Now continue as in Example 1. This time, you will arrive at $4I = \ldots$(See **Two for you.**)

Two for you.

1)(a) Finish Example 2: $\int \sec^5(x)\,dx$

(b) Evaluate: $\int \sec(x)\tan^2(x)\,dx$ (Hint: Let $u = \tan(x)$ and $dv = \sec(x)\tan(x)\,dx$.
Also, after doing I by P, use the substitution $\sec^2(x) = \tan^2(x) + 1$.)

2)(a) Evaluate: $\int \csc^3(x)\,dx$ (b) $\int \csc^5(x)\,dx$

$$\boxed{\begin{array}{ll} \multicolumn{2}{c}{\text{Hint: Special Toolbox for } \int \csc^3(x)\,dx \text{ and } \int \csc^5(x)\,dx} \\ \cot^2(x) = \csc^2(x) - 1 & u = \csc(x) \Rightarrow du = -\csc(x)\cot(x)\,dx; \\ \int \csc^2(x)\,dx = -\cot(x) + C & \int \csc(x)\,dx = \ln|\csc(x) - \cot(x)| + C \\ u = \csc^3(x) = (\csc(x))^3 \Rightarrow du = 3(\csc(x))^2(-\csc(x)\cot(x))\,dx = -3\csc^3(x)\cot(x)\,dx \end{array}}$$

Answers 1)(a) $\dfrac{1}{4}\sec^3(x)\cdot\tan(x) + \dfrac{3}{8}\big(\sec(x)\cdot\tan(x) + \ln|\sec(x) + \tan(x)|\big) + C$

(b) $\dfrac{1}{2}\big(\sec(x)\tan(x) - \ln|\sec(x) + \tan(x)|\big) + C$

2)(a) $\dfrac{1}{2}\big(\ln|\csc(x) - \cot(x)| - \csc(x)\cot(x)\big) + C$

(b) $\dfrac{3}{8}\big(\ln|\csc(x) - \cot(x)| - \csc(x)\cot(x)\big) - \dfrac{1}{4}\csc^3(x)\cot(x) + C$

The Derivative of an Integral

This is an application of my favourite Theorem: **The Fundamental Theorem of Calculus**— "**the**" Fundamental Theorem. **The big one!** In this application, we take the derivative of an integral. You might expect the answer to be the original question. It is. Almost.

Example 1) Evaluate: (a) $\dfrac{d}{dx}\left(\displaystyle\int_{t=1}^{x} t^3 + 1 \; dt\right)$ (b) $\dfrac{d}{dx}\left(\displaystyle\int_{t=1}^{x} t^3 + t + 5 \; dt\right)$

Solution (a) $\dfrac{d}{dx}\left(\displaystyle\int_{t=1}^{x} t^3 + 1 \; dt\right) = \dfrac{d}{dx}\left(\dfrac{t^4}{4} + t\right)\Big|_1^x = \dfrac{d}{dx}\left(\dfrac{x^4}{4} + x - \left(\dfrac{1}{4} + 1\right)\right) = x^3 + 1$

We are back where we started except that t is replaced by x! Knowing this happens...

(b) $\dfrac{d}{dx}\left(\displaystyle\int_{t=1}^{x} t^3 + t + 5 \; dt\right)$ $\boxed{\text{The answer is the original integrand with } t \text{ replaced by } x!}$ $= \; x^3 + x + 5$

Example 2) (a) $\dfrac{d}{dx}\left(\displaystyle\int_{t=\sin(x)}^{\tan(x)} t^3 + 1 \; dt\right)$ (b) $\dfrac{d}{dx}\left(\displaystyle\int_{t=B(x)}^{T(x)} f(t) \; dt\right)$ $\boxed{\begin{array}{l}T \text{ for } Top \\ B \text{ for } Bottom\end{array}}$

Solution (a) $\dfrac{d}{dx}\left(\displaystyle\int_{t=\sin(x)}^{\tan(x)} t^3 + 1 \; dt\right)$ $\boxed{\begin{array}{l}\text{This is just like} \\ \text{Example 1(a) so far.}\end{array}}$ $= \dfrac{d}{dx}\left(\dfrac{t^4}{4} + t\right)\Big|_{\sin(x)}^{\tan(x)}$

$= \dfrac{d}{dx}\left(\dfrac{\tan^4(x)}{4} + \tan(x) - \left(\dfrac{\sin^4(x)}{4} + \sin(x)\right)\right)$

$\boxed{\begin{array}{l}\text{NOW WE NEED} \\ \text{THE \textbf{CHAIN RULE}!}\end{array}}$ $= \; \tan^3(x)\sec^2(x) + \sec^2(x) - \left(\sin^3(x)\cos(x) + \cos(x)\right)$

$\boxed{\begin{array}{l}\text{Factor out the "}\sec^2(x)\text{"} \\ \text{and "}\cos(x)\text{" terms.}\end{array}}$ $= \; (\tan^3(x) + 1)\sec^2(x) - \left(\sin^3(x) + 1\right)\cos(x)$

Here, we come back to the original integrand, but "t" is replaced **first** with "$\tan(x)$" and the chain rule made us multiply by $\dfrac{d\tan(x)}{dx} = \sec^2(x)$, then by "$\sin(x)$" and the chain rule made us multiply by $\dfrac{d\sin(x)}{dx} = \cos(x)$. So, knowing that this is what happens...

(b) $\dfrac{d}{dx}\left(\displaystyle\int_{t=B(x)}^{T(x)} f(t) \; dt\right) = f(T(x))\dfrac{d(T(x))}{dx} - f(B(x))\dfrac{d(B(x))}{dx}$ $\boxed{\text{in short...}}$ $= \; f(T)T' - f(B)B'$

Two for you.

Evaluate the following:

1) $\dfrac{d}{dx}\left(\displaystyle\int_{t=e^x}^{x^2+1} \cos t \ \ln t + t \ dt\right)$ (Hint: remember $\ln(e^x) = x$.)

2) $\dfrac{d}{dx}\left(\displaystyle\int_{\ln x}^{x} x + \ln x \ dx\right)$

Answers 1) $2x\left(\cos(x^2+1)\ \ln(x^2+1) + x^2+1\right) - e^x\left(x\cos\left(e^x\right) + e^x\right)$

2) $x + \ln x - \dfrac{\ln x + \ln(\ln x)}{x}$

(Note: the variable in the integrand, "x" or "t", **does not matter!**)

Finding the Inverse of a Function

Let $f(x) = x^3 + 1$. Then $f(2) = 9$. In the inverse function, we should have $f^{-1}(9) = 2$. In other words, since the point $(2, 9)$ satisfies f, the point $(9, 2)$ must satisfy f^{-1}. The key to inverses is that **the roles of x and y are INTERCHANGED!** So to find the inverse of a function, we 1) **interchange x and y** and then 2) **solve for y.**

Example 1)(a) Find the inverse function for $f(x) = x^3 + 1$.

(b) Verify that $f^{-1}(f(x)) = x$ for $x \in \text{dom}(f)$ and $f(f^{-1}(x)) = x$ for $x \in \text{dom}(f^{-1})$.

(c) In general, how are the domains and ranges of f and f^{-1} related?

(d) Draw the graphs of f, f^{-1}, and $y = x$ on the same set of axes. How are the three graphs related?

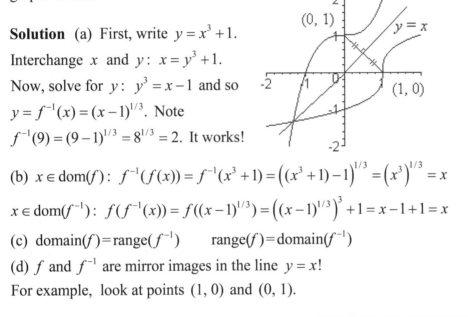

Solution (a) First, write $y = x^3 + 1$.

Interchange x and y: $x = y^3 + 1$.

Now, solve for y: $y^3 = x - 1$ and so

$y = f^{-1}(x) = (x-1)^{1/3}$. Note

$f^{-1}(9) = (9-1)^{1/3} = 8^{1/3} = 2$. It works!

(b) $x \in \text{dom}(f)$: $f^{-1}(f(x)) = f^{-1}(x^3 + 1) = \left((x^3 + 1) - 1\right)^{1/3} = \left(x^3\right)^{1/3} = x$

$x \in \text{dom}(f^{-1})$: $f(f^{-1}(x)) = f((x-1)^{1/3}) = \left((x-1)^{1/3}\right)^3 + 1 = x - 1 + 1 = x$

(c) $\text{domain}(f) = \text{range}(f^{-1})$ $\text{range}(f) = \text{domain}(f^{-1})$

(d) f and f^{-1} are mirror images in the line $y = x$!

For example, look at points $(1, 0)$ and $(0, 1)$.

Note: **given the function $y = f(x)$, the inverse will be a function only if f is one to one!** For example, if $f(x) = x^2$, then the inverse **relation** is $f^{-1}(x) = \pm\sqrt{x}$. Since $f(3) = f(-3) = 9$, therefore $f^{-1}(9) = \pm 3$; f^{-1} is **not** a function!

Example 2)(a) Find the inverse of $y = f(x) = \ln(x+1)$.

(b) State the domain and range for each of f and f^{-1}.

Solution (a) Set $x = \ln(y+1)$. $\therefore$ $y + 1 = e^x$ and so $y = f^{-1}(x) = e^x - 1$.

(b) Domain of f: $x + 1 > 0$ and so $x > -1$. Range of f: $y \in \mathbb{R}$.

Domain of f^{-1}: $x \in \mathbb{R}$. Range of f^{-1}: $y = e^x - 1 > -1$.

The domains and ranges of f and f^{-1} are interchanged!

Two for you.

Find f^{-1} for each of the following: 1) $f(x) = x^5 + 5$ 2) $f(x) = e^{2x+1}$

Answers 1) $f^{-1}(x) = (x-5)^{1/5}$ 2) $f^{-1}(x) = \dfrac{\ln x - 1}{2}$

Derivatives of Inverse Functions

Let $y = f(x)$. Then $\dfrac{dy}{dx} = f'(x)$. For the inverse, we want x and y to switch roles, so the derivative of the inverse should be, at least in notation, $\dfrac{dx}{dy}$. But remember that we can treat dx and dy as separate quantities (run and rise along the tangent line – see **Estimating Using the Differential** on page 205!) So, from Grade 5 arithmetic,

$\dfrac{dx}{dy} \overset{\text{should}}{=} \dfrac{1}{\left(\dfrac{dy}{dx}\right)}$. **AND IT DOES!** However, there is a **subtle** part: we have switched

x and y. We evaluate $\dfrac{dx}{dy}$ at the point (y, x) while we evaluate $\dfrac{dy}{dx}$ at (x, y).

A MOUTHFUL BUT TRUE!
The derivative of the inverse function at the point (y, x) is the reciprocal of the derivative of the original function at the point (x, y).

Example 1) Let $y = f(x) = x^3 + 1$. (a) Find $f^{-1}(x)$, $f'(x)$, and $(f^{-1})'(x)$.

(b) Note that $f(2) = 9$. Verify that $(f^{-1})'(9) = \dfrac{1}{f'(2)}$.

Solution (a) In $y = f(x) = x^3 + 1$, interchange x and y: $x = y^3 + 1$.

Now solving for y, $y^3 = x - 1$ and so $y = f^{-1}(x) = (x-1)^{1/3}$.

Therefore, $f'(x) \overset{\boxed{f(x)=x^3+1}}{=} 3x^2$ and $(f^{-1})'(x) \overset{\boxed{f^{-1}(x)=(x-1)^{1/3}}}{=} \dfrac{1}{3(x-1)^{2/3}}$.

(b) $f'(2) = 12$ and $(f^{-1})'(9) = \dfrac{1}{3(8)^{2/3}} = \dfrac{1}{12} = \dfrac{1}{f'(2)}$

Example 2) Suppose $f(7) = 8$ and $f'(7) = \dfrac{4}{5}$. Find (i) $(f^{-1})'(8)$ (ii) $(f^{-1})'(7)$

Solution (i) $(f^{-1})'(8) = \dfrac{1}{f'(7)} = \dfrac{5}{4}$ (ii) You don't have enough information!

Two for you.

For the function $y = f(x) = x^2 + 4$, find $(f^{-1})'$ at each of these points of f:

1) $(2, 8)$ and 2) $(-2, 8)$

Answers 1) $\dfrac{1}{4}$ 2) $-\dfrac{1}{4}$

(Note that there would be a problem asking for "$(f^{-1})'(8)$"! Since $f(x)$ is not a one to one function, f^{-1} is **NOT A FUNCTION!** For example, $f(2) = f(-2) = 8$.

We **can't** have $(f^{-1})'(8) = \dfrac{1}{f'(2)}$ and $(f^{-1})'(8) = \dfrac{1}{f'(-2)}$.)

Polar Coordinates

POSITIVE angles are drawn **COUNTER-CLOCKWISE** from the positive x axis.

NEGATIVE angles are drawn **CLOCKWISE** from the positive x axis.

POSITIVE RADIUS : Given the point P with polar coordinates (r, θ), with $r > 0$, plot P, with the angle θ, r units from the pole (or origin).

NEGATIVE RADIUS : Given the point P with polar coordinates (r, θ), with $r < 0$, plot a point **(not P!)**, with the angle θ, $-r$ units from the pole (or origin). Then **reflect** this point through the pole. **The reflected point is P!**

Example 1) Plot each of the following points which are given in polar coordinates.

(a) $(3, \pi/4)$ (b) $(1, -\pi/3)$ (c) $(2, 0)$ (d) $(2, \pi)$

Solution

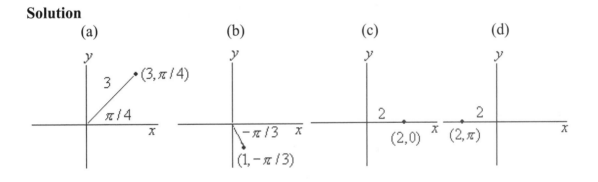

Example 2) Plot each of the following points which are given in polar coordinates.

(a) $(-3, \pi/4)$ (b) $(-1, -\pi/3)$ (c) $(-2, 0)$ (d) $(-2, \pi)$

Solution

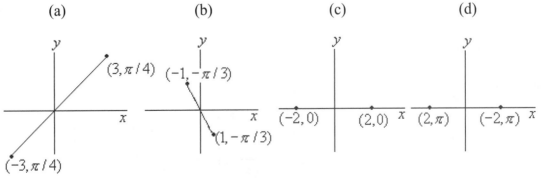

245

Two for you.

1) Plot the points with polar coordinates $(2, 30°)$ and $(2, -30°)$.

2) Plot the points with polar coordinates $(-2, 30°)$ and $(-2, -30°)$.

Answers

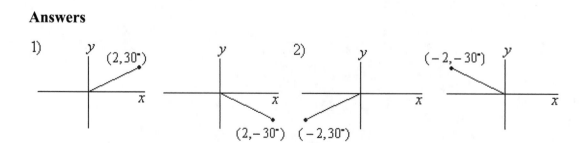

Polar to Rectangular Coordinates
Rectangular to Polar Equations

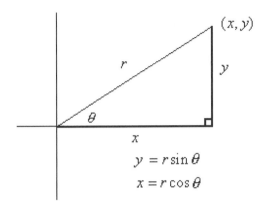

$$y = r\sin\theta$$

$$x = r\cos\theta$$

The problem with math teachers when it comes to things like polar and rectangular coordinates is this: how are students to know whether (a, b) is supposed to be in **polar** (a is the radius and b is the angle) coordinates or **rectangular** (a is the horizontal distance and b is the vertical distance) coordinates?

Good answer: teachers would label points something like this: $(a, b)_{PC}$ and $(a, b)_{RC}$!
"Get Real" answer: you are either told explicitly or you pick it up from the context.
Sometimes life is cruel and teachers can be (though this is rare) inconsiderate!

Example 1) Convert each of the following points from polar to rectangular coordinates:

(a) $(3, \pi/4)$ (b) $(2, -\pi/3)$ (c) $(-2, 0)$ (d) $(2, \pi/2)$ (e) $(2, -\pi/2)$

Solution (a) $x = 3\cos(\pi/4) = 3\left(\dfrac{1}{\sqrt{2}}\right) = \dfrac{3}{\sqrt{2}}$ and $y = 3\sin(\pi/4) = 3\left(\dfrac{1}{\sqrt{2}}\right) = \dfrac{3}{\sqrt{2}}$

(b) $x = 2\cos(-\pi/3) = 2\left(\dfrac{1}{2}\right) = 1$ and $y = 2\sin(-\pi/2) = 2\left(-\dfrac{\sqrt{3}}{2}\right) = -\sqrt{3}$

(c) $x = -2\cos 0 = 2(1) = -2$ and $y = -2\sin 0 = 0$

(d) $x = 2\cos(\pi/2) = 0$ and $y = 2\sin(\pi/2) = 2$

(e) $x = 2\cos(-\pi/2) = 0$ and $y = 2\sin(-\pi/2) = -2$

Example 2) Convert these rectangular equations to polar equations:

(a) $y = x^2$ (b) $x^2 + y^2 = 16$

Solution (a) $r\sin\theta = r^2\cos^2\theta$ $\therefore$ $r = 0$ or $r = \dfrac{\sin\theta}{\cos^2\theta} = \tan\theta\sec\theta$.

Note that when $\theta = 0$ in the second equation, $r = 0$. So, we only need $r = \tan\theta\sec\theta$.

(b) $r^2\cos^2\theta + r^2\sin^2\theta = 16$ and factoring out r^2, we have $r^2(\cos^2\theta + \sin^2\theta) = 16$.

Everybody knows that $\cos^2\theta + \sin^2\theta = 1$ and so the polar equation is $r^2 = 16$.

Therefore, $r = 4$ or $r = -4$. However, these are two polar equations for the same curve, the circle around the origin of radius 4. So $r = 4$ will do!

Two for you.

1) Convert these polar coordinates to rectangular: (a) $(5, 5\pi/4)$ (b) $(-2, \pi)$

2) Find a polar equation from the rectangular equation $y = x$.

Answers 1)(a) $\left(-\dfrac{5}{\sqrt{2}}, -\dfrac{5}{\sqrt{2}} \right)$ (b) $(2,0)$ 2) $\tan\theta = 1$

Rectangular to Polar Coordinates
Polar to Rectangular Equations

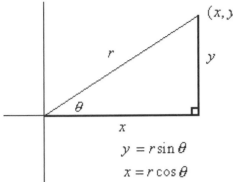

(x, y) $r^2 = x^2 + y^2$ and so $r = \pm\sqrt{x^2 + y^2}$ $\tan\theta = \dfrac{y}{x}$

Use your calculator or math software to solve $\tan\theta = $ constant, if it isn't an "easy" ratio.

> **Set your calculator to radians for now :**
> **constant 2nd function tan =**

Be careful! Your calculator will only give you an answer for θ between $-\pi/2$ and $\pi/2$.

$y = r\sin\theta$

$x = r\cos\theta$

Strategy: (x, y) is...

...in one of the four quadrants
OR
...on the positive y axis $(x = 0, \ y > 0)$
OR
...on the negative y axis $(x = 0, \ y < 0)$.

The picture at the right shows how to choose r and θ in each case.

$\theta = \pi/2$
$r = y > 0$

$\theta \in (-\pi/2, 0)$
$r = -\sqrt{x^2 + y^2}$

$\theta \in [0, \pi/2)$
$r = \sqrt{x^2 + y^2}$

$r = 0$

$\theta \in [0, \pi/2)$
$r = -\sqrt{x^2 + y^2}$

$\theta \in (-\pi/2, 0)$
$r = \sqrt{x^2 + y^2}$

$\theta = -\pi/2$
$r = -y > 0$

Example 1) Convert each of the points from rectangular to polar coordinates:

(a) $(2, 2)$ (b) $(-1, \sqrt{3})$ (c) $(0, -5)$

Solution (a) $\tan\theta = \dfrac{2}{2} = 1$ and the point is in the first quadrant.

$\therefore \ \theta = \pi/4$ and $r = +\sqrt{2^2 + 2^2} = \sqrt{8} = 2\sqrt{2}$

(b) $\tan\theta = -\sqrt{3}$ and the point is in the second quadrant.

$\therefore \ \theta = -\pi/3$ and $r = -\sqrt{(-1)^2 + \sqrt{3}^2} = -\sqrt{4} = -2$

(c) $\tan\theta$ is undefined. Since $y < 0$, we can choose $\theta = -\pi/2$ and $r = 5$.

Example 2) Convert $r\sin\theta = 5$ to an equation in rectangular coordinates.

Solution $\pm\sqrt{x^2 + y^2}\left(\dfrac{y}{\pm\sqrt{x^2 + y^2}}\right) = 5$ which becomes simply $y = 5$.

Two for you.

1) Convert rectangular coordinates $(-3,-3)$ to polar coordinates.

2) Find a rectangular equation corresponding to $r = \sin\theta$.

Answers 1) $\theta = \pi/4$ and $r = -3\sqrt{2}$ 2) $x^2 + y^2 = y$ or $x^2 + \left(y - \dfrac{1}{2}\right)^2 = \dfrac{1}{4}$

(Very) Basic Vectors

Let's review the basics of vectors. Vectors are usually denoted with an italicized letter capped by an arrow, for example, $\vec{v}$, or by a bold letter, such as **v**, or both: $\vec{\boldsymbol{v}}$. The length (or magnitude) is denoted $\|\vec{v}\|$.

$\mathbb{R}^2$
Let $\vec{v}=(a,b)$, $\vec{w}=(c,d)$, and $k\in\mathbb{R}$.
$\vec{v}\pm\vec{w}=(a\pm c,b\pm d)$
$k\vec{v}=(ka,kb)$ $\|\vec{v}\|=\sqrt{a^2+b^2}$

$\mathbb{R}^3$
Let $\vec{v}=(a,b,c)$, $\vec{w}=(d,e,f)$, and $k\in\mathbb{R}$.
$\vec{v}\pm\vec{w}=(a\pm d,b\pm e,c\pm f)$
$k\vec{v}=(ka,kb,kc)$ $\|\vec{v}\|=\sqrt{a^2+b^2+c^2}$

Example 1) Let the vector $\vec{v}=(1,2)$.

(a) Illustrate $\vec{v}$ as a directed line segment beginning at (i) $(0,0)$ (ii) $(-3,-3)$.

(b) Find and illustrate $\vec{w}=-2\vec{v}$ starting at $(0,2)$ using your picture in (a).

(c) Find the length of (i) $\vec{v}$ and (ii) $\vec{w}$.

Solution (a) and (b)

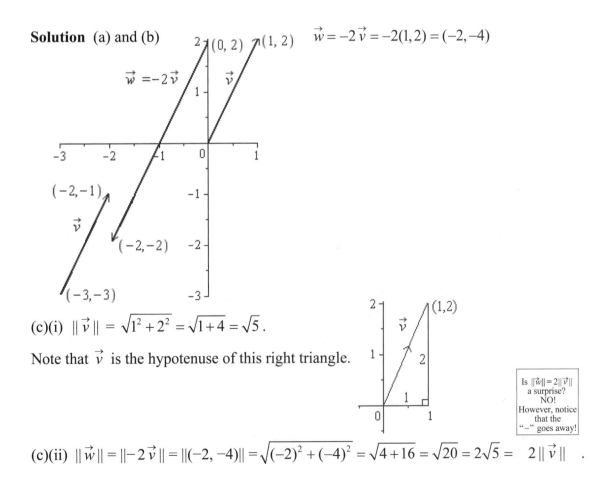

$\vec{w}=-2\vec{v}=-2(1,2)=(-2,-4)$

(c)(i) $\|\vec{v}\| = \sqrt{1^2+2^2} = \sqrt{1+4} = \sqrt{5}$.

Note that $\vec{v}$ is the hypotenuse of this right triangle.

Is $\|\vec{w}\|=2\|\vec{v}\|$ a surprise? NO! However, notice that the "−" goes away!

(c)(ii) $\|\vec{w}\| = \|-2\vec{v}\| = \|(-2,-4)\| = \sqrt{(-2)^2+(-4)^2} = \sqrt{4+16} = \sqrt{20} = 2\sqrt{5} = 2\|\vec{v}\|$.

251

Two for you.

1) Let the vector $\vec{v} = (-1, 2)$.

(a) Illustrate $\vec{v}$ as a directed line segment beginning at the **point** (i) (0,0) (ii) (2,1).

(b) Find and illustrate $\vec{w} = -2\vec{v}$ starting at (0,0) using your picture in (a).

(c) Find the length of (i) $\vec{v}$ and (ii) $\vec{w}$.

2) Let $\vec{v} = (1, 2, 3)$ and $\vec{w} = (-2, 1, 3)$.

(a) Find $\vec{v} + \vec{w}$.

(b) Find the lengths of $\vec{v}$, $\vec{w}$ and $\vec{v} + \vec{w}$.

(c) Note that $\| \vec{v} + \vec{w} \| < \| \vec{v} \| + \| \vec{w} \|$. The three vectors $\vec{v}$, $\vec{w}$ and $\vec{v} + \vec{w}$ can be positioned to form the sides of triangle. The inequality is an example of the **Side Inequality Theorem: The sum of the lengths of two sides of a triangle is always...** (finish this statement.)

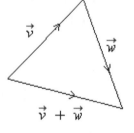

Answers 1)(a) and (b)

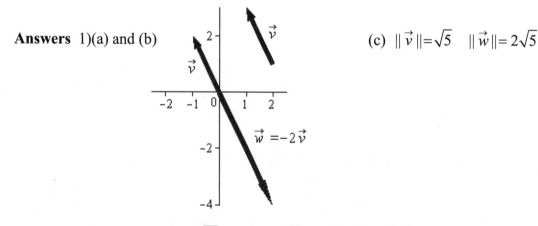

(c) $\| \vec{v} \| = \sqrt{5}$ $\| \vec{w} \| = 2\sqrt{5}$

2)(a) $(-1, 3, 6)$ (b) $\| \vec{v} \| = \sqrt{14}$ $\| \vec{w} \| = \sqrt{14}$ $\| \vec{v} + \vec{w} \| = \sqrt{46}$
(c) **...greater than the length of the third side.**

The Dot or Scalar or Inner Product of Two Vectors

The dot product is also called the "**scalar product**" because it is a form of vector multiplication which yields a scalar, **not a vector!** Why is it called the "**inner product**" as well? See ** on the last line of the **Definition** below.

Definition The dot or scalar product of the

two vectors $\vec{a}$ and $\vec{b}$ is $\vec{a} \cdot \vec{b} = \|\vec{a}\| \|\vec{b}\| \cos\theta$,

where θ is the angle between $\vec{a}$ and $\vec{b}$,

$0 \le \theta \le \pi$. If, as in the diagram, $\vec{a} = (a_1, a_2)$

and $\vec{b} = (b_1, b_2)$, it turns out that

$\vec{a} \cdot \vec{b} = \|\vec{a}\| \|\vec{b}\| \cos\theta = a_1 b_1 + a_2 b_2$.

If we are dealing with more dimensions,

$\vec{a} = (a_1, a_2, ..., a_n)$ and $\vec{b} = (b_1, b_2, ..., b_n)$,

then $\vec{a} \cdot \vec{b} = a_1 b_1 + a_2 b_2 + ... + a_n b_n$.**

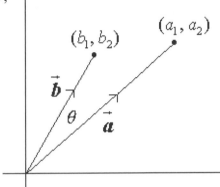

Example 1) Given $\vec{a} = (3, 4, 0)$ and $\vec{b} = (-1, 2, \sqrt{11})$, find

(a) $\vec{a} \cdot \vec{b}$ (b) $\|\vec{a}\|$ and $\|\vec{b}\|$ (c) θ, the angle between $\vec{a}$ and $\vec{b}$.

Solution (a) $\vec{a} \cdot \vec{b} = (3, 4, 0) \cdot (-1, 2, \sqrt{11}) = 3 \times (-1) + 4 \times 2 + 0 \times \sqrt{11} = 5$

(b) $\|\vec{a}\| = \sqrt{3^2 + 4^2 + 0^2} = \sqrt{25} = 5$ $\|\vec{b}\| = \sqrt{(-1)^2 + 2^2 + \sqrt{11}^2} = \sqrt{16} = 4$

(c) From $\vec{a} \cdot \vec{b} = \|\vec{a}\| \|\vec{b}\| \cos\theta = a_1 b_1 + a_2 b_2 + a_3 b_3$

$\cos\theta = \dfrac{a_1 b_1 + a_2 b_2 + a_3 b_3}{\|\vec{a}\| \|\vec{b}\|} = \dfrac{5}{5 \times 4} = \dfrac{1}{4} = 0.25$

| Put your calculator in RADIAN mode! |
| 0.25 SecondFunction Cos= |

| Put your calculator in DEGREE mode! |
| 0.25 SecondFunction Cos= |

$\therefore$ θ $\doteqdot$ 1.32 radians or $\therefore$ θ $\doteqdot$ 75.5°

Example 2) What can you conclude about θ or $\vec{a}$ or $\vec{b}$ if $\vec{a} \cdot \vec{b}$ is

(a) 0?   (b) $\|\vec{a}\| \|\vec{b}\|$?

Solution (a) If $\vec{a} \cdot \vec{b} = \|\vec{a}\| \|\vec{b}\| \cos\theta = 0$, then either $\vec{a} = \vec{0}$ or $\vec{b} = \vec{0}$ or $\theta = \pi/2$.

(b) If $\vec{a} \cdot \vec{b} = \|\vec{a}\| \|\vec{b}\| \cos\theta = \|\vec{a}\| \|\vec{b}\|$, then $\cos\theta = 1$ and so $\theta = 0$.

Two for you.

1) Find the angle between $\vec{a}$ and $\vec{b}$ if $\vec{a} = (1, -1)$ and $\vec{b} = (-1, 2)$.

2) What can you conclude about θ or $\vec{a}$ or $\vec{b}$ if the value of $\vec{a} \cdot \vec{b}$ is $-\|\vec{a}\|\,\|\vec{b}\|$?

Answers 1) $\theta \doteq 2.8$ radians or $\theta \doteq 161.6°$ 2) $\theta = \pi$ or $\vec{a} = \vec{0}$ or $\vec{b} = \vec{0}$

The Vector or Cross Product of Two Vectors

The cross product is also called the "**vector product**" because it is a type of vector multiplication which, unlike the dot product, **does yield a vector!** In fact, the cross product of $\vec{a}$ and $\vec{b}$ (which are vectors in $\mathbb{R}^3$) is a vector **perpendicular to the plane** (when $\vec{a}$ and $\vec{b}$ are linearly independent) **spanned by** $\vec{a}$ **and** $\vec{b}$!

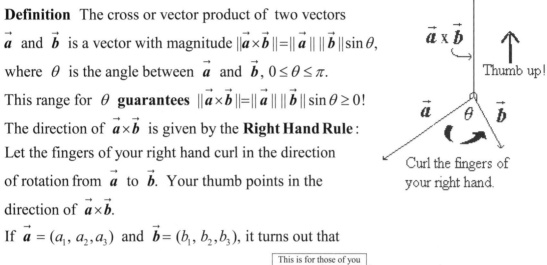

Definition The cross or vector product of two vectors $\vec{a}$ and $\vec{b}$ is a vector with magnitude $\|\vec{a} \times \vec{b}\| = \|\vec{a}\| \, \|\vec{b}\| \sin \theta$, where θ is the angle between $\vec{a}$ and $\vec{b}$, $0 \le \theta \le \pi$. This range for θ **guarantees** $\|\vec{a} \times \vec{b}\| = \|\vec{a}\| \, \|\vec{b}\| \sin \theta \ge 0$!

The direction of $\vec{a} \times \vec{b}$ is given by the **Right Hand Rule**: Let the fingers of your right hand curl in the direction of rotation from $\vec{a}$ to $\vec{b}$. Your thumb points in the direction of $\vec{a} \times \vec{b}$.

If $\vec{a} = (a_1, a_2, a_3)$ and $\vec{b} = (b_1, b_2, b_3)$, it turns out that

$$\vec{a} \times \vec{b} = (a_2 b_3 - a_3 b_2, \ a_3 b_1 - a_1 b_3, \ a_1 b_2 - a_2 b_1) \quad \underset{\substack{\text{This is for those of you} \\ \text{who are comfortable with} \\ \text{the } \textbf{DETERMINANT} \\ \text{of a } 3 \times 3 \text{ matrix.}}}{=} \quad \begin{vmatrix} \vec{i} & \vec{j} & \vec{k} \\ a_1 & a_2 & a_3 \\ b_1 & b_2 & b_3 \end{vmatrix}.$$

> Here is an easy pattern for $\vec{a} \times \vec{b}$!
> The **1st** coordinate uses **2, 3**; the **2nd** uses **3, 1**; the **3rd** uses **1, 2**.

Example 1) Given $\vec{a} = (1, 2, 3)$ and $\vec{b} = (4, 5, 6)$, find $\vec{a} \times \vec{b}$. Which quadrant is θ in?

Solution $\vec{a} \times \vec{b} = (1, 2, 3) \times (4, 5, 6) = (2 \times 6 - 5 \times 3, \ 3 \times 4 - 6 \times 1, \ 1 \times 5 - 4 \times 2) = (-3, 6, -3)$

Note that $\vec{a} \cdot \vec{b} = 4 + 10 + 18 = 32 > 0$.

$\therefore \ \cos \theta \ \underset{\boxed{\text{We used this formula on the previous page!}}}{=} \ \dfrac{\vec{a} \cdot \vec{b}}{\|\vec{a}\| \, \|\vec{b}\|} > 0$ and so $\theta \in (0, \pi/2)$.

Example 2) Let $\vec{a} = (a_1, a_2, a_3) \ne \vec{0}$, $\vec{b} = (b_1, b_2, b_3) \ne \vec{0}$, and $\vec{a} \nparallel \vec{b}$, so $\vec{a} \times \vec{b} \ne \vec{0}$.

Prove $\vec{a} \times \vec{b} \perp \vec{a}$. (We define $\vec{0}$ to be orthogonal to all vectors.)

Solution $(\vec{a} \times \vec{b}) \cdot \vec{a} = (a_2 b_3 - a_3 b_2, \ a_3 b_1 - a_1 b_3, \ a_1 b_2 - a_2 b_1) \cdot (a_1, a_2, a_3)$

$= a_1 a_2 b_3 - a_1 a_3 b_2 + a_2 a_3 b_1 - a_2 a_1 b_3 + a_3 a_1 b_2 - a_3 a_2 b_1 \underset{\boxed{\substack{\text{The terms cancel} \\ \text{out in pairs!}}}}{=} 0.$ If θ is the angle

between $\vec{a} \times \vec{b}$ and $\vec{a}$, then $(\vec{a} \times \vec{b}) \cdot \vec{a} = \|\vec{a} \times \vec{b}\| \, \|\vec{a}\| \cos \theta \ \therefore \cos \theta = 0$ and so $\theta = \dfrac{\pi}{2}$.

Two for you.

1) Find $\vec{a} \times \vec{b}$ if $\vec{a} = (1, 2, 3)$ and $\vec{b} = (1, 2, 3)$.

2) What can you conclude about $\vec{a} \times \vec{b}$, if anything, if $\vec{a}$ is parallel to $\vec{b}$?

Answers 1) $\vec{a} \times \vec{b} = \vec{0}$ 2) $\vec{a} \times \vec{b} = \vec{0}$

Vector Equation of a Line: $\overrightarrow{OP} = \overrightarrow{OP_0} + t\vec{v}$

To find the vector equation of a line, we need:
(i) a point P_0 on the line and

(ii) a vector $\vec{v}$ parallel to the line.
Then, if P is any point on the line, we can write

$\overrightarrow{OP} = \overrightarrow{OP_0} + t\vec{v}$. ($\overrightarrow{OP_0}$ gets us **onto the line** and

then $t\vec{v}$ lets us **travel along the line**!)

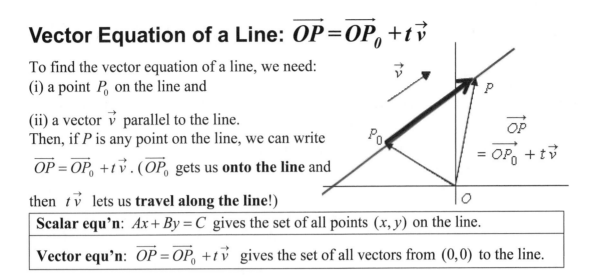

Scalar equ'n: $Ax + By = C$ gives the set of all points (x, y) on the line.

Vector equ'n: $\overrightarrow{OP} = \overrightarrow{OP_0} + t\vec{v}$ gives the set of all vectors from $(0,0)$ to the line.

Example 1) Find (a) vector (b) parametric and (c) symmetric equations of the line through $P_0(1,2)$ and parallel to $\vec{v} = (2,-3)$.

Solution (a) **Vector Equation**: $\overrightarrow{OP} \overset{\boxed{\overrightarrow{OP}=\overrightarrow{OP_0}+t\vec{v}}}{=} (1,2) + t(2,-3)$, or $(x,y) = (1,2) + t(2,-3)$

(b) **Parametric Equations**: $x \overset{\boxed{\text{Equate the first coordinates in the vector equation.}}}{=} 1 + 2t$, $y \overset{\boxed{\text{Equate the second coordinates in the vector equation.}}}{=} 2 - 3t$

(c) **Symmetric Equations**: $t \overset{\boxed{\text{Solve for } t \text{ in the parametric equations.}}}{=} \dfrac{x-1}{2} = \dfrac{y-2}{-3}$

Example 2) Find (a) vector (b) parametric and (c) symmetric equations of the line through $P_0(1,2,-1)$ and parallel to $\vec{v} = (2,-3,4)$.

Solution (a) **Vector**: $\overrightarrow{OP} = (1,2,-1) + t(2,-3,4)$ or $(x,y,z) = (1,2,-1) + t(2,-3,4)$.
(b) **Parametric**: $x = 1 + 2t$, $y = 2 - 3t$, $z = -1 + 4t$

(c) **Symmetric**: $t = \dfrac{x-1}{2} = \dfrac{y-2}{-3} = \dfrac{z+1}{4}$

Example 3) Find (a) vector (b) parametric and (c) symmetric equations of the line through $P_0(1,2,-1)$ and parallel to $\vec{v} = (2,0,0)$.

Solution (a) **Vector**: $\overrightarrow{OP} = (1,2,-1) + t(2,0,0)$, or $(x,y,z) = (1,2,-1) + t(2,0,0)$.

(b) **Parametric**: $x = 1 + 2t$, $y = 2$, $z = -1$

(c) **Symmetric**: $t = \dfrac{x-1}{2}$, $y = 2$, $z = -1$

Note: Here, y and z are constant and so there is only the one symmetric equation. This line is parallel to the x axis, through the point $(1,2,-1)$. For comparison, the x axis itself, in $\mathbb{R}^3$ has symmetric equation $t = x$ with $y = 0$, $z = 0$.

Two for you.

1) Find (a) vector (b) parametric and (c) symmetric equations of the line through $P_0(-1,3)$ and parallel to $\vec{v} = (2,1)$.

2) Find (a) vector (b) parametric and (c) symmetric equations of the line through $P_0(1,2,-1)$ and parallel to the line given by $\overrightarrow{OP} = (3,5,-3) + t(2,-3,4)$.
(Hint: Any normal to the plane will be parallel to the line.)

Answers

1) **Vector:** $\overrightarrow{OP} = (-1,3) + t(2,1)$

    Parametric: $x = -1 + 2t, \ y = 3 + t$

    Symmetric: $t = \dfrac{x+1}{2} = \dfrac{y-3}{1}$

2) **Vector:** $\overrightarrow{OP} = (1,2,-1) + t(2,-3,4)$

    Parametric: $x = 1 + 2t, \ y = 2 - 3t, \ z = -1 + 4t$

    Symmetric: $t = \dfrac{x-1}{2} = \dfrac{y-2}{-3} = \dfrac{z+1}{4}$

Vector Equation of a Plane: $\overrightarrow{OP}=\overrightarrow{OP_0}+s\,\vec{v}+t\,\vec{w}$

To find the vector equation of a plane, we need:

(i) a point P_0 on the plane and

(ii) two **NON-PARALLEL** direction vectors

$\vec{v}$ and $\vec{w}$ for the plane.
Then, if P is any point on the plane, we can write

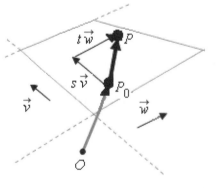

$\overrightarrow{OP}=\overrightarrow{OP_0}+s\,\vec{v}+t\,\vec{w}$. ($\overrightarrow{OP_0}$ gets us **onto the plane**

and then $s\,\vec{v}+t\,\vec{w}$ lets us **travel along the plane to the required point** P !)

Example 1) Find (a) vector and (b) parametric equations of the plane through

$P_0(1,2,1)$ and parallel to vectors $\vec{v}=(2,-3,1)$ and $\vec{w}=(0,2,3)$.

Solution Note $\vec{v}$ and $\vec{w}$ are independent (which, for two vectors, means non-parallel!)

> You should take the time NOW to show that $\vec{v}$ and $\vec{w}$ are
>
> independent/non-parallel, that is, show $a\,\vec{v}+b\,\vec{w}=(0,0,0)\Rightarrow a=b=0$.
>
> In fact, you are showing that neither $\vec{v}$ nor $\vec{w}$ is a multiple of the other.

(a) **Vector Equation**:

$$\overrightarrow{OP}\ \overset{\boxed{\overrightarrow{OP}=\overrightarrow{OP_0}+s\vec{v}+t\vec{w}}}{=}\ (1,2,1)+s\,(2,-3,1)+t\,(0,2,3)\ \text{ or }\ (x,y,z)=(1,2,1)+s\,(2,-3,1)+t\,(0,2,3)$$

> For x, equate the first coordinates in the vector equation;
> for y, equate the second coordinates; for z, the third

(b) **Parametric Equations:** $x=1+2s,\ y=2-3s+2t,\ z=1+s+3t$

(Just in case you are wondering, we don't have symmetric equations of a plane!)

Example 2) Find (a) vector and (b) parametric equations of the plane through $P_0(0,0,0)$

and parallel to the plane given by $\overrightarrow{OP}=(1,2,1)+s\,(1,0,0)+t\,(0,1,0)$

Solution For two independent direction vectors, we can use

$\vec{v}=(1,0,0)$ and $\vec{w}=(0,1,0)$.

(a) **Vector Equation**: $\overrightarrow{OP}=(0,0,0)+s\,(1,0,0)+t\,(0,1,0)=s\,(1,0,0)+t\,(0,1,0)$

(b) **Parametric Equations:** $x=s,\ y=t,\ z=0$ **Note:** This is the xy plane in $\mathbb{R}^3$.

Two for you.

1) Find (a) vector and (b) parametric equations of the plane through $P_0(-2,3,5)$

and parallel to vectors $\vec{v} = (3,2,1)$ and $\vec{w} = (2,5,1)$.

2) Find (a) vector and (b) parametric equations of the plane through $P_0(0,0,1)$ and perpendicular to the planes given by $x+y+z=3$ and $-x+2y-4z=7$.
(Hint: A normal to, for example, the plane given by $x+y+z=3$ is a direction vector for the required plane.)

Answers 1)(a) **vector:** $\overrightarrow{OP} = (-2,3,5) + s\,(3,2,1) + t\,(2,5,1)$
(b) **parametric:** $x = -2 + 3s + 2t,\ y = 3 + 2s + 5t,\ z = 5 + s + t$
2)(a) **vector:** $\overrightarrow{OP} = (0,0,1) + s\,(1,1,1) + t\,(-1,2,-4)$
(b) **parametric:** $x = s - t,\ y = s + 2t,\ z = 1 + s - 4t$

The Scalar Equation of a Plane: $Ax+By+Cz=D$

A mathematics philosophical digression: When a mathematical explorer is first venturing into new territory, she has to define what she deems to be critical concepts and then conjecture and prove theorems that connect those concepts. Unlike the texts that come later, this is rarely a smooth, linear process. But when brilliant insight leads to just the right concepts, intellectual power and beauty emerge. Someone defined the dot product and showed that the dot product of perpendicular vectors is 0. From that simple yet profound observation…

Let $\vec{n} = (A, B, C)$ be perpendicular to a plane

(that is, $\vec{n}$ is **normal** to the plane) and $P_0(x_0, y_0, z_0)$ be a given point on the plane. If $P(x, y, z)$ is any point on the plane,

$\vec{n} \perp \overrightarrow{P_0P}$ and so $\vec{n} \cdot \overrightarrow{PP_0} = 0$.

So $(A, B, C) \cdot (x - x_0, y - y_0, z - z_0) = 0$.

This leads to $Ax + By + Cz = D$,

where $D = Ax_0 + By_0 + Cz_0$.

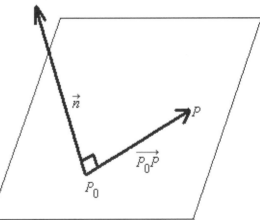

…we get the equation of a plane. Simple, yet powerful.

Using $\vec{n} = (A, B)$ and point $P_0(x_0, y_0)$, the same process shows that the equation of a line is $Ax + By = C$.

Example 1) Find the scalar equation of the plane through $P_0(1, 2, 1)$ with normal $\vec{n} = (2, -3, 1)$.

Solution If $P(x, y, z)$ is any point on the plane, then $\vec{n} \perp \overrightarrow{P_0P}$ and so

$\vec{n} \cdot \overrightarrow{PP_0} = 0$, ie., $(2, -3, 1) \cdot (x - 1, y - 2, z - 1) = 0$

$\therefore 2x - 2 - 3y + 6 + z - 1 = 0$ and so $2x - 3y + z = -3$

Example 2) What is the best way to find the scalar equation of a plane if you are given three **non-collinear** points P, Q, and R?

Solution Because the points are non-collinear, $\overrightarrow{PQ}$ and $\overrightarrow{PR}$ are non-parallel direction vectors for the plane. Therefore, $\vec{n} = \overrightarrow{PQ} \times \overrightarrow{PR}$ is a normal to the plane. Now using normal $\vec{n}$ and any one of the points P, Q, and R, proceed as in Example 1.

Two for you.

1) Find the scalar equation of the plane through $(1,2,3)$ and parallel to the plane $-2x + 3z = 7$. (Hint: a normal to this plane is $(-2, 0, 3)$.)

2) Find the scalar equation of the plane with vector equation $\overrightarrow{OP} = (4,1,3) + s(1,2,3) + t(1,-2,-4)$. (Hint: take the **cross product** of the two direction vectors to obtain a **normal** to the plane.)

Answers 1) $-2x + 3z = 7$ 2) $-2x + 7y - 4z = -13$

Two Lines in $\mathbb{R}^3$: Parallel/Coincident

With two lines in $\mathbb{R}^3$, there are four possible scenarios. The lines can be:
(1) coincident   (2) parallel   (3) intersect in exactly one point   (4) "skew".
Here we will deal with (1) and (2).

Critical Note: When the direction vectors from two vector equations of lines are multiples of one another, the lines **must** have...

> **...NO** points in common (**parallel** lines) or **ALL** points in common (**coincident** lines).

So, if we have two such direction vectors, take **ANY** point on one of the lines. If the point is on the other line, the lines are coincident. If not, the lines are parallel.

Another Critical Note: In the first **Critical Note**, be careful to distinguish between lines and vectors. Vectors have direction. Lines don't.

Geometry	Algebraic Example	What to do
(1) The two lines are coincident.	L1: $\overrightarrow{OP} = (1,1,1) + s\,(1,2,3)$ L2: $\overrightarrow{OP} = (-1,-3,-5) + t\,(-2,-4,-6)$	Note that the two direction vectors are **multiples of one one another** and then show there **is** a common point.
(2) The two lines are parallel.	L1: $\overrightarrow{OP} = (1,1,1) + s\,(1,2,3)$ L2: $\overrightarrow{OP} = (-1,-3,-4) + t\,(-2,-4,-6)$	Note that the two direction vectors are **multiples of one another** and then show there **is no** common point.

(1) L1 has direction vector $(1,2,3)$ and L2 has direction vector $(-2,-4,-6)$. These are clearly multiples of one another, so L1 and L2 are either parallel or coincident. Letting $s = 0$ shows $(1,1,1)$ is a point on L1. Now, let's check whether it is also on L2.

$$(1,1,1) = (-1,-3,-5) + t\,(-2,-4,-6)$$
$$\Leftrightarrow\ 1 = -1 - 2t \qquad 1 = -3 - 4t \qquad 1 = -5 - 6t$$
$$\Leftrightarrow\ 2 = -2t \qquad\quad 4 = -4t \qquad\quad 6 = -6t$$
$$\Leftrightarrow\ t = -1 \qquad\quad t = -1 \qquad\quad t = -1$$

$\therefore\ (1,1,1) = (-1,-3,-5) - (-2,-4,-6)$ and so $(1,1,1)$ is on L2.

So this point **is on both lines**. Therefore, the lines are coincident.

(2) The direction vectors are clearly multiples of each other. $s = 0$ shows $(1,1,1)$ is a point on L1. Now, let's check whether it is also on L2.

$$(1,1,1) = (-1,-3,-4) + t\,(-2,-4,-6)$$
$$\Leftrightarrow 1 = -1 - 2t \qquad 1 = -3 - 4t \qquad 1 = -4 - 6t$$
$$\Leftrightarrow 2 = -2t \qquad\quad 4 = -4t \qquad\quad 5 = -6t$$
$$\Leftrightarrow t = -1 \qquad\quad t = -1 \qquad\quad t = -\frac{5}{6}. \ \text{Since we do not have a common } t \text{ value,}$$

$(1,1,1)$ cannot be on L2. Therefore, L1 is parallel to L2.

Two for you.

1)(a) Are these two lines coincident, parallel, skew, or do they intersect in a single point? If they intersect, find the intersection point.

L1: $\overrightarrow{OP} = (1,1,1) + s(1,1,1)$

L2: $\overrightarrow{OP} = (-1,-3,-5) + t(4,4,4)$

(b) If the lines were coincident, what value of s shows that $(-1,-3,-5)$ is on L1?

2)(a) Are these two lines coincident, parallel, skew, or do they intersect in a single point? If they intersect, find the intersection point.

L1: $\overrightarrow{OP} = (19,17,15) + s(1,1,1)$

L2: $\overrightarrow{OP} = (-1,-3,-5) + t(4,4,4)$

(b) If the lines are coincident, what value of s shows that $(-1,-3,-5)$ is on L1?

Answers 1)(a) parallel (b) non applicable since $(-1,-3,-5)$ is **not** on L1.
2)(a) coincident (b) $s = -20$

Two Lines in $\mathbb{R}^3$: Non-Parallel/Non-Coincident

With two lines in $\mathbb{R}^3$, there are four possible scenarios. The lines can be
(1) coincident or (2) parallel or (3) intersect in exactly one point or (4) "skew".
Here we will deal with (3) and (4).

Critical Note: When the direction vectors from two vector equations of lines are **NOT** multiples of one another, the lines **must** intersect in a unique point or not at all (skew).

Geometry	Algebraic Example	What to do
(3) The two lines intersect in a single point.	L1: $\overrightarrow{OP} = (1,1,1) + s\,(1,2,3)$ L2: $\overrightarrow{OP} = (-2,0,2) + t\,(1,1,1)$	Note the direction vectors are not multiples of one another. Equate the x, y, and z parametric equations of each line and then **row reduce** to find a **unique** solution for s and t.
(4) The two lines do not intersect ("skew" lines).	L1: $\overrightarrow{OP} = (1,1,1) + s\,(1,2,3)$ L2: $\overrightarrow{OP} = (-2,0,1) + t\,(1,1,1)$	Note the direction vectors are not multiples of one another. Equate the x, y, and z parametric equations of each line and then **row reduce** to show the system of equations is inconsistent.

3) The direction vectors clearly are **not** multiples of each other.
Parametric Equations for L1: $x = 1+s$, $y = 1+2s$, $z = 1+3s$

Parametric Equations for L2: $x = -2+t$, $y = 0+t$, $z = 2+t$

$\begin{aligned} x &= 1+s = -2+t \\ y &= 1+2s = t \\ z &= 1+3s = 2+t \end{aligned}$	Rewrite these three equations as equations in variables s and t and then **row reduce** the new equations. $\Leftrightarrow$ **SEE PAGE 45 TO REVIEW ROW REDUCING A SYSTEM OF EQUATIONS!**	$\begin{aligned} \text{E1:} \quad & s-t=-3 \\ \text{E2:} \quad & 2s-t=-1 \\ \text{E3:} \quad & 3s-t=1 \end{aligned}$	$\begin{aligned} \text{E4} &= \text{E1} \\ \text{E5} &= -2\text{E1}+\text{E2} \\ \text{E6} &= -3\text{E1}+\text{E3} \end{aligned}$ $\Leftrightarrow$	$\begin{aligned} \text{E4:} \quad & s-t=-3 \\ \text{E5:} \quad & t=5 \\ \text{E6:} \quad & 2t=10 \end{aligned}$

So $t = 5$ and $s = -3+5 = 2$. Subbing into either set of parametric equations gives intersection point $(3,5,7)$.

4) The direction vectors are **not** multiples of each other.
Parametric Equations for L1: $x = 1+s$, $y = 1+2s$, $z = 1+3s$

Parametric Equations for L2: $x = -2+t$, $y = 0+t$, $z = 1+t$

$\begin{aligned} 1+s &= -2+t \\ 1+2s &= t \\ 1+3s &= 1+t \end{aligned}$ $\Rightarrow$	$\begin{aligned} \text{E1:} \quad & s-t=-3 \\ \text{E2:} \quad & 2s-t=-1 \\ \text{E3:} \quad & 3s-t=0 \end{aligned}$	$\begin{aligned} \text{E4} &= \text{E1} \\ \text{E5} &= -2\text{E1}+\text{E2} \\ \text{E6} &= -3\text{E1}+\text{E3} \end{aligned}$ $\Leftrightarrow$	$\begin{aligned} \text{E4:} \quad & s-t=-3 \\ \text{E5:} \quad & t=5 \\ \text{E6:} \quad & 2t=9 \end{aligned}$	$\begin{aligned} \text{E7} &= \text{E4} \\ \text{E8} &= \text{E5} \\ \text{E9} &= -2\text{E5}+\text{E6} \end{aligned}$ $\Leftrightarrow$	$\begin{aligned} \text{E7:} \quad & s-t=-3 \\ \text{E8:} \quad & t=5 \\ \text{E9:} \quad & 0=-1 \end{aligned}$

E9 shows the system has no solution (**inconsistent!**) and so there is no intersection point.

Think of two swimmers where one swims the **length** of a pool doing the **front crawl** while the other swims the **width** of the pool **underwater**. The two trace out (perpendicular) non-intersecting lines, that is, skew lines!

Two for you.

1)(a) Are these two lines coincident, parallel, skew, or do they intersect in a single point?

L1: $\overrightarrow{OP} = (1,1,1) + s(1,2,3)$

L2: $\overrightarrow{OP} = (8,3,-2) + t(3,2,1)$

(b) If they intersect in a single point, find this point. Give the values of s and t in L1 and L2 respectively which produce this intersection point.

2)(a) Are these two lines coincident, parallel, skew, or do they intersect in a single point? If they intersect, find the intersection point.

L1: $\overrightarrow{OP} = (1,1,1) + s(1,2,3)$

L2: $\overrightarrow{OP} = (-1,-3,5) + t(3,2,1)$

(b) If they intersect in a single point, find this point. Give the values of s and t in L1 and L2 respectively which produce this intersection point.

Answers 1)(a) intersect in a single point (b) $(-1,-3,-5)$, $s = -2$, $t = -3$
2)(a) skew   (b) not applicable since the lines do not intersect.

Intersection of Two Planes

Note: For this topic, we will work with **scalar** equations of planes.

When we have two planes in $\mathbb{R}^3$, there are three possibilities:

Remember: Plane $Ax + By + Cz = D$ has normal $\vec{n} = (A, B, C)$.

Geometry	Algebraic Example	Picture
(1) The two planes are coincident, that is, they are the same plane. This only happens if the two equations are **exact multiples of one another!**	E1: $x + y - z = 1$ E2: $2x + 2y - 2z = 2$ Here, E2 $= 2 \times$ E1.	
(2) The two planes are parallel. This only happens if the **normals** of the two equations are **exact multiples of one another but the equations are not!**	E1: $x + y - z = 1$ E2: $2x + 2y - 2z = 3$ $\vec{n_1} = (1,1,-1);\ \vec{n_2} = (2,2,-2)$ Here, $\vec{n_2} = 2\vec{n_1}$ but E2 is not a multiple of E1!	
(3) The two planes are not parallel. In this case, they **must** intersect in a straight line. The normals will **not** be multiples of one another.	E1: $x + y - z = 1$ E2: $x + 2y - 2z = 1$	

Example 1) For each of the following pairs of equations of planes, decide whether the planes are coincident, parallel, or intersect in a line. If they intersect, find a set of parametric equations and a vector equation of the line.

(a)	(b)	(c)
E1: $x + 2y + 3z = 4$ E2: $-4x - 8y - 12z = -16$	E1: $x + 2y + 3z = 4$ E2: $-4x - 8y - 12z = 10$	E1: $x - 2y + 3z = 4$ E2: $x - y + 4z = -1$

Solution

(a) Since E2 $= -4$E1, the planes are coincident.

(b) Since $\vec{n_2} = -4\vec{n_1}$ but E2 $\neq -4$E1, the planes are parallel.

(c) Since the normals are not multiples of one another, the planes intersect in a line.

$$\boxed{\text{E1: } x - 2y + 3z = 4 \quad \text{E2: } x - y + 4z = -1}$$
$$\begin{array}{c} \text{E3} = \text{E1} \\ \text{E4} = -\text{E1} + \text{E2} \\ \Leftrightarrow \\ \boxed{\text{SEE PAGE 45 TO REVIEW ROW REDUCING A SYSTEM OF EQUATIONS!}} \end{array}$$
$$\boxed{\text{E3: } x - 2y + 3z = 4 \quad \text{E4: } y + z = -5}$$

From E4, we have $y = -5 - z$. Substitute this into E1:

$x - 2(-5 - z) + 3z = 4 \Leftrightarrow x + 10 + 5z = 4 \Leftrightarrow x = -6 - 5z$ Let $z = t$.

Parametric Equations : $x = -6 - 5t,\ y = -5 - t,\ z = t$

$\therefore$ We have point $(-6, -5, 0)$ and, from the t coefficients, direction vector $(-5, -1, 1)$.

Vector Equation : $(x, y, z) = (-6, -5, 0) + t(-5, -1, 1)$

Three for you.

1)(a) Are these two planes coincident, parallel, or do they intersect in a line?

E1: $5x + 2y - z = 1$

E2: $-10x - 4y + 2z = 0$

(b) If they intersect in line, find a set of parametric equations for the line.

2)(a) Are these two planes coincident, parallel, or do they intersect in a line?

E1: $5x + 2y - z = 1$

E2: $-10x - 4y + 2z = -2$

(b) If they intersect in line, find a set of parametric equations for the line.

3)(a) Are these two planes coincident, parallel, or do they intersect in a line?

E1: $x - y + 4z = 1$

E2: $5x + 2y - z = -2$

(b) If they intersect in line, find a set of parametric equations for the line.

Answers 1)(a) parallel (The normals are multiples but the equations are not.)
(b) not applicable since the planes do not intersect

2)(a) coincident (The equations are multiples of each other.)
(b) not applicable since the planes are coincident

3)(a) The planes intersect in a line.   (b) $x = -t, \ y = -1 + 3t, \ z = t$

Intersection of Three Planes: Parallel/Coincident Case

Note: For this topic, we will work with **scalar** equations of planes.

A common refrain on this topic: **"HELP!"**

Well, at your service are three **crucial** facts from **The Intersection of Two Planes**:

I) Equation E1 is a multiple of equation E2 ⇔ The two planes are coincident.

II) E1 and E2 aren't multiples but normals $\vec{n}_1$ and $\vec{n}_2$ are ⇔ The two planes are ∥.

III) Otherwise, the two planes must intersect in a line.

There are **EIGHT** possible scenarios with three planes. **DON'T BE FRIGHTENED.** Here, we will deal with the five where at least two of the planes are either parallel or coincident. The very good news: you can determine the answer *just by looking* at the equations. It's easy! Trust me, it really is! **DON'T BE FRIGHTENED!**

Planes E1, E2, E3 (with normals $\vec{n}_1, \vec{n}_2, \vec{n}_3$) ...	...which, row reduced*, become... *See page 45.	Geometrical description	Picture	What are multiples of what?
(1) $x+y+z=1$ $2x+2y+2z=2$ $3x+3y+3z=3$	$x+y+z=1$ $0=0$ $0=0$	3 coincident planes		E1, E2, E3; $\vec{n}_1, \vec{n}_2, \vec{n}_3$
(2) $x+y+z=1$ $2x+2y+2z=2$ $3x+3y+3z=4$	$x+y+z=1$ $0=0$ $0=-1$	2 coincident planes and a ∥ plane		E1, E2; $\vec{n}_1, \vec{n}_2, \vec{n}_3$
(3) $x+y+z=1$ $x+2y+2z=2$ $2x+2y+2z=2$	$x+y+z=1$ $y+z=1$ $0=0$	2 coincident planes intersecting the 3rd in a line**		E1, E3; $\vec{n}_1, \vec{n}_3$
(4) $x+y+z=1$ $x+y+z=2$ $x+y+z=3$	$x+y+z=1$ $0=-1$ $0=-2$	3 ∥ planes		$\vec{n}_1, \vec{n}_2, \vec{n}_3$
(5) $x+y+z=1$ $x+2y+3z=4$ $x+y+z=2$	$x+y+z=1$ $y+2z=3$ $0=-1$	2 ∥ planes, each intersecting the 3rd plane in a line		$\vec{n}_1, \vec{n}_3$

See **Intersection of Two Planes (page 267) for details on finding the line of intersection.

So in all five parallel/coincident cases, you can just eyeball the **original** equations (you don't need to row reduce!) and the answer will be obvious. For example, in (5), the first and third planes are parallel because their normals are multiples but their equations are not. The middle normal is not a multiple of either of the others so the middle plane must intersect the first in a line and the third in a line. Planes one and three never meet so neither do these intersection lines. In fact, we can say more: the intersection lines are parallel. How can you prove this?

One (BIG TABLE) for you.

1) Complete the table.

Three Planar Equations	Which equations and which normals are multiples of one another?	Geometric Description
E1: $3x+2y+z=1$ E2: $6x+4y+2z=2$ E3: $3x+3y+3z=3$		
E1: $3x+2y+z=1$ E2: $6x+4y+2z=5$ E3: $-3x-2y-z=3$		
E1: $3x+2y+z=1$ E2: $6x+4y+2z=2$ E3: $9x+6y+3z=5$		
E1: $3x+2y+z=1$ E2: $6x+4y+2z=-2$ E3: $3x+3y+3z=3$		

Answer

Three Planar Equations	Which equations and which normals are multiples of one another?	Geometric Description
E1: $3x+2y+z=1$ E2: $6x+4y+2z=2$ E3: $3x+3y+3z=3$	E1, E2; $\vec{n_1}, \vec{n_2}$	2 coincident planes intersecting the 3rd in a line
E1: $3x+2y+z=1$ E2: $6x+4y+2z=5$ E3: $-3x-2y-z=3$	$\vec{n_1}, \vec{n_2}, \vec{n_3}$	3 ∥ planes
E1: $3x+2y+z=1$ E2: $6x+4y+2z=2$ E3: $9x+6y+3z=5$	E1, E2; $\vec{n_1}, \vec{n_2}, \vec{n_3}$	2 coincident planes and a ∥ plane
E1: $3x+2y+z=1$ E2: $6x+4y+2z=-2$ E3: $3x+3y+3z=3$	$\vec{n_1}, \vec{n_2}$	2 ∥ planes, each intersecting the 3rd plane in a line

Intersection of Three Planes: Non-Parallel/Non-Coincident

Note: For this topic, we will work with **scalar** equations of planes.

A common refrain on this topic: **"HELP!"**
Well, at your service are three **crucial** facts from **The Intersection of Two Planes**:
I) E1 is a multiple of E2 $\Leftrightarrow$ The two planes are coincident.

II) E1 and E2 aren't multiples but $\vec{n_1}$ and $\vec{n_2}$ are $\Leftrightarrow$ The two planes are parallel.

III) Otherwise, the two planes must intersect in a line.

There are **EIGHT** possible scenarios with three planes. **DON'T BE FRIGHTENED.** We dealt with the five parallel/coincident cases in the previous section. Here, we will deal with the next three where **none** of the planes are parallel or coincident. The very good news: you can determine the answer *just by looking* at the **row reduced** equations. It's easy! Trust me, it really is!* **DON'T BE FRIGHTENED!**

*Well, it's easy when you know how to row reduce equations! See page 45.

Planes E1, E2, E3 (with normals $\vec{n_1}, \vec{n_2}, \vec{n_3}$) ...	... which, row reduced*, become... *See page 45.*	Geometrical description	Picture	What are multiples of what?
(6) $x+y+z=1$ $x+2y+2z=2$ $2x+3y+3z=4$	$x+y+z=1$ $y+z=1$ $0=1$	None are $\parallel$. There are 3 $\parallel$ lines of intersection!		none
(7) $x+y+z=1$ $2x+3y+3z=3$ $x+2y+2z=2$	$x+y+z=1$ $y+z=1$ $0=0$	None are $\parallel$. There is one common line of intersection.		none
(8) $x+y+z=1$ $2x+3y+3z=4$ $x+2y+3z=2$	$x+y+z=1$ $y+z=2$ $z=-1$	None are $\parallel$. There is a unique intersection point.		none

Here is the row reduction for (6):

E1: $\quad x+y+z=1$ E2: $x+2y+2z=2$ E3: $2x+3y+3z=4$	$\begin{array}{l}E4 = E1\\ E5 = -E1+E2\\ E6 = -2E1+E3\end{array}$ $\Leftrightarrow$	E4: $x+y+z=1$ E5: $\quad y+z=1$ E6: $\quad y+z=2$	$\begin{array}{l}E7 = E4\\ E8 = E5\\ E9 = -E5+E6\end{array}$ $\Leftrightarrow$	E7: $x+y+z=1$ E8: $\quad y+z=1$ E9: $\quad 0=1$

Now you do the row reductions for (7) and (8)!

One (BIG TABLE) for you

1) Complete the table.

Three planar equations…	… when row reduced, become…	Geometrical description	Picture
E1: $x - 2y - z = 1$ E2: $x - y - 2z = 2$ E3: $3x - 5y + z = -1$			
E1: $x - 2y - z = 1$ E2: $x - y - 2z = 2$ E3: $5x - 8y - 7z = 7$			
E1: $x + y + z = 1$ E2: $x + 2y + 2z = 2$ E3: $3x + 4y + 4z = 5$			

Answer

Three planar equations…	… when row reduced, become…	Geometrical description	Picture
E1: $x - 2y - z = 1$ E2: $x - y - 2z = 2$ E3: $3x - 5y + z = -1$	$x - 2y - z = 1$ $y - z = 1$ $z = -1$	None are ‖. There is a unique intersection point.	
E1: $x - 2y - z = 1$ E2: $x - y - 2z = 2$ E3: $5x - 8y - 7z = 7$	$x - 2y - z = 1$ $y - z = 1$ $0 = 0$	None are ‖. There is one common line of intersection.	
E1: $x + y + z = 1$ E2: $x + 2y + 2z = 2$ E3: $3x + 4y + 4z = 5$	$x + y + z = 1$ $y + z = 1$ $0 = 1$	None are ‖. There are 3 ‖ lines of intersection!	

Summation Notation and Common SUM $\equiv \sum$ Formulas

Let m and n be natural numbers with $1 \le m \le n$.

$$\sum_{i=1}^{n} f(i) = f(1) + f(2) + f(3) + \dots + f(n) \qquad \sum_{i=m}^{n} f(i) = f(m) + f(m+1) + \dots + f(n)$$

$$\sum_{i=1}^{n} cf(i) = c \sum_{i=1}^{n} f(i) \qquad \sum_{i=1}^{n} (f(i) \pm g(i)) = \sum_{i=1}^{n} f(i) \pm \sum_{i=1}^{n} g(i)$$

$$\sum_{i=1}^{n} c = cn \qquad \sum_{i=1}^{n} i = \frac{n(n+1)}{2} \qquad \sum_{i=1}^{n} i^2 = \frac{n(n+1)(2n+1)}{6} \qquad \sum_{i=1}^{n} i^3 = \frac{n^2(n+1)^2}{4} = \left(\sum_{i=1}^{n} i\right)^2$$

Example 1) Evaluate each of (a) and (b) and expand (c) into THREE sums.

(a) $\displaystyle\sum_{i=1}^{11} 2i$ 　　(b) $\displaystyle\sum_{i=4}^{8} i^3$ 　　(c) $\displaystyle\sum_{i=1}^{n} (1+i)^2$

Solution (a) $\displaystyle\sum_{i=1}^{11} 2i = 2\sum_{i=1}^{11} i = 2\left(\frac{11 \cdot 12}{2}\right) = 132$

(b) $\displaystyle\sum_{i=4}^{8} i^3 \overset{\boxed{\sum_{i=1}^{8} i^3 - \sum_{i=1}^{3} i^3}}{=} \left(\frac{8 \cdot 9}{2}\right)^2 - \left(\frac{3 \cdot 4}{2}\right)^2 = 36^2 - 36 = 1260$

(c) $\displaystyle\sum_{i=1}^{n} (1+i)^2 = \sum_{i=1}^{n} (1 + 2i + i^2) = \sum_{i=1}^{n} 1 + 2\sum_{i=1}^{n} i + \sum_{i=1}^{n} i^2$

Example 2) Write the following in summation notation and evaluate the sum:

$$S = \frac{2}{n}\left(\frac{2}{n}\right)^2 + \frac{2}{n}\left(\frac{4}{n}\right)^2 + \frac{2}{n}\left(\frac{6}{n}\right)^2 + \dots + \frac{2}{n}\left(\frac{2i}{n}\right)^2 + \dots + \frac{2}{n}\left(\frac{2n}{n}\right)^2$$

Solution $\displaystyle S = \frac{2}{n}\left(\frac{2}{n}\right)^2 + \frac{2}{n}\left(\frac{4}{n}\right)^2 + \frac{2}{n}\left(\frac{6}{n}\right)^2 + \dots + \frac{2}{n}\left(\frac{2i}{n}\right)^2 + \dots + \frac{2}{n}\left(\frac{2n}{n}\right)^2$

$$= \sum_{i=1}^{n} \frac{2}{n}\left(\frac{2i}{n}\right)^2 \overset{\boxed{\text{Factor out the } \frac{2}{n} \text{ and the } \left(\frac{2}{n}\right)^2 !}}{=} \frac{2}{n}\left(\frac{2}{n}\right)^2 \sum_{i=1}^{n} i^2 = \frac{8}{n^3} \frac{n(n+1)(2n+1)}{6} = \frac{4(n+1)(2n+1)}{3n^2}$$

Note : for evaluating integrals from definition (where a sum like this usually arises),

we would continue $\dfrac{4(n+1)(2n+1)}{3n^2} = \dfrac{4}{3}\left(\dfrac{n+1}{n}\right)\left(\dfrac{2n+1}{n}\right) = \dfrac{4}{3}\left(1 + \dfrac{1}{n}\right)\left(2 + \dfrac{1}{n}\right).$

Two for you.

1) Evaluate: $\displaystyle\sum_{i=1}^{10}\left(2i-i^{2}\right)$

2) Expand into THREE sums: $\displaystyle\sum_{i=1}^{n}\frac{3}{n}\left(1+\frac{3i}{n}\right)^{2}$

Answers 1) -275 2) $\displaystyle\frac{3}{n}\sum_{i=1}^{n}1+\frac{18}{n^{2}}\sum_{i=1}^{n}i+\frac{27}{n^{3}}\sum_{i=1}^{n}i^{2}$

Arithmetic and Geometric Sequences and Series

The nth term of an **arithmetic** sequence with first term a_1 and common difference d is $a_n = a_1 + (n-1)d$. The sum is $S_n = \sum_{i=1}^{n} a_i = \frac{n}{2}(2a_1 + (n-1)d) \overset{\boxed{\text{also}}}{=} n\left(\frac{a_1 + a_n}{2}\right)$.

The nth term of a **geometric** sequence with first term a_1 and common ratio r is $a_n = a_1 r^{n-1}$. The sum is $S_n = \sum_{i=1}^{n} a_1 r^{i-1} \overset{\boxed{\text{Use this when } r > 1.}}{=} a_1\left(\frac{r^n - 1}{r - 1}\right) \overset{\boxed{\text{Use this when } r < 1.}}{=} a_1\left(\frac{1 - r^n}{1 - r}\right)$.

Here are the corresponding formulas for i starting at 0.		
Arithmetic: $\begin{aligned} a_n &= a_0 + nd \\ S_n &= \frac{n+1}{2}(a_0 + a_n) \end{aligned}$	Geometric:	$\begin{aligned} a_n &= a_0 r^n \\ S_n &= a_0\left(\frac{1 - r^{n+1}}{1 - r}\right) \end{aligned}$

Example 1) Given an arithmetic series with $a_1 = 7$ and common difference $d = 2$, find a_6 and S_6.

Solution $a_6 \overset{\boxed{a_1 = 7,\ n = 6,\ d = 2}}{=} a_1 + (6-1)2 = 7 + 5(2) = 17$

$S_6 \overset{\boxed{a_1 = 7,\ n = 6,\ d = 2}}{=} \frac{6}{2}(2(7) + (6-1)2) = 3(14 + 10) = 72$ **OR** $S_6 \overset{\boxed{a_1 = 7,\ a_6 = 17}}{=} \frac{6}{2}(7 + 17) = 72$

Example 2) Given a geometric sequence with first term $a_1 = 3$ and common ratio $r = 2$, find a_6 and S_6.

Solution $a_6 = a_1 r^5 \overset{\boxed{a_1 = 3,\ r = 2}}{=} 3(2^5) = 96$ $\qquad S_6 = a_1\left(\frac{r^6 - 1}{r - 1}\right) \overset{\boxed{a_1 = 3,\ r = 2}}{=} 3\left(\frac{2^6 - 1}{2 - 1}\right) = 189$

Example 3) An arithmetic sequence has $a_4 = 16$ and $a_{12} = 56$. Find a_1 and d.

Solution $a_{12} = a_1 + 11d = 56$ and $a_4 = a_1 + 3d = 16$. Subtracting these two equations gives $8d = 40$ so $d = 5$. Substituting: $a_4 = a_1 + 15 = 16$ and so $a_1 = 1$.

Example 4) A geometric sequence has $a_4 = 10\ 000$ and $a_7 = 10$. Find a_1 and r.

Solution $a_4 = a_1 r^3 = 10000$ and $a_7 = a_1 r^6 = 10$.

$\dfrac{a_7}{a_4} = \dfrac{a_1 r^6}{a_1 r^3} = r^3 = \dfrac{10}{10\ 000} = \dfrac{1}{1000}$ and so $r = \dfrac{1}{10}$. Substituting in a_4 gives

$a_1\left(\dfrac{1}{10}\right)^3 = 10\ 000$ and so $a_1 = 10\ 000\ 000$.

Two for you.

1) Given an arithmetic sequence with 5th term 50 and 13th term 26, find a_1 and d.

2) Given a geometric sequence with 5th term 2 and 12th term 256, find a_1 and r.

Answers 1) $d = -3$ and $a_1 = 62$ 2) $r = 2$ and $a_1 = \dfrac{1}{8}$

Combinations and Permutations: Choosing and Arranging

For any natural numbers n and r, where $n \geq r$,

$$C(n, r) \overset{\text{Another Notation!}}{=} \binom{n}{r} \overset{\text{Another Notation!!}}{=} {}_nC_r = \frac{n!}{(n-r)!\, r!} = \binom{n}{n-r} \text{ calculates}$$

the number of COMBINATIONS of r **objects you can make from** n **objects.**

$$P(n, r) \overset{\text{Another Notation!}}{=} {}_nP_r = \frac{n!}{(n-r)!} \text{ calculates}$$

the number of ARRANGEMENTS of r **objects you can make from** n **objects.**

Remember, $0! = 1! = 1$ and $i! = i(i-1)(i-2)...(3)(2)(1)$.

$$C(n, 0) = C(n, n) = 1 \qquad P(n, 0) = 1 \qquad P(n, n) = n!$$

Example 1) How many possible ways are there of choosing a president, vice-president, and treasurer from a group of 8 candidates for a student math club? **(Yes, there are student math clubs!)**

Solution We are looking for the number of **arrangements** of 3 people from 8.

Order IS important! The required number is $P(8,3) = \dfrac{8!}{(8-3)!} = \dfrac{8!\,\overset{8 \times 7 \times 6}{}}{5!} = 336.$

Example 2) How many possible ways are there of choosing 3 members for the executive of the math club from 8 candidates?

Solution We are looking for the number of **combinations** of 3 people from 8. **Order is NOT important!**

The required number is $C(8,3) = \dfrac{8!}{(8-3)!3!} = \dfrac{8!\,\overset{8 \times 7}{}}{5!3!} = 56.$

Two for you.

1) How many different poker hands (5 cards from a 52 card deck) contain the Ace and Jack of Spades?

2) For the word "utopia", how many possible ways are there of arranging

(a) exactly 4 of all the letters?   (b) just the vowels?

Answers 1) $C(50,3) = 19600$ 2)(a) $P(6,4) = 360$ (b) $P(4,4) = 24$

Mean, Median, Mode, and Standard Deviation

Given numbers $X_1 \leq X_2 \leq X_3 \leq ... \leq X_n$, we have **THREE** kinds of averages:

$$\textbf{Mean} = \frac{X_1 + X_2 + X_3 + ... + X_n}{n} = \frac{\sum\limits_{i=1}^{n} X_i}{n}$$

Median The numbers have been listed from lowest to highest. The median is

$$\begin{cases} \text{the middle number } X_{\frac{n+1}{2}}, \text{ if } n \text{ is odd;} \\ \\ \text{the average } \dfrac{X_{\frac{n}{2}} + X_{\frac{n}{2}+1}}{2}, \text{ if } n \text{ is even.} \end{cases}$$

Mode The mode is the number that occurs most often in the list.
There may be several modes.

The **Standard Deviation** is a measure of how the data is scattered about the mean.
If the mean $= \bar{X}$, then

$$\textbf{Standard Deviation} = \sqrt{\frac{\sum\limits_{i=1}^{n}(X_i - \bar{X})^2}{n}}. \text{ Note that } \frac{\sum\limits_{i=1}^{n}(X_i - \bar{X})^2}{n} \text{ is itself a "mean".}$$

It is the **MEAN of the squares of the distances of the data points to the MEAN of the original data**. What a mouthful!

Example 1) A group of 13 customers in a women's shoe store have these shoe sizes: 6, 6.5, 7, 7, 7, 7.5, 7.5, 8, 8, 8, 9, 9, 10. Find the mean, median, mode(s), and standard deviation for this data.

Solution Mean $= \dfrac{6 + 6.5 + 7 \times 3 + 7.5 \times 2 + 8 \times 3 + 9 \times 2 + 10}{13} = \bar{X} \doteq 7.7$

Median $= X_{\frac{13+1}{2}} = X_7 = 7.5$

Mode There are two modes: both 7 and 8 occur three times in the list.

The **Standard Deviation**

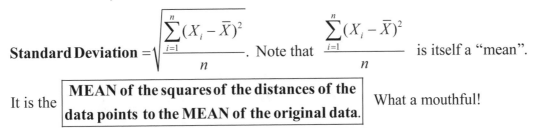

$$= \sqrt{\frac{(6 - \bar{X})^2 + (6.5 - \bar{X})^2 + 3(7 - \bar{X})^2 + 2(7.5 - \bar{X})^2 + 3(8 - \bar{X})^2 + 2(9 - \bar{X})^2 + (10 - \bar{X})^2}{13}}$$

$\doteq 1.07$

One for you.

1) Find

(a) the mean   (b) the median   (c) the mode(s)   (d) the standard deviation

for the data points 1, 2, 3, 3, 3, 3, 4, 4, 5, 8.

Answers (a) 3.6   (b) $\dfrac{X_5 + X_6}{2} = 3$ (c) 3   (d) 1.8

The Binomial Theorem

For any natural number n,

$$(a+b)^n = \sum_{i=0}^{n} \binom{n}{i} a^{n-i} b^i$$

$$= \binom{n}{0} a^n + \binom{n}{1} a^{n-1} b + \binom{n}{2} a^{n-2} b^2 + \dots + \binom{n}{i} a^{n-i} b^i + \dots + \binom{n}{n-1} a^1 b^{n-1} + \binom{n}{n} b^n,$$

where $\binom{n}{i} = \dfrac{n!}{(n-i)!\,i!} = \binom{n}{n-i}$, and in particular, $\binom{n}{0} = \binom{n}{n} = 1$.

Remember, $0! = 1! = 1$ and $i! = i(i-1)(i-2)\dots(3)(2)(1)$.

Some students think "3!" means "!!!**THREE**!!!"

Example 1) Expand $(2+x)^5$.

Solution $(2+x)^5 = \binom{5}{0} 2^5 + \binom{5}{1} 2^4 x + \binom{5}{2} 2^3 x^2 + \binom{5}{3} 2^2 x^3 + \binom{5}{4} 2x^4 + \binom{5}{5} x^5$

$$= 32 + 5(16)x + 10(8)x^2 + 10(4)x^3 + 5(2)x^4 + x^5$$

$$= 32 + 80x + 80x^2 + 40x^3 + 10x^4 + x^5$$

Example 2) Find the coefficient of x^{15} in the expansion of $\left(2x^3 + \dfrac{1}{4x^2}\right)^{10}$.

Solution $\left(2x^3 + \dfrac{1}{4x^2}\right)^{10} = \sum_{i=0}^{10} \binom{10}{i} (2x^3)^{10-i} \left(\dfrac{1}{4x^2}\right)^i$

$\boxed{\text{Expand, using properties of exponents.}}$
$$= \sum_{i=0}^{10} \binom{10}{i} \dfrac{2^{10-i} x^{30-3i}}{4^i x^{2i}} \quad \boxed{\text{Rewrite } 4^i \text{ in base 2.}} \quad = \sum_{i=0}^{10} \binom{10}{i} \dfrac{2^{10-i} x^{30-3i}}{2^{2i} x^{2i}}$$

$\boxed{\text{Combine exponents!}}$
$$= \sum_{i=0}^{10} \binom{10}{i} 2^{10-3i} x^{30-5i}.$$

We want $30 - 5i = 15$. $\therefore -5i = -15$ and so $i = 3$.

The required coefficient is

$$\binom{10}{3} 2^{10-3(3)} = \dfrac{10!}{7!3!} 2^1 = \dfrac{(10)(9)(8)}{(3)(2)(1)} (2) = 240.$$

Two for you.

1) Expand: $\left(\dfrac{2}{x^2} - \dfrac{y}{3} \right)^4$

2) Find the coefficient of x^{-4} in the expansion of $\left(\dfrac{3}{x^2} + \dfrac{x^2}{9} \right)^4$.

Answers 1) $\dfrac{16}{x^8} - \dfrac{32y}{3x^6} + \dfrac{8y^2}{3x^4} - \dfrac{8y^3}{27x^2} + \dfrac{y^4}{81}$ 2) 12

INDEX

How to... How to... How to...

Get an "A" in MATH!

1 After class, **DON'T** do your homework! Instead, *read over your class notes*. When you come to an example done in class...

2 **DON'T** read the example. Copy out the question, set your notes aside, and do the question yourself. Maybe you will get stuck. Even if you thought you understood the example completely when the teacher went over it in class, you may get stuck.

And this is **GOOD NEWS!** Now, you know what you don't know. So, consult your notes, look in the text, see your teacher/professor. Do whatever is necessary to figure out the steps in the example that troubled you.

Once you have sweated through the example, **DO IT AGAIN! And again**. Do it as often as you need so that it becomes, if not easy, then at least straightforward. Make sure you not only understand each line in the solution, but why each line is needed for the solution.

In part, you have memorized the solution. More importantly, you have made the subtleties of the problem unsubtle!

This is the great equalizer step. If your math or science aptitude is strong, then maybe you will have the example down pat after doing it twice. If not so strong, you may have to do it several times. But after you have done this for every class example...

3 **DO** YOUR HOMEWORK! If you follow this method and if the teacher chose the examples well, then most of the homework questions will relate easily back to problems done in class and the rest should extend or synthesize the ideas behind those problems.

Guess what you'll find on 80% or more of your tests and exams? The same kinds of problems! And you will have your "A". Good luck, although if you use this method, luck will have nothing to do with your INEVITABLE success.

THE MATHEMATICS SURVIVAL KIT
FEEDBACK

What topic did you need that you didn't find in **The Mathematics Survival Kit**?

Send me your topic*. If I use it in a future edition of the MSK, I will send you a copy of the new edition hot off the press. In it, you will find a page with your topic, and at the bottom of the page, **your name and school!** Be famous and help me improve the MSK. Send me your topic!

Poster versions of **"How to Get an 'A' in Math"** and **"How to Get Extra Help"** are available for a nominal price. Please email me for details.

Good luck with your studies in general and mathematics especially.

Best wishes,

Jack Weiner

Professor Jack Weiner
Department of Mathematics and Statistics
University of Guelph
Guelph, Ontario, Canada
N1G 2W1

*Email your suggested topic or comments about **The Mathematics Survival Kit** to
jweiner@uoguelph.ca

For updates, go to
www.mathematicssurvivalkit.ca

Notes

Notes

Notes

Notes

Notes

Notes

Every Exact Trig Ratio You'd Ever Want to Know and Probably More!

degrees	radians	sin	cos	tan	csc	sec	cot
0	0	0	1	0	undefined	1	undefined
30	$\dfrac{\pi}{6}$	$\dfrac{1}{2}$	$\dfrac{\sqrt{3}}{2}$	$\dfrac{1}{\sqrt{3}}$	2	$\dfrac{2}{\sqrt{3}}$	$\sqrt{3}$
45	$\dfrac{\pi}{4}$	$\dfrac{1}{\sqrt{2}}$	$\dfrac{1}{\sqrt{2}}$	1	$\sqrt{2}$	$\sqrt{2}$	1
60	$\dfrac{\pi}{3}$	$\dfrac{\sqrt{3}}{2}$	$\dfrac{1}{2}$	$\sqrt{3}$	$\dfrac{2}{\sqrt{3}}$	2	$\dfrac{1}{\sqrt{3}}$
90	$\dfrac{\pi}{2}$	1	0	undefined	1	undefined	0
120	$\dfrac{2\pi}{3}$	$\dfrac{\sqrt{3}}{2}$	$-\dfrac{1}{2}$	$-\sqrt{3}$	$\dfrac{2}{\sqrt{3}}$	-2	$-\dfrac{1}{\sqrt{3}}$
135	$\dfrac{3\pi}{4}$	$\dfrac{1}{\sqrt{2}}$	$-\dfrac{1}{\sqrt{2}}$	-1	$\sqrt{2}$	$-\sqrt{2}$	-1
150	$\dfrac{5\pi}{6}$	$\dfrac{1}{2}$	$-\dfrac{\sqrt{3}}{2}$	$-\dfrac{1}{\sqrt{3}}$	2	$-\dfrac{2}{\sqrt{3}}$	$-\sqrt{3}$
180	π	0	-1	0	undefined	-1	undefined
210	$\dfrac{7\pi}{6}$	$-\dfrac{1}{2}$	$-\dfrac{\sqrt{3}}{2}$	$\dfrac{1}{\sqrt{3}}$	-2	$-\dfrac{2}{\sqrt{3}}$	$\sqrt{3}$
225	$\dfrac{5\pi}{4}$	$-\dfrac{1}{\sqrt{2}}$	$-\dfrac{1}{\sqrt{2}}$	1	$-\sqrt{2}$	$-\sqrt{2}$	1
240	$\dfrac{4\pi}{3}$	$-\dfrac{\sqrt{3}}{2}$	$-\dfrac{1}{2}$	$\sqrt{3}$	$-\dfrac{2}{\sqrt{3}}$	-2	$\dfrac{1}{\sqrt{3}}$
270	$\dfrac{3\pi}{2}$	-1	0	undefined	-1	undefined	0
300	$\dfrac{5\pi}{3}$	$-\dfrac{\sqrt{3}}{2}$	$\dfrac{1}{2}$	$-\sqrt{3}$	$-\dfrac{2}{\sqrt{3}}$	2	$-\dfrac{1}{\sqrt{3}}$
315	$\dfrac{7\pi}{4}$	$-\dfrac{1}{\sqrt{2}}$	$\dfrac{1}{\sqrt{2}}$	-1	$-\sqrt{2}$	$\sqrt{2}$	-1
330	$\dfrac{11\pi}{6}$	$-\dfrac{1}{2}$	$\dfrac{\sqrt{3}}{2}$	$-\dfrac{1}{\sqrt{3}}$	-2	$\dfrac{2}{\sqrt{3}}$	$-\sqrt{3}$
360	2π	0	1	0	undefined	1	undefined

$\sqrt{2} \doteq 1.4142$	$\dfrac{1}{\sqrt{2}} \doteq 0.7071$	$\sqrt{3} \doteq 1.7321$	$\dfrac{1}{\sqrt{3}} \doteq 0.5774$	$\dfrac{\sqrt{3}}{2} \doteq 0.8660$	$\dfrac{2}{\sqrt{3}} \doteq 1.1547$

The Rationale Behind Fractions $\dfrac{\sqrt{3}}{2} = 0.8660$

$$\frac{a}{b} + \frac{c}{d} = \frac{ad + bc}{bd} \qquad \frac{\left(\dfrac{a}{b}\right)}{\left(\dfrac{c}{d}\right)} = \frac{a}{b} \times \frac{d}{c} \qquad \frac{\left(\dfrac{a}{b}\right)}{c} = \frac{a}{bc} \qquad \frac{a}{\left(\dfrac{b}{c}\right)} = \frac{ac}{b}$$

Factoring Productively

$$ax + ay = a(x + y) \qquad x^2 - y^2 = (x - y)(x + y) \qquad x^3 \pm y^3 = (x \pm y)(x^2 \mp xy + y^2)$$

$$x^n - y^n = (x - y)(x^{n-1} + x^{n-2}y + x^{n-3}y^2 + \ldots + xy^{n-2} + y^{n-1}), \text{ for } n \in \mathbb{N}$$

$$x^n + y^n = (x + y)(x^{n-1} - x^{n-2}y + x^{n-3}y^2 - \ldots - xy^{n-2} + y^{n-1}), \text{ for } n \in \mathbb{N}, n \text{ odd}$$

The Power of Binomials

$$(x \pm y)^2 = x^2 \pm 2xy + y^2 \qquad (x \pm y)^3 = x^3 \pm 3x^2y + 3xy^2 \pm y^3$$

Advocating Exponents

$$a^x a^y = a^{x+y} \qquad \frac{a^x}{a^y} = a^{x-y} \qquad \left(a^x\right)^y = a^{xy} \qquad \left(\frac{ab}{c}\right)^x = \frac{a^x b^x}{c^x} \qquad a^0 = 1 \qquad a^{-1} = \frac{1}{a}$$

Getting Powerful with Logs

$$\log_a(xy) = \log_a(x) + \log_a(y) \qquad \log_a\left(\frac{x}{y}\right) = \log_a(x) - \log_a(y) \qquad \log_a(x^y) = y \log_a(x)$$

$$\log_a(x^y) \overset{\boxed{\text{Please note!}}}{\neq} \left[\log_a(x)\right]^y \qquad \log_a(1) = 0 \qquad \log_a(a) = 1 \qquad \log_a\left(\frac{1}{a}\right) = -1$$

Inverse formulas: $a^{\log_a(x)} = x \qquad \log_a(a^x) = x$ **Change of base**: $\log_a(x) = \dfrac{\log_b(x)}{\log_b(a)} \qquad \log_a(b) = \dfrac{1}{\log_b(a)}$

Rooting for the Quadratic Formula

$$ax^2 + bx + c = 0 \Rightarrow x = \frac{-b \pm \sqrt{b^2 - 4ac}}{2a} \qquad \text{Sum of roots} = -\frac{b}{a} \qquad \text{Product of roots} = \frac{c}{a}$$

The Slant on Slopes and Lines

Slope through points (x_1, y_1) and $(x_2, y_2) = \dfrac{y_2 - y_1}{x_2 - x_1}$; line $l_1 \perp$ line $l_2 \Rightarrow$ slope of $l_1 = -\dfrac{1}{\text{slope of } l_2}$.

The equation of the line through (x_1, y_1) with slope m: $y - y_1 = m(x - x_1)$.

Trig Truths

$\pi \text{ radians} = 180° \qquad \sin^2(A) + \cos^2(A) = 1 \qquad 1 + \tan^2(A) = \sec^2(A) \qquad \cot^2(A) + 1 = \csc^2(A)$

$$\sin\left(\frac{\pi}{2} - A\right) = \cos(A) \qquad \cos\left(\frac{\pi}{2} - A\right) = \sin(A) \qquad \tan\left(\frac{\pi}{2} - A\right) = \cot(A)$$

$$\sin(-A) = -\sin(A) \qquad \cos(-A) = \cos(A) \qquad \tan(-A) = -\tan(A)$$

$$\sin(A \pm B) = \sin(A)\cos(B) \pm \cos(A)\sin(B) \qquad \sin(2A) = 2\sin(A)\cos(A) \qquad \sin^2(A) = \frac{1 - \cos(2A)}{2}$$

$$\cos(A \pm B) = \cos(A)\cos(B) \mp \sin(A)\sin(B) \qquad \cos(2A) = \cos^2(A) - \sin^2(A) \qquad \cos^2(A) = \frac{1 + \cos(2A)}{2}$$

Sine Law: $\dfrac{\sin(A)}{a} = \dfrac{\sin(B)}{b} = \dfrac{\sin(C)}{c}$

Cosine Law (eg): $a^2 = b^2 + c^2 - 2bc\cos(A)$